MACHINE DRAWING

A TEXT AND PROBLEM BOOK
FOR TECHNICAL STUDENTS
AND DRAFTSMEN

BY

CARL L. SVENSEN, B.S., M.E., LL.D.

Member-Secretary Texas State Board of Registration for Professional Engineers;
Registered Professional Engineer in Texas, Florida, and New Mexico;
Member American Society of Mechanical Engineers;
National Society of Professional Engineers;
Society for Promotion of Engineering Education

THIRD EDITION, SECOND PRINTING

NEW YORK
D. VAN NOSTRAND COMPANY, Inc.
250 FOURTH AVENUE

First Published, *August 1921*

*Reprinted, December 1922, November 1923, July
1927, April 1928, August 1929, January 1931*

Second Edition, *January 1933*

*Reprinted, February 1935, November 1936, October 1937,
August 1939, October 1940, December 1941, March 1943*

Third Edition, *January 1945*

Reprinted, January 1946

PRINTED IN THE U. S. A.

LANCASTER PRESS, INC., LANCASTER, PA.

PREFACE TO THIRD EDITION

Machine drawing has come to occupy an extremely important place in the engineering and manufacturing world. The complexity and variety of materials, operations, and processes is such that a course in mechanical or engineering drawing will no longer suffice as adequate preparation.

The purpose of this revision is to bring the text up to date, to include new material, and to add a large number of new problems. The text has been rewritten where improvements could be made, but features of proven value in former editions have been retained. Changes throughout the text are such as to improve the value of the book for both teaching and reference purposes.

Again the author expresses his thanks to the many users of this book in the past and hopes that their suggestions for its improvement will make it of greater service to them in the future. Mention should be made of the interest of Mr. George J. Frey, and of the assistance of Mr. Herbert Brasher in the preparation of new illustrations.

C. L. S.

PREFACE TO FIRST EDITION

Machine drawing may be considered as:
1. A final stage of a course in mechanical drawing.
2. A course in practical drafting.
3. A transition course between mechanical drawing and machine design.
4. An introductory or first course in machine design.
5. A course for the correlation of drawing and engineering.

The importance of such a course is well recognized but the means of attaining success is not so readily available as for many other courses. This book is planned to make available a guide for the development of an understanding of the relation of machine drawing to engineering. The text is kept as brief as a clear presentation of the subject matter permits. It is designed for advanced courses for students who have had previous instruction in mechanical drawing. A brief chapter on elementary principles is given as an introduction to the course and for review purposes or reference.

A complete treatment of the subject of working drawings, drafting-room practice and idiomatic expressions of the engineering language is followed by a chapter on the principles and practice of dimensioning. The classification of size specification by means of two kinds of dimensions, six cases of the elements of dimensioning, and four systems of dimensioning will, it is hoped, make this subject a definite study.

A study of the common machine details, empirical machine design, jigs and fixtures, etc., is included as properly belonging to an advanced course in machine drawing.

A textbook obtains much of its value from the number, variety, and character of the problems which it contains. The collection of problems in this book (about two hundred) is arranged under headings in a single chapter where they can be conveniently found. Necessary instructions, hints, and references to the text are given so that the student has a definite task whether assigned a simple machine part or the study of a complete machine. The problems are presented by layouts or other specifications so that the instructor is relieved of the preliminary details which ordinarily arise when assigning machine drawing studies.

The scope of the text and the variety and extent of the illustrations and problems are such that it is believed that the special needs of thorough courses in machine drawing in technical institutions can be efficiently served.

C. L. S.

COLUMBUS, OHIO,
   September, 1921

CONTENTS

vii

CONTENTS

CONTENTS

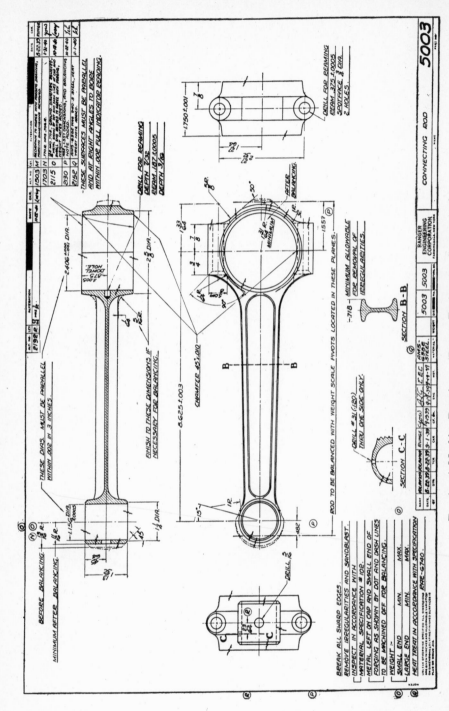

Fig. 1. A Machine Drawing. (Ranger Engineering Corporation.)

MACHINE DRAWING

CHAPTER I

ELEMENTARY PRINCIPLES

1. Machine drawings are the result of the practical application of mechanical drawing to the representation and specification of machinery (Fig. 1). There is a universal dependence upon such drawings in the practice of engineering in connection with the specifications for machine constructions—machine tools, power generation and transmission machinery, transportation machines such as locomotives, airplanes, ships,

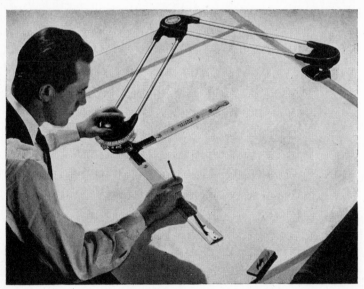

Fig. 2. A Drafting Machine. (*Eugene Dietzgen Co.*)

and automobiles, machinery for operations such as manufacturing, road building, engineering projects, and farming, and machinery in general.

Experience in the industrial uses of drawing has indicated the desirability of certain "idioms of the engineering language"—practical modifi-

1

cations and variations from the theory of mechanical drawing and descriptive geometry. Machine drawing reflects the current practice in graphic description as used by design engineers.

2. The equipment used for machine drawing consists of the usual drafting tools with a drafting machine (Fig. 2) as the basic tool. The ordinary triangles (30°–60° and 45°) and T-square, with either the flat scale or the triangular scale, can, of course, be used if a drafting machine is not available.

FIG. 3.   A Flat Scale.

3. Scales are used for "laying off" measurements on drawings. The mechanical engineers' scale, with various portions proportionally divided to represent feet and inches, is used for machine drawings. A set of flat scales, one of which is illustrated in Fig. 3, is preferred by professional draftsmen and engineers. They are more convenient than the "triangular" scale sometimes used (Fig. 4).

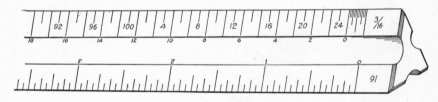

FIG. 4.   A Triangular Scale.

The following scales are used on machine drawings, $3'' = 1$ ft., $1^1/_2'' = 1$ ft., $1'' = 1$ ft., $^1/_2'' = 1$ ft., $^3/_8'' = 1$ ft., $^1/_4'' = 1$ ft., $^3/_{16}'' = 1$ ft., and $^1/_8'' = 1$ ft. The scale of $3'' = 1$ ft. is often called quarter size, and $1^1/_2'' = 1$ ft. is called eighth size. These two reductions are much used on detail drawings.

4. The scale of $3'' = 1$ ft. means that the measurements on the drawings are one-fourth the measurements of the actual object, or that each one-fourth inch on the drawing represents one inch on the object. In this case a distance equal to three inches is divided into 12 parts, each part representing one inch. These parts are further divided to represent quarter inches and other fractions.

Half size (6″ = 1 ft.) drawings are worked from the full size scale. In such cases use the half inch for an inch.

The views which describe a machine or part are drawn full size when it is practicable to do so. When this is not possible, proportional or reduced scales are used to lay off the distances on the drawing. *Never* divide the dimensions of the piece when drawing to a reduced scale. Measure with

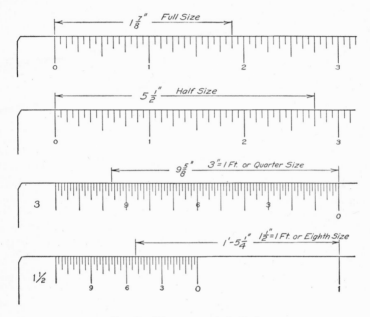

Fig. 5. Measurements to Scale.

the reduced scale and *think full size*. Dimensions put on the drawing are *always* full size of the machine or part regardless of the scale used. Distances measured full size with different scales are illustrated in Fig. 5. Very small parts may be drawn to an enlarged scale of two, four, or ten times full size. Measurements in decimals may be laid off with the civil engineers' scale which has divisions of 10, 20, 30, 40, 50, 60, 80, and 100 parts to the inch. Metric scales are used for measurements in that system.

5. American Standard sizes for drawings are based on the commercial letterhead, $8\frac{1}{2}″$ x 11″, and are as follows: *A*, $8\frac{1}{2}$ x 11; *B*, 11 x 17; *C*, 17 x 22; *D*, 22 x 34; *E*, 34 x 44. These are trimmed sizes for paper or cloth.

6. Line Symbols.—American Standard kinds of lines are illustrated in Fig. 6. Three widths of lines are indicated for inked drawings—*thick*, *medium*, and *thin*. For rapid practice two widths may be used on either inked or penciled drawings, *medium* for outlines, hidden, cutting plane, short breaks, adjacent part and alternate position lines, and *thin* for section, center, dimension, long break, and ditto lines.

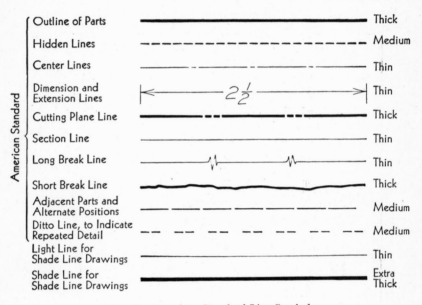

FIG. 6.   American Standard Line Symbols.

A certain amount of contrast gives character to drawings and makes them easier to read. This can be done by using wide lines for large simple drawings and thinner lines for smaller or intricate drawings. The lines illustrated are suitable for the general run of drawings. Note that hidden lines are composed of short dashes of uniform length with very short spaces between them. There is a tendency to use longer dashes for hidden lines, in the interest of speed.

7. Lettering.—Definiteness is an essential requirement in engineering work of all kinds. This is particularly true of drawings of machinery where legibility is necessary for quick and correct understanding. As so often stated poor lettering ruins the appearance of a drawing. This is important to the extent that it affects the usefulness of the drawing.

In general lettering equipment might include pencils, pens, drawing ink, erasers, T-square, triangles, dividers, guide-line instruments and practice paper.

For pencil letters, use an H or F pencil, with a well-sharpened long conical point. Have the point smooth and coinciding with the axis of the lead. Uniformity of line can be maintained by rotating the pencil in the fingers after every two or three letters.

For inking, use a ball-point pen for somewhat coarse letters, and Gillott's 404 or 303 for ordinary figures and notes. The pen may be dipped into the ink and the surplus shaken back into the bottle or the quill may be used as with the ruling pen. For good work the pen must be kept clean, requiring frequent wiping. The pen point should be kept pointed toward the top of the paper. Do not turn the pen or change its position in the hand when making lines in different directions. Do not grip a pen or pencil too tightly as it is difficult to control the movements and the fingers become cramped.

FIG. 6A.   Variations in Letters.   FIG. B6.

8. Proportions and Forms.—The proportions and forms of the letters should be studied by skething them in a large size. The proportions of letters are not definitely fixed but all the letters in an alphabet have a general relation to one another which allows of only a small variation. The appearance may be changed by using "compressed" or "extended" letters, shown in comparison with "normal" letters in Fig. 6A. Other effects may be obtained by using "light face" or "bold face" letters, Fig. 6B.

The proportions of both vertical and inclined engineering letters are shown in Figs. 7 and 8. Arrows indicate the directions in which the various strokes are drawn. The general proportions are indicated by the series of division lines. All proportions are approximate.

FIG. 7.   Vertical Letters.

For inclined letters the American Standard recommended slope is two horizontal units to five vertical units.

The proportions of fractions in comparison with whole numbers are shown in Fig. 9. The division line is horizontal with a small space between the fraction numbers and the line.

9. Titles for drawings vary a great deal as an inspection of a few blueprints will show. Titles for drawings may include such information as the name and location of the company, name of part or machine, size, material, capacity, number required, names of details, scale, date, names or initials of draftsman, checker, engineer, etc. A "free title" is shown in Fig. 10, a form of "printed box title" in Fig. 11, and a record strip title in Fig. 12.

Fig. 8. Inclined Letters.

$1\frac{1}{2}$ $2\frac{3}{4}$ $3\frac{5}{16}$ $4\frac{7}{8}$

Fig. 9. Fractions.

10. Penciling.—For good work it is necessary to have pencils of uniform quality and of the right degree of hardness. Use an H or F pencil for lettering, a 4H for ordinary detail drawings, and a 6H for design drawings. An H or 2H pencil is used for pencil tracings.

Speed and quality of work depend largely upon keeping the pencil point properly sharpened. Remove the wood with a draftsmen's special

      MACHINE DRAWING

SUCTION HEAD FOR $1\frac{1}{2}$" S.E.D. PUMP

SCALE 6"= 1'-0"   JUNE 24, 19—

WARREN STEAM PUMP CO.

WARREN, MASSACHUSETTS

FIG. 10.   A Free Title.

GAS PIPELINE CROSSING ON THE CANADIAN RIVER BRIDGE U.S. HIGHWAY 87 POTTER CO.,TEX. AMARILLO OIL CO., OWNER	CARL L. SVENSEN CONSULTING ENGINEER				
	1509 AVENUE K			LUBBOCK, TEXAS	
	DATE	JOB NO.	DRAWN BY	CHECKED BY	REVISED

FIG. 11.   A Printed Box Title.

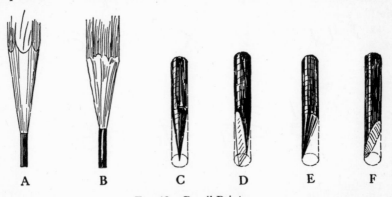

FIG. 12.   A Record Strip Title.

cutter (or with a knife) as at **A** or **B** in Fig. 13.   Then use a sandpaper pad or a file to form the lead to a long conical point, as at **C**.   The flattened or wedge shape shown at **D** is desirable for large drawings with long lines. The points at **E** and **F** are for use in the compasses and bow pencil.

A   B   C   D   E   F

FIG. 13.   Pencil Points.

Most drawings are now made directly in pencil on tracing paper or pencil tracing cloth.   The starting and blocking-in lines should be light thin lines which can be easily erased if necessary.   The completed drawing should have definite lines of uniform width and density.

11. Hidden lines should be drawn with care. A hidden line starts with a dash when it represents the extent of a surface as at **A** (Fig. 14), but when it is a continuation of a visible outline a space is left before the first dash starts as at **B**. When an angle is represented the two dashes at the vertex should touch as at **C, D,** and **E**. Hidden arcs always start at tangent points as at **F, G,** and **H**, which illustrate a "one-dash," a "two-dash,"

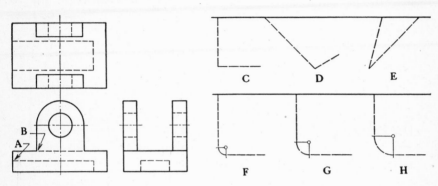

FIG. 14. Hidden Lines and Arcs.

and a "three-dash" arc. Note the positions of the centers and the tangent points. The dashes should be of uniform length and spacing whether used for arcs or straight lines.

12. The order of penciling when making a working drawing is given in Art. 93.

FIG. 15. Joining Lines and Arcs.

13. Inking.—It is sometimes necessary or desirable to ink drawings on either paper or tracing cloth. Black waterproof drawing ink is used for this purpose. Lines are drawn with the ruling pen. Ink is placed between the nibs of the pen with the filler attached to the ink bottle stopper. Care must be taken to prevent ink from getting on the outside of the pen. The proper amount of ink varies from $3/16$ inch to about $5/16$ inch according to the widths and lengths of lines to be drawn.

When inking, the pen should be held in a nearly vertical position and guided by a scale arm of the drafting machine, by the T-square blade, or by a triangle. Do not hold the pen too tightly or press against the guide. Both nibs of the pen must touch the surface. *Keep the pen clean.*

The pens for the compasses and bow pen are filled and cared for as described for the ruling pen. The legs of the compasses should be perpendicular to the surface. When drawing small circles or short arcs, a smaller amount of ink should be used to avoid wider "spots" at the ends of the arcs. When setting to a radius, the ink line should come exactly over the pencil line to insure good tangent joints as at **A** in Fig. 15, which also shows the effect of inking on the inside or outside of the pencil line.

The order of inking when making a working drawing is given in Art. 95. The general order is arcs and circles, horizontal lines, vertical lines, inclined lines.

14. Accuracy and Neatness.—The question of time or efficiency enters into all work and should be considered in studying engineering subjects. Accuracy and neatness not only save time in the study of drafting but are absolute essentials if worth while progress is to be made.

Be sure that the paper is tacked down *flat* on the board. Keep all instruments clean and in proper adjustment, ready for use. Always clean lettering and ruling pens before filling and after using. Keep the pencil points sharp *all the time.* Draw lightly—do not groove the paper.

Pencil lines may run a short distance beyond corners when first laying out but do not draw them clear across the sheet. Do not draw extra lines as it takes time to erase them. Consider the order in which the lines of the different views are drawn, working from the general center and "block in" lines to the details. Make similar measurements at one time. Have a system and follow it.

Do not slight small details or have "fuzzy" indistinct corners and joints. Make every part of the drawing accurately to scale and perfectly clear. Too much freehand work, dull pencils, lack of contrast in lines, inaccurate measurements, and lack of exactness in representation make "sloppy" drawings which often prove very expensive. Clear thinking should be expressed in clear, easily read drawings.

15. Cleaning and Erasing.—Drawings which have been worked over for a length of time become soiled, due to rubbing over the pencil lines, perspiration from the hands, and the dust which settles on them. For this reason, the drawing board, tools, and instruments should be wiped with a piece of cloth before starting work. Do not sharpen a pencil over the drawing or board. Keep the hands clean, especially if they have a tendency to become moist. All the tools should be cleaned occasionally with a damp cloth and thoroughly dried before using. Sometimes the part of the drawing not being worked on can be covered with an extra sheet of paper.

16. Either pencil or ink lines can be erased with a medium soft pencil eraser. Most drafting rooms are equipped with an electric erasing machine. Always erase in the direction of the line. Do not use a knife or ink eraser as it destroys the surface of the paper or cloth. Be sure that an ink line is dry before making an erasure. Do not "dig" into the paper or overheat the eraser by attempting to remove a line too quickly. An erasing shield of celluloid or metal is convenient to protect lines which are not to be removed. Art gum is useful to erase pencil lines and for cleaning the completed drawing.

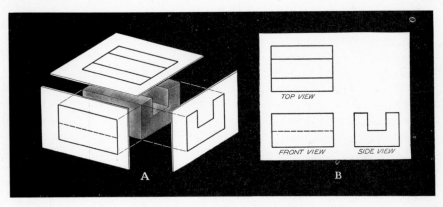

FIG. 16. Orthographic Projection.

17. Shop drawings for machinery are composed of views obtained by orthographic projection and arranged in conformity with the third angle. This is indicated at **A** in Fig. 16 where the views are pictured on planes in front of, above, and to the side of an object. The views of a drawing are arranged as at **B**.

Drawings with two or three views suffice for most objects. Each view shows the part as seen from a different position; from in front (front view), from above (top view), and from one side (side view) as in Fig. 17. These are called the three principal views.

A two-view drawing is shown in Fig. 18. Three views of a blacksmith's "sow" are given in Fig. 19. The top view shows surfaces A', B, and A. The meaning of the horizontal lines which limit surface B in the

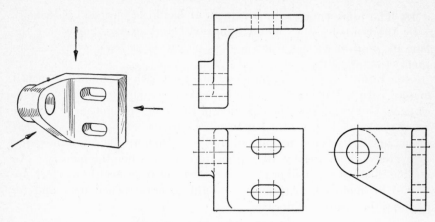

FIG. 17.   A Three-View Drawing.

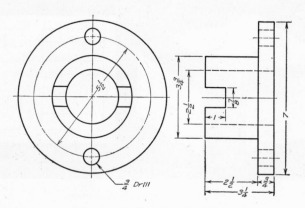

FIG. 18.   A Two-View Drawing.

top view cannot be under-
stood without looking at
the side view which shows
that surface *B* is on a
lower level than surfaces
A and *A'*. The representation of a sloping sur-
face is shown in the drawing of the "swage" in
Fig. 20.

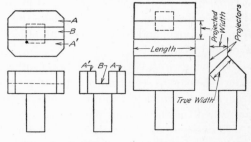

FIG. 19.   Reading
a Drawing.

FIG. 20.   Projected Area.

18. The representation of a cylindrical surface is illustrated in Fig. 21 by the shaded areas.   If a cylinder has its axis perpendicular to a plane its projection (view) on that plane is a circle.   When the axis is parallel to a plane the cylinder appears as a rectangle.

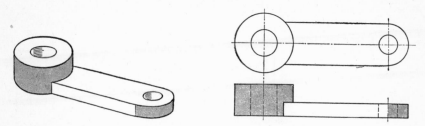

FIG. 21.   Projection of Curved Surfaces.

19. Placing Views.—Views may be drawn from six positions and placed according to American Standards as shown in Fig. 22.   All six views would seldom, if ever, be used.   The usual selection and arrangement is shown in Fig. 23 at **A**, with the *right-side view in the first position*.   Sometimes, however, it is desirable to revolve the side plane as shown in Fig. 23 at **B** which gives the *second position of the right-side view*.   The second

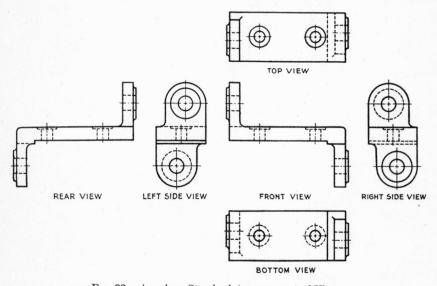

FIG. 22.   American Standard Arrangement of Views.
(*From American Standards.*)

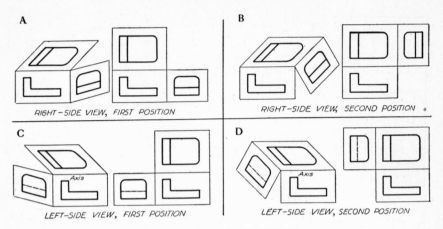

A

RIGHT-SIDE VIEW, FIRST POSITION

B

RIGHT-SIDE VIEW, SECOND POSITION

C

Axis

LEFT-SIDE VIEW, FIRST POSITION

D

Axis

LEFT-SIDE VIEW, SECOND POSITION

Fig. 23.   Positions for the Side View.

position is desirable when a part is rather flat and wide.   It allows a larger scale to be used.   Sometimes it is the only way in which the views can be contained on a given size of drawing paper.   The first position of the left-side view is shown in Fig. 23 at C and the second position in Fig. 23 at D.

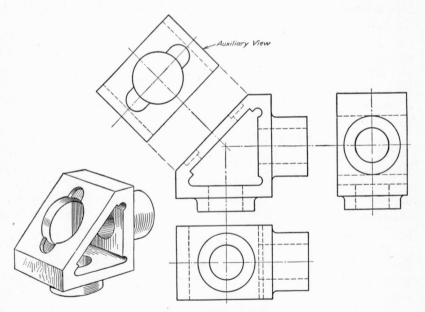

Auxiliary View

Fig. 24.   An Auxiliary View.

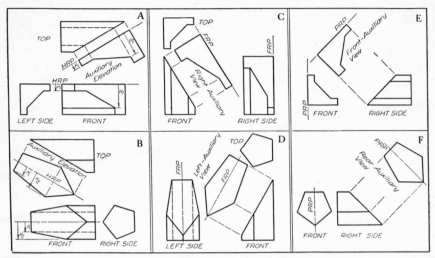

Fig. 25.   Classes of Auxiliary Views.

20. Auxiliary Views.—When it is necessary to show the true size or shape of an inclined surface, an *auxiliary view* is drawn (Fig. 24).   The different classes of auxiliary views are illustrated and named in Fig. 25.   In spaces **A** and **B** the *auxiliary elevation* is obtained by projecting from the top view, and taking measurements perpendicular to HRP (horizontal reference plane) in the front view as shown for H_1 and H_2.   In spaces **C** and **D** the *right-* and *left-auxiliary views* are obtained by projecting from the front view and taking measurements perpendicular to FRP (frontal reference plane).   In spaces **E** and **F**, points are projected from the side view and measured from PRP (profile, or side, reference plane).

21. Sectional Views.—When it is necessary to show the interior of an object or machine more clearly than can be done with hidden lines, an imaginary cutting plane is used.   The part of the object in front of the cutting plane is removed as illustrated in Fig. 26.   The cut surface is indicated by *section lines* and the view is called a section.   Various kinds of sections and treatments of sectional views are illustrated and described in Chapter IV.

22. Reference Material.—The value of handbooks for designers and engineers is too well established to require comment.   There is a mass of detail information and dimensions rather well established, which must be adhered to when making machine drawings.   Every engineer should possess at least one handbook which bears directly upon his work, and should become thoroughly familiar with its contents.

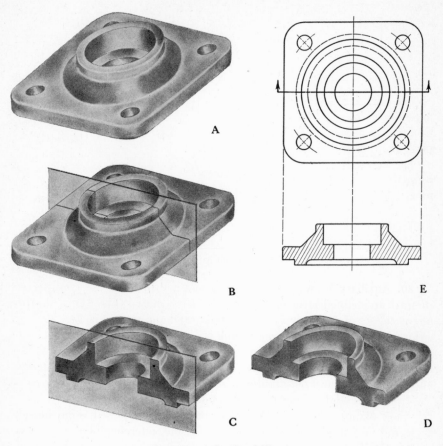

A

B

E

C

D

FIG. 26. A Sectional View.

23. The American Standards Association (A.S.A.) approves and issues standards sponsored by the various engineering societies and other interested agencies. American Standards have become a very important part of American engineering practice. Information as to standards available, date of issue, prices, and projects under way may be secured from the American Standards Association, 70 East 45th St., New York City (17).

Data, dimensions, and standards in general use for many purposes will be found in the publications of various engineering societies. There are certain Government Standards issued by various agencies, including the National Bureau of Standards of the U. S. Department of Commerce, AN (Army Navy), AC (Air Corps), NAF (Naval Aircraft Factory), etc.

CHAPTER II

THREADED FASTENINGS

24. Kinds of Fastenings.—Practical requirements of manufacture necessitate the use of separate pieces in the construction of machinery. Common methods of fastening include the use of screws, bolts, rivets, pins, keys, hooks, slides and welding.

25. Screw-Threads.—In addition to their application as fastenings, screw-threads are used to transmit motion, apply force and for the adjustment of parts. A screw-thread, Fig. 27, is defined as " a ridge of uniform

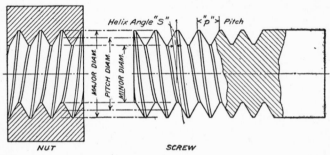

Fig. 27. Screw Thread Terminology.

section in the form of a helix (Art. 201) on the external or internal surface of a cylinder or cone " (A.S.A.).*

26. Screw-Thread Profiles.—A section through the axis of a screw will show the profile or form of thread. A number of screw-thread profiles are shown in Fig. 28. The American Standard, British Standard and V-threads are well adapted for fastening parts together. The British Association Standard uses a smaller angle and smaller pitches. The International Standard Thread (Metric System) has the same form as the American Standard. The pitches and diameters are given in millimeters. The Dardelet thread uses an angle of 29° but has a taper contact which makes it self locking. This patented thread is of French design but is made in the United States by the Dardelet Thread Cor-

---

* References to the American Standards Association will be designated by the initials, A.S.A.

16   MACHINE DRAWING

poration of New York. The square thread and the Acme thread are used for the transmission of force and motion. The Acme thread permits the use of a split nut. The worm thread with proportions as shown is used on *worms*. A worm is similar to a screw but is used in a form of gearing (as worm and wheel, Art. 177). The buttress or breechlock

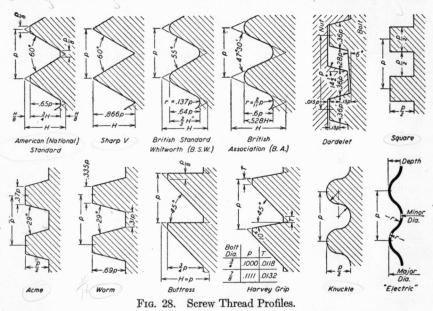

FIG. 28.   Screw Thread Profiles.

thread is designed to take pressure in only one direction. This form has the strength in shear of the V form but avoids the tendency to burst the nut. The Harvey grip thread is similar to the buttress thread. It is used on railroad track bolts in two sizes, $3/4''$ dia., 10 threads per inch and $7/8''$ dia., 9 threads per inch.

The knuckle or rounded thread can be cast in a mold. A similar thread rolled in sheet metal is used for screw caps, electric lamps, plugs, receptacles, etc. American Standard rolled threads for screw shells of electric sockets and lamp bases are specified in A.S.A. C44-1931. Sizes are as follows:

Size	Miniature	Candelabra	Intermediate	Medium	Mogul
Threads per inch	14	10	9	7	4
Depth of thread	.020	.025	.027	.033	.050
Radius	.0210	.0312	.0353	.0470	.0906

27. Pitch and Lead.—The pitch of a screw is the distance from one thread point to the next, measured parallel to the axis. The lead is the distance which the screw will advance axially during one revolution. For a single thread the pitch and lead are equal, Fig. 29 at I. When a

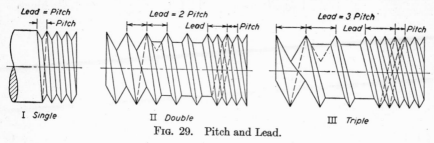

FIG. 29. Pitch and Lead.

long travel or lead is required with a small diameter, the depth of a single thread will reduce the minor diameter as shown in Fig. 29 at II. To avoid this, two parallel ridges may be used to form the thread. The result is a double thread. Similarly a triple thread may be formed. As indicated the lead for a double thread is two times the pitch. For a triple thread it is three times the pitch.

A **right-hand thread** requires the screw to be turned in a clockwise direction to enter the nut. A left-hand thread must be turned counterclockwise to enter the nut.

28. Conventional Representation of Screw-Threads.—It is not often necessary to draw the helix representing a screw-thread, as there are a number of conventional representations in use which serve the purpose as well and which save time. The methods shown in Fig. 30 meet the

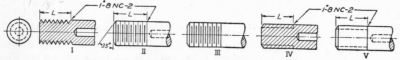

FIG. 30. American Standard Thread Symbols.

requirements of good practice. When the representations of I, II and III are used, the pitch is not drawn to scale but is arranged to avoid crowding the lines.

The representations of Fig. 31 are given for reference as they are all in use to some extent. When the pitch lines are drawn at an angle the slope is determined by one-half the pitch for single threads, Fig. 31 at II, III, IV and XI, or the whole pitch for double threads, as at XII. Representations for square threads are shown at XIII, XIV and XV.

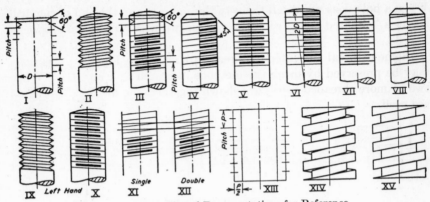

Fig. 31.   Screw Thread Representations for Reference.

29. Threaded Holes and Threads in Section.—Representations of threaded holes in plan, elevation and section are shown by the American Standard symbols in Fig. 32. Regular symbols for threaded holes in section are shown at III, VI, and X. Two weights of lines may be used as in the illustration or the lines may be of equal weight. Simplified

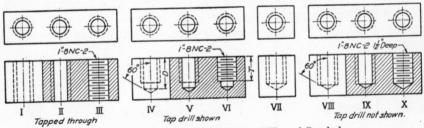

Fig. 32.   American Standard Internal Thread Symbols.

symbols are shown at II, V and IX. Simplified symbols for threaded holes in elevation are shown at I, IV and VIII. For a bottoming tap use the symbol at VII. Regular symbols for threaded holes in elevation are the same as for sections except, of course, that hidden lines are used.

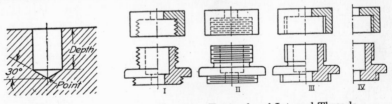

Fig. 33.   Fig. 34.   External and Internal Threads.

When a hole does not go all the way through a piece, the end of the drill leaves a " pointed " hole which may be drawn with 30° lines as shown in Fig. 33.

Some external and internal threads are shown in Fig. 34. Clearness may be preserved by using the methods indicated at I and III. When two or more threaded pieces are shown together, the methods of Fig. 35 are used.

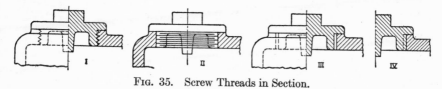

FIG. 35. Screw Threads in Section.

30. American Standard Screw-Threads.—Screw-threads for bolts, machine screws, nuts and commercially tapped holes have been standardized in form, thread series, fits and tolerances by the American Standards Association. Such threads are known as American (National) Standard threads, and have the profile shown in Fig. 36. This is the

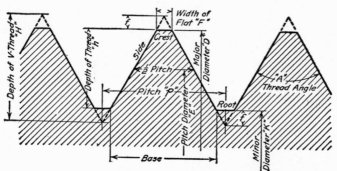

FIG. 36. American (National) Standard Thread Form.

thread formerly known as the United States or Sellers Standard. The angle between the sides of the thread is 60°. The flat at the root and crest has a width of $F = p/8$. The depth $h = p \times .64952$. The pitch, p, is in inches.

Five screw-thread series are provided in the American Standard report.

The American Standard Coarse-Thread Series (NC) comprises the former "United States Standard" supplemented by a part of the A.S.M.E. (American Society of Mechanical Engineers) standards for Machine Screws for sizes below $1/4''$.

MACHINE DRAWING

TABLE 1

COARSE-THREAD SERIES—GENERAL DIMENSIONS *

1	2	3	4	5	6	7
Identification		Basic Diameters			Thread Data	
Sizes	Threads per Inch (n)	Major Diameter (D) (Inches)	Pitch Diameter (E) (Inches)	Minor Diameter (K) (Inches)	Pitch † (p) (Inches)	Basic Depth of Thread (h) (Inches)
1	64	0.0730	0.0629	0.0527	0.0156250	0.01014
2	56	0.0860	0.0744	0.0628	0.0178571	0.01160
3	48	0.0990	0.0855	0.0719	0.0208333	0.01353
4	40	0.1120	0.0958	0.0795	0.0250000	0.01624
5	40	0.1250	0.1088	0.0925	0.0250000	0.01624
6	32	0.1380	0.1177	0.0974	0.0312500	0.02030
8	32	0.1640	0.1437	0.1234	0.0312500	0.02030
10	24	0.1900	0.1629	0.1359	0.0416667	0.02706
12	24	0.2160	0.1889	0.1619	0.0416667	0.02706
$1/4$	20	0.2500	0.2175	0.1850	0.0500000	0.03248
$5/16$	18	0.3125	0.2764	0.2403	0.0555556	0.03608
$3/8$	16	0.3750	0.3344	0.2938	0.0625000	0.04060
$7/16$	14	0.4375	0.3911	0.3447	0.0714286	0.04640
$1/2$	13	0.5000	0.4500	0.4001	0.0769231	0.04996
$9/16$	12	0.5625	0.5084	0.4542	0.0833333	0.05413
$5/8$	11	0.6250	0.5660	0.5069	0.0909091	0.05905
$3/4$	10	0.7500	0.6850	0.6201	0.1000000	0.06495
$7/8$	9	0.8750	0.8028	0.7307	0.1111111	0.07217
1	8	1.0000	0.9188	0.8376	0.1250000	0.08119
$1 1/8$	7	1.1250	1.0322	0.9394	0.1428571	0.09279
$1 1/4$	7	1.2500	1.1572	1.0644	0.1428571	0.09279
$1 1/2$	6	1.5000	1.3917	1.2835	0.1666667	0.10825
$1 3/4$	5	1.7500	1.6201	1.4902	0.2000000	0.12990
2	$4 1/2$	2.0000	1.8557	1.7113	0.2222222	0.14434
$2 1/4$	$4 1/2$	2.2500	2.1057	1.9613	0.2222222	0.14434
$2 1/2$	4	2.5000	2.3376	2.1752	0.2500000	0.16238
$2 3/4$	4	2.7500	2.5876	2.4252	0.2500000	0.16238
3	4	3.0000	2.8376	2.6752	0.2500000	0.16238

* The dimensions of screw-thread gages and other important information on the gaging of screw-threads will be found in the second report of this Committee entitled "Gages and Gaging of Screw-threads."

† This column is given to seven decimal places for computation purposes only.

TABLE 2

FINE-THREAD SERIES—GENERAL DIMENSIONS *

1	2	3	4	5	6	7
Identification		Basic Diameters			Thread Data	
Sizes	Threads per Inch (n)	Major Diameter (D) (Inches)	Pitch Diameter (E) (Inches)	Minor Diameter (K) (Inches)	Pitch † (p) (Inches)	Basic Depth of Thread (h) (Inches)
0	80	0.0600	0.0519	0.0438	0.0125000	0.00812
1	72	0.0730	0.0640	0.0550	0.0138889	0.00902
2	64	0.0860	0.0759	0.0657	0.0156250	0.01014
3	56	0.0990	0.0874	0.0758	0.0178571	0.01160
4	48	0.1120	0.0985	0.0849	0.0208333	0.01353
5	44	0.1250	0.1102	0.0955	0.0227273	0.01476
6	40	0.1380	0.1218	0.1055	0.0250000	0.01624
8	36	0.1640	0.1460	0.1279	0.0277778	0.01804
10	32	0.1900	0.1697	0.1494	0.0312500	0.02030
12	28	0.2160	0.1928	0.1696	0.0357143	0.02319
$1/4$	28	0.2500	0.2268	0.2036	0.0357143	0.02319
$5/16$	24	0.3125	0.2854	0.2584	0.0416667	0.02706
$3/8$	24	0.3750	0.3479	0.3209	0.0416667	0.02706
$7/16$	20	0.4375	0.4050	0.3725	0.0500000	0.03248
$1/2$	20	0.5000	0.4675	0.4350	0.0500000	0.03248
$9/16$	18	0.5625	0.5264	0.4903	0.0555556	0.03608
$5/8$	18	0.6250	0.5889	0.5528	0.0555556	0.03608
$3/4$	16	0.7500	0.7094	0.6688	0.0625000	0.04060
$7/8$	14	0.8750	0.8286	0.7822	0.0714286	0.04640
1	14	1.0000	0.9536	0.9072	0.0714286	0.04640
$1 1/8$	12	1.1250	1.0709	1.0167	0.0833333	0.05413
$1 1/4$	12	1.2500	1.1959	1.1417	0.0833333	0.05413
$1 1/2$	12	1.5000	1.4459	1.3917	0.0833333	0.05413

* The dimensions of screw-thread gages and other important information on the gaging of screw-threads will be found in the second report of this Committee entitled "Gages and Gaging of Screw-threads."

† This column is given to seven decimal places for computation purposes only.

TABLE 3

EXTRA-FINE THREAD SERIES (S. A. E.)

Dia.	Threads per Inch	Dia.	Threads per Inch	Dia.	Threads per Inch
$1/4$	36	$3/4$	20	2	16
$5/16$	32	$7/8$	20	$2 1/4$	16
$3/8$	32	1	20	$2 1/2$	16
$7/16$	28	$1 1/8$	18	$2 3/4$	16
$1/2$	28	$1 1/4$	18	3	16
$9/16$	24	$1 1/2$	18	Over 3 to 6	16
$5/8$	24	$1 3/4$	16	Over 6	16

The **American Standard Fine-Thread Series** (NF) comprises the regular screw-thread series of the S.A.E. (Society of Automotive Engineers) supplemented below $1/4''$ by sizes selected from the A.S.M.E. standard.

The **8-Pitch Series** ($8N$) has eight threads per inch on all sizes ($1''$ to $6''$ inclusive).

The **12-Pitch Series** ($12N$) has twelve threads per inch on all sizes ($1/2''$ to $6''$ inclusive).

The **16-Pitch Series** ($16N$) has sixteen threads per inch on all sizes ($3/4''$ to $4''$ inclusive).

In addition to these five A.S.A. series there is the Extra-Fine-Thread Series of the S.A.E. It has the same form of thread and is suited to aeronautic and other applications where screw threads finer than the present fine screw-thread series are necessary.

General dimensions for the various series of screw threads are given in Tables 1, 2, and 3.

31. Classes of Fits.—Classes of screw-thread fits are described in the American Standards Screw-Thread Report which also includes detail specifications, characteristics, and tables of allowances and tolerances. There are four classes of fits.

Class 1 Fit. The Class 1 fit is recommended only for screw thread work where clearance between mating parts is essential for rapid assembly and where shake or play is not objectionable.

Class 2 Fit. Class 2 represents a high quality of commercial screw thread product and is recommended for the great bulk of interchangeable screw thread work.

Class 3 Fit. Class 3 represents an exceptionally high grade of commercially threaded product and is recommended only in cases where the high cost of precision tools and continual checking of tools is warranted.

Class 4 Fit. Class 4 is intended to meet very unusual requirements more exacting than those for which Class 3 is intended. It is a selective fit if initial assembly by hand is required. It is not, as yet, adaptable to quantity production.

32. Specifications of Screw Threads.—The American (National) Standard Screw-Thread symbols are based upon the items of specification in the following order.

Diameter in inches (or screw number).

Number of threads per inch (Arabic).

Initials of the series: NC for coarse threads; NF for fine threads; EF for extra-fine threads; N for other series or to indicate American (National) Standard form.

Class of fit by Arabic numeral.

For a left-hand thread add *LH* after the class of fit. No symbol is required for right-hand threads. Aircraft practice omits all inch marks.

For example: $1^1/_2''$-6NC-2 specifies $1^1/_2''$ diameter, 6 threads per inch, coarse thread standard and class 2 fit. $2^1/_2''$-16N16-3 specifies $2^1/_2''$ diameter, 16 threads per inch, 16-pitch series and class 3 fit. For American form with a special pitch specify as follows: $^7/_8''$-7N-3, which specifies $^7/_8''$ diameter, 7 threads per inch, Am. Std. form, and class 3 fit. For British Standard, Whitworth, or English threads use the symbol B.S.W., and for British Standard fine threads use the symbol B.S.F. For square or Acme threads spell out the word.

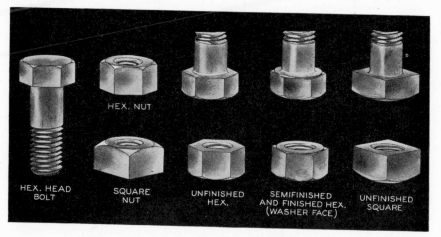

FIG. 37. American Standard Bolt Heads and Nuts.

33. American Standard Bolt Heads and Nuts.—The A.S.A.-B18.2 report states that "these standards are intended for general use by all industries and to replace such other series of dimensions as have been used."

Three series of standards are provided:

"Regular series bolt heads and nuts are for general use."

"Heavy series bolt heads and nuts are for use where a greater bearing surface is necessary, that is, where a large clearance between the bolt and hole or a greater wrench bearing is considered essential."

"Light series nuts have smaller dimensions across flats than regular series nuts."

Three kinds of finish are provided:

TABLE 4

AMERICAN STANDARD REGULAR BOLT HEADS AND NUTS

(Unfinished; square and hexagon. Semifinished (also Finished); hexagon only)

Diameter D	Bolts					Nuts				
	Flats, W Sq. and Hex.	Corners		Height, H		Flats, W Sq. and Hex.	Corners		Thickness, N	
		Sq.	Hex.	Unfin.	Semifin.		Sq.	Hex.	Unfin.	Semifin.
1/4	3/8	1/2	27/64	11/64	5/32	7/16	19/32	31/64	7/32	13/64
5/16	1/2	43/64	17/32	13/64	3/16	9/16	49/64	5/8	17/64	1/4
3/8	9/16	3/4	5/8	1/4	15/64	5/8	27/32	45/64	21/64	5/16
7/16	5/8	53/64	11/16	19/64	9/32	3/4	1	27/32	3/8	23/64
1/2	3/4	1	53/64	21/64	19/64	13/16	1 3/32	29/32	7/16	27/64
9/16	7/8	1 11/64	31/32	3/8	11/32	7/8	1 5/32	31/32	1/2	31/64
5/8	15/16	1 1/4	1 3/64	27/64	25/64	1	1 11/32	1 7/64	35/64	17/32
3/4	1 1/8	1 1/2	1 1/4	1/2	15/32	1 1/8	1 1/2	1 1/4	21/32	41/64
7/8	1 5/16	1 3/4	1 29/64	19/32	9/16	1 5/16	1 3/4	1 29/64	49/64	3/4
1	1 1/2	2	1 21/32	21/32	19/32	1 1/2	2	1 21/32	7/8	55/64
1 1/8	1 11/16	2 1/4	1 55/64	3/4	11/16	1 11/16	2 1/4	1 55/64	1	31/32
1 1/4	1 7/8	2 1/2	2 5/64	27/32	25/32	1 7/8	2 1/2	2 5/64	1 1/32	1 1/16
1 3/8	2 1/16	2 3/4	2 9/32	29/32	27/32	2 1/16	2 3/4	2 9/32	1 13/64	1 11/64
1 1/2	2 1/4	3	2 31/64	1	15/16	2 1/4	3	2 31/64	1 5/16	1 9/32
1 5/8	2 7/16	3 1/4	2 11/16	1 1/32	1 1/32	2 7/16	3 1/4	2 11/16	1 27/64	1 25/64
1 3/4	2 5/8	3 1/2	2 29/32	1 5/32	1 3/32	2 5/8	3 1/2	2 29/32	1 17/32	1 1/2
1 7/8	2 13/16	3 3/4	3 7/64	1 1/4	1 3/16	2 13/16	3 3/4	3 7/64	1 41/64	1 39/64
2	3	4	3 5/16	1 11/32	1 1/4	3	4	3 5/16	1 3/4	1 23/64
2 1/4	3 3/8	4 1/2	3 47/64	1 1/2	1 3/8	3 3/8	4 1/2	3 47/64	1 31/32	1 59/64
2 1/2	3 3/4	5	4 5/64	1 21/32	1 17/32	3 3/4	5	4 5/64	2 3/16	2 5/64
2 3/4	4 1/8	5 1/2	4 35/64	1 13/16	1 11/16	4 1/8	5 1/2	4 35/64	2 13/32	2 23/64
3	4 1/2	6	4 31/32	2	1 7/8	4 1/2	6	4 31/32	2 5/8	2 37/64

"Unfinished bolt heads or nuts are not machined except in the threads."

"Semifinished bolt heads or nuts are machined or otherwise formed or treated on the bearing surface so as to provide for nuts either a washer face or a circular bearing surface formed by chamfering the edges, and for bolt heads a washer face."

"Finished bolt heads and nuts are the same as semifinished except that the surfaces other than the bearing surface have been so treated as to provide a special appearance. The finish desired on all non-bearing surfaces of finished bolt heads and nuts should be specified by the purchaser."

Bolt heads and nuts are illustrated in Fig. 37. The dimensions in Tables 4 and 5 are abridged from American Standards. For complete information the report mentioned at the beginning of this Article should be consulted. In general, the regular series unfinished bolt heads and nuts may be used unless others are specified.

TABLE 5

AMERICAN STANDARD HEAVY BOLT HEADS AND NUTS

(Unfinished; square and hexagon. Semifinished (also Finished); hexagon only)

Diameter D	Bolts					Nuts				
	Flats, W Sq. and Hex.	Corners		Height, H		Flats, W Sq. and Hex.	Corners		Thickness, N	
		Sq.	Hex.	Unfin.	Semifin.		Sq.	Hex.	Unfin.	Semifin.
1/4						1/2	43/64	9/16	1/4	15/64
5/16						19/32	51/64	43/64	5/16	19/64
3/8						11/16	59/64	49/64	3/8	23/64
7/16						25/32	1 3/64	7/8	7/16	27/64
1/2	7/8	1 11/64	63/64	7/16	13/32	7/8	1 11/64	63/64	1/2	31/64
9/16	15/16	1 1/4	1 3/64	15/32	7/16	15/16	1 1/4	1 3/64	9/16	35/64
5/8	1 1/16	1 27/64	1 3/16	17/32	1/2	1 1/16	1 27/64	1 3/16	5/8	39/64
3/4	1 1/4	1 43/64	1 25/64	5/8	19/32	1 1/4	1 43/64	1 25/64	3/4	47/64
7/8	1 7/16	1 59/64	1 19/32	23/32	11/16	1 7/16	1 59/64	1 19/32	7/8	55/64
1	1 5/8	2 11/64	1 51/64	13/16	3/4	1 5/8	2 11/64	1 51/64	1	63/64
1 1/8	1 13/16	2 27/64	2 1/64	29/32	27/32	1 13/16	2 27/64	2 1/64	1 1/8	1 7/64
1 1/4	2	2 43/64	2 7/32	1	15/16	2	2 43/64	2 7/32	1 1/4	1 7/32
1 3/8	2 3/16	2 59/64	2 27/64	1 3/32	1 1/32	2 3/16	2 59/64	2 27/64	1 3/8	1 11/32
1 1/2	2 3/8	3 11/64	2 5/8	1 3/16	1 1/8	2 3/8	3 11/64	2 5/8	1 1/2	1 15/32
1 5/8	2 9/16	3 13/32	2 53/64	1 9/32	1 7/32	2 9/16	3 13/32	2 53/64	1 5/8	1 19/32
1 3/4	2 3/4	3 21/32	3 3/64	1 3/8	1 5/16	2 3/4	3 9/16	3 3/64	1 3/4	1 23/32
1 7/8	2 15/16	3 29/32	3 1/4	1 15/32	1 13/32	2 15/16	3 29/32	3 1/4	1 7/8	1 27/32
2	3 1/8	4 5/32	3 29/64	1 9/16	1 7/16	3 1/8	4 5/32	3 29/64	2	1 31/32
2 1/4	3 1/2	4 21/32	3 7/8	1 3/4	1 5/8	3 1/2	4 21/32	3 7/8	2 1/4	2 13/64
2 1/2	3 7/8	5 5/32	4 9/32	1 15/16	1 13/16	3 7/8	5 5/32	4 9/32	2 1/2	2 29/64
2 3/4	4 1/4	5 21/32	4 45/64	2 1/8	2	4 1/4	5 21/32	4 45/64	2 3/4	2 45/64
3	4 5/8	6 5/32	5 7/64	2 5/16	2 3/16	4 5/8	6 5/32	5 7/64	3	2 61/64
3 1/4						5	6 21/32	5 33/64	3 1/4	3 3/16
3 1/2						5 3/8	7 9/64	5 15/16	3 1/2	3 7/16
3 3/4						5 3/4	7 41/64	6 11/32	3 3/4	3 11/16
4						6 1/8	8 9/64	6 49/64	4	3 15/16

34. Regular unfinished hexagonal and square bolt heads and nuts have the following proportions. Chamfer: 30° for hexagonal, 25° for square. Width across flats of head, $W = 1^1/_2D$, adjusted to sixteenths. Height of head, $H = {}^2/_3D$, adjusted to fractions. Width across flats of nut, $W = 1^1/_2D + {}^1/_{16}$ for sizes $^1/_4$ to $^5/_8$ and $W = 1^1/_2D$ for sizes $^3/_4$ to 3. Thickness of nut, $N = {}^7/_8D$. See Table 4 for dimensions.

35. Regular semifinished (also finished) hexagonal bolt heads and nuts have the following proportions. Width across flats of head, $W = 1^1/_2D$. Height of head, $H = {}^2/_3D - {}^1/_{64}$ for sizes $^1/_4$ to $^7/_{16}$. $H = {}^2/_3D - {}^1/_{32}$ for sizes $^1/_2$ to $^7/_8$. $H = {}^2/_3D - {}^1/_{15}$ for sizes 1 to $1^7/_8$. $H = {}^2/_3D - {}^1/_8$ for sizes 2 to 3. Width across flats of nut, $W = 1^1/_2D + {}^1/_{16}$ for sizes $^1/_4$ to $^5/_8$. $W = 1^1/_2D$ for sizes $^3/_4$ to 3. Thickness of nut, $N = {}^7/_8D - {}^1/_{64}$ for sizes

$^{1}/_{4}$ to $1^{1}/_{8}$, $N = ^{7}/_{8}D - ^{1}/_{32}$ for sizes $1^{1}/_{4}$ to 2. $N = ^{7}/_{8}D - ^{3}/_{64}$ for sizes $2^{1}/_{4}$ to 3. See Table 4 for dimensions.

36. Heavy unfinished hexagonal and square bolt heads and nuts have the following proportions: Width across flats of head, $W = 1^{1}/_{2}D + ^{1}/_{8}$. Height of head, $H = ^{3}/_{4}D + ^{1}/_{16}$. Width across flats of nut, $W = 1^{1}/_{2}D + ^{1}/_{8}$. Thickness of nut $= D$. See Table 5 for dimensions.

37. Heavy semifinished (also finished) hexagonal bolt heads and nuts have the following proportions. Width across flats of head, $W = 1^{1}/_{2}D + ^{1}/_{8}$. Height of head, $H = ^{3}/_{4}D - ^{1}/_{32}$ for sizes $^{1}/_{2}$ to $^{7}/_{8}$. $H = ^{3}/_{4}D$ for sizes 1 to $1^{7}/_{8}$. $H = ^{3}/_{4}D - ^{1}/_{16}$ for sizes 2 to 3. Width across flats of nut, $W = 1^{1}/_{2}D + ^{1}/_{8}$. Thickness of nut, $N = D - ^{1}/_{64}$ for sizes $^{1}/_{4}$ to $1^{1}/_{8}$. $N = D - ^{1}/_{32}$ for sizes $1^{1}/_{4}$ to 2. $N = D - ^{3}/_{64}$ for sizes $2^{1}/_{4}$ to 3. $N = D - ^{1}/_{16}$ for sizes $3^{1}/_{4}$ to 4. See Table 5 for dimensions.

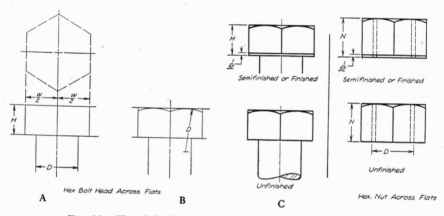

A   Hex Bolt Head Across Flats   B   C

Fig. 38. Hex. Bolt Head Across Flats.   Fig. 39. Hex. Nut.

38. To Draw a Hexagonal Bolt Head or Nut Across Flats.—For a bolt head refer to Fig. 38 at **A**. Draw the center line, a line locating the under side of the head, and lay off the diameter of the bolt. Lay off $^{1}/_{2}W$ (half the distance across flats) on each side of the center line and lay off H (the height of the head). Draw the outline of the head as shown. With **D** as a radius and center half way between center line and outer line, draw arcs as at **B**, and complete the view as at **C** for the unfinished or semifinished head as shown.

For a nut, Fig. 39, proceed in the same way as for a bolt head. Note that the thickness, N, for a nut is greater than the height of a bolt head. Also draw the thread representation as shown.

38A. To Draw a Hexagonal Bolt Head or Nut Across Corners.—For a bolt head refer to Fig. 40 at **A**. Draw the center line, diameter of bolt, and a line locating the under side of the head. Lay off $^1/_2W$ (half the distance across flats) from the center line and draw the 30° line to construct the triangle to obtain the distance $2E$ = one-half distance across corners. Lay off $2E$ on each side of the center line and lay off H (the height of the head). Draw center arc with radius of $1^1/_2D$ and side arcs with radii of $^3/_8D$ as shown at **B**. Draw 30° chamfer line, and complete the view as at **C** for the unfinished or semifinished head as shown.

For a nut, Fig. 41, proceed in the same way as for a bolt head. Note that the thickness, N, for a nut is greater than the height of a bolt head. Also draw the thread representation as shown.

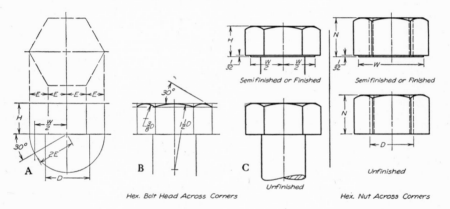

Hex. Bolt Head Across Corners.   Semi finished or Finished   Semifinished or Finished   Unfinished   Hex. Nut Across Corners

Fig. 40. Hex. Bolt Head Across Corners.   Fig. 41. Hex. Nut.

39. To Draw a Square Bolt Head or Nut Across Flats.—For a bolt head refer to Fig. 42 at **A**. Draw center line, lay off W and H. Draw arc with radius R_1 and complete as at **B**. A square nut is drawn at **C** in the same way except that the thickness, N, is greater than H.

39A. To Draw a Square Bolt Head or Nut Across Corners.—For a bolt head refer to Fig. 43 at **A**. Lay off $^1/_2W$ and draw the 45° line to obtain $^1/_2C$ = one-half distance across corners. Lay off $^1/_2C$ and H as shown. Draw arcs with radius R_2 as at **B**. Draw chamfer lines and complete the view.

A nut is drawn at **C** in the same way except that the thickness, N, is greater than H.

39B. A regular hex head bolt and nut may be drawn as in Fig. 44. A heavy square head bolt and nut may be drawn as in Fig. 45.

40. Bolts and Studs.—Three common forms of machine bolts are shown in Fig. 46, the through bolt, the tap bolt, and the stud or stud

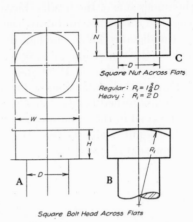

Square Bolt Head Across Flats

FIG. 42. Square Bolt Head and Nut Across Flats.

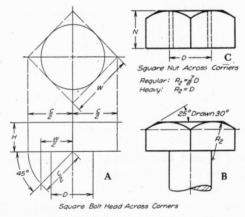

Square Bolt Head Across Corners

FIG. 43. Square Bolt Head and Nut Across Corners.

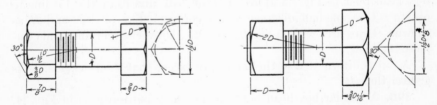

FIG. 44. Hex. Head Bolt and Nut.　　FIG. 45. Square Head Bolt and Nut.

bolt. When possible the through bolt should be used as it requires only drilled holes. The tap bolt is used as a permanent fastening in cases where a cap screw is not desired. When there are parts which must be removed often or where threads might rust in, studs are used if through bolts are not practicable. The length of thread must be designated in all cases and is indicated in the figures.

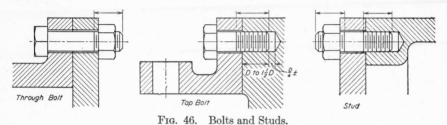

FIG. 46. Bolts and Studs.

A stud may be made tight in a hole by having the threads jam near the bottom or the top of the hole. For the second condition clearance must be allowed.

Since bolt heads and nuts are standard, only three dimensions are necessary on a drawing. For a bolt these are diameter, length from under side of head, and length of thread measured from end of bolt. For a stud, give the diameter, total length, and length of thread measured from each end. A bolt drawing is shown in Fig. 289.

41. Cap Screws.—American Standard finished hexagonal head cap screws are shown in Fig. 47 with dimensions in Table 6. The top is a

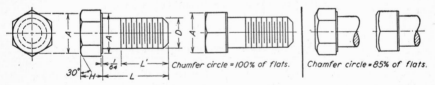

FIG. 47. American Standard Cap Screws.

flat circle with a diameter of 85 to 100 per cent of the width across flats. Cap screws have a washer face $1/_{64}''$ thick, and a diameter equal to width across flats. For lengths of $1''$ or less, thread full length. Over $1''$ long, thread length is $1^1/_2 D + 1/_4''$ or more. Coarse- or fine-thread series may be used, with class 2 fit.

American Standard slotted head cap screws are shown in Fig. 48, with dimensions in Table 7. Thread length is $2 D + 1/_4''$. When length of screw is less than $2 D + 1/_4''$, thread full length.

TABLE 6
FINISHED HEXAGONAL CAP SCREW HEADS (FIG. 47)

Diameter of Screw D	Width across Flats		Minimum Width across Corners	Height		
	Maximum	Minimum		Nominal	Maximum	Minimum
$^1/_4$ 0.2500	$^7/_{16}$ 0.4375	0.428	0.488	$^3/_{16}$	0.194	0.181
$^5/_{16}$ 0.3125	$^1/_2$ 0.5000	0.489	0.558	$^{15}/_{64}$	0.242	0.227
$^3/_8$ 0.3750	$^9/_{16}$ 0.5625	0.551	0.628	$^9/_{32}$	0.289	0.274
$^7/_{16}$ 0.4375	$^5/_8$ 0.6250	0.612	0.699	$^{21}/_{64}$	0.337	0.319
$^1/_2$ 0.5000	$^3/_4$ 0.7500	0.737	0.840	$^3/_8$	0.385	0.365
$^9/_{16}$ 0.5625	$^{13}/_{16}$ 0.8125	0.798	0.910	$^{27}/_{64}$	0.433	0.411
$^5/_8$ 0.6250	$^7/_8$ 0.8750	0.860	0.980	$^{15}/_{32}$	0.481	0.457
$^3/_4$ 0.7500	1 1.0000	0.983	1.120	$^9/_{16}$	0.576	0.549
$^7/_8$ 0.8750	$1^1/_8$ 1.1250	1.106	1.261	$^{21}/_{32}$	0.672	0.641
1 1.0000	$1^5/_{16}$ 1.3125	1.291	1.474	$^3/_4$	0.768	0.733
$1^1/_8$ 1.1250	$1^1/_2$ 1.5000	1.477	1.686	$^{27}/_{32}$	0.863	0.824
$1^1/_4$ 1.2500	$1^{11}/_{16}$ 1.6875	1.663	1.898	$^{15}/_{16}$	0.959	0.916

All dimensions in inches. D = diameter of bolts.

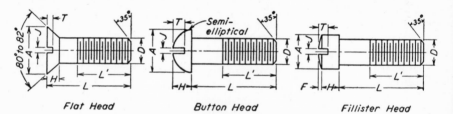

Flat Head   Button Head   Fillister Head

FIG. 48.   American Standard Cap Screws.

TABLE 7
SLOTTED HEAD CAP SCREWS (FIG. 48)

Dia. of Screw D	Width of Slot J	Flat Head			Button Head			Fillister Head			
		A	H	T	A	H	T	A	H	F	T
$^1/_4$	.070	$^1/_2$	.146	.073	$^7/_{16}$	.191	.117	$^3/_8$	$^{11}/_{64}$	.044	.097
$^5/_{16}$	.079	$^5/_8$	.183	.091	$^9/_{16}$	.246	.151	$^7/_{16}$	$^{13}/_{64}$	.050	.115
$^3/_8$	.088	$^3/_4$	.220	.110	$^5/_8$	.273	.167	$^9/_{16}$	$^1/_4$	.064	.142
$^7/_{16}$	.098	$^{13}/_{16}$	.220	.110	$^3/_4$	.328	.202	$^5/_8$	$^{19}/_{64}$	.071	.168
$^1/_2$	.110	$^7/_8$	.220	.110	$^{13}/_{16}$	.355	.219	$^3/_4$	$^{21}/_{64}$	.084	.188
$^9/_{16}$	.123	1	.256	.128	$^{15}/_{16}$	.410	.253	$^{13}/_{16}$	$^3/_8$	.091	.214
$^5/_8$	.138	$1^1/_8$	.293	.146	1	.438	.270	$^7/_8$	$^{27}/_{64}$	.099	.240
$^3/_4$	.154	$1^3/_8$	.366	.183	$1^1/_4$	.547	.337	1	$^1/_2$	.112	.283
$^7/_8$	.173							$1^1/_8$	$^{19}/_{32}$	.126	.334
1	.194							$1^5/_{16}$	$^{21}/_{32}$	.146	.372

42. Machine Screws are especially adapted for use with small parts of machines. The heads are made in different forms as shown in Fig. 49. For lengths of $1^1/_4''$ or less, thread full length. Over $1^1/_4''$ long, thread

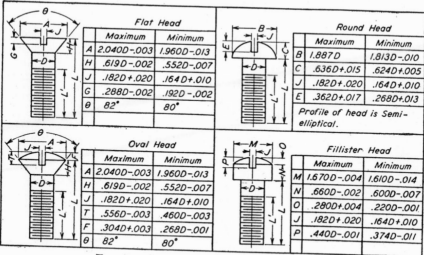

Fig. 49. American Standard Machine Screws.

length is not less than $1^1/_4''$. Coarse- or fine-thread series may be used, with class 2 fit. Some American Standard dimensions are given in Table 8.

TABLE 8

MAXIMUM DIMENSIONS FOR MACHINE SCREW HEADS (FIG. 49)

Nominal Size	D	A	B	C	E	F	G	H	J	M	N	O	P	T
2	.086	.172	.162	.070	.048	.029	.023	.051	.036	.140	.055	.028	.037	.045
3	.099	.199	.187	.078	.053	.033	.027	.059	.038	.161	.063	.032	.043	.052
4	.112	.225	.211	.086	.058	.037	.030	.067	.040	.183	.072	.035	.048	.059
5	.125	.252	.236	.095	.062	.041	.034	.075	.043	.205	.081	.039	.054	.067
6	.138	.279	.260	.103	.067	.045	.038	.083	.045	.226	.089	.043	.060	.074
8	.164	.332	.309	.119	.076	.053	.045	.100	.050	.270	.106	.050	.071	.088
10	.190	.385	.359	.136	.086	.061	.053	.116	.055	.313	.123	.057	.083	.103
12	.216	.438	.408	.152	.095	.069	.060	.132	.059	.357	.141	.064	.094	.117
$^1/_4$	.250	.507	.472	.174	.108	.079	.070	.153	.066	.414	.163	.074	.109	.136
$^5/_{16}$	.3125	.636	.591	.214	.130	.098	.088	.192	.077	.519	.205	.092	.137	.171
$^3/_8$	.375	.762	.708	.254	.153	.117	.106	.230	.088	.622	.246	.109	.164	.208

For threads per inch see Tables 1 and 2.

43. Set Screws.—For holding pulleys on shafts and otherwise preventing relative motion, set screws may be used. Several forms are

illustrated in Fig. 50. Any combination of head and point can be made.
A projecting set screw on a revolving pulley is a source of danger. The
many forms of headless and hollow set screws available make the use of

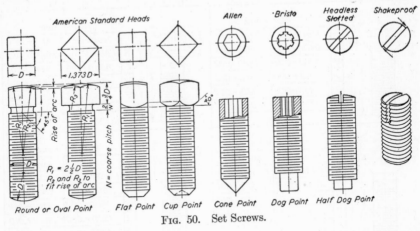

Fig. 50. Set Screws.

other forms unnecessary in such cases. Dimensions of American Standard set screw heads are given in Table 9. Coarse- or fine-thread series
may be used.

TABLE 9

AMERICAN STANDARD SET SCREW HEADS

Diameter of Screw D	Width across Flats		Height		
	Maximum	Minimum	Nominal	Maximum	Minimum
$1/4$	$1/4$ 0.2500	0.241	$3/16$	0.197	0.179
0.2500					
$5/16$ 0.3125	$5/16$ 0.3125	0.302	$15/64$	0.245	0.224
$3/8$ 0.3750	$3/8$ 0.3750	0.362	$9/32$	0.293	0.270
$7/16$ 0.4375	$7/16$ 0.4375	0.423	$21/64$	0.341	0.315
$1/2$ 0.5000	$1/2$ 0.5000	0.484	$3/8$	0.389	0.361
$9/16$ 0.5625	$9/16$ 0.5625	0.545	$27/64$	0.437	0.407
$5/8$ 0.6250	$5/8$ 0.6250	0.607	$15/32$	0.485	0.452
$3/4$ 0.7500	$3/4$ 0.7500	0.729	$9/16$	0.582	0.544
$7/8$ 0.8750	$7/8$ 0.8750	0.852	$21/32$	0.678	0.635
1 1.0000	1 1.0000	0.974	$3/4$	0.774	0.726
$1 1/8$ 1.1250	$1 1/8$ 1.1250	1.097	$27/32$	0.870	0.817
$1 1/4$ 1.2500	$1 1/4$ 1.2500	1.219	$15/16$	0.967	0.909
$1 1/2$ 1.5000	$1 1/2$ 1.5000	1.464	$1 1/8$	1.159	1.091

All dimensions in inches. D = diameter of bolts.

44. S.A.E. Bolts, Nuts and Threads.—The American Standards for regular bolts, nuts, threads, etc., given in previous paragraphs are a part of the S.A.E. accepted standards.

An extra-fine thread series is provided by the S.A.E. as given in Table 3.

The S.A.E. Annual Handbook should be consulted for automotive and aeronautical standards for bolts, nuts, threads and other details.

45. Locking Devices.—The vibration of machinery often causes nuts to become loose if they are not provided with some means of locking or holding. A common method is to use two nuts, both full size or one full size and one thin nut. American Standard Jam Nuts are shown in Fig. 51. Several forms of special nuts and lock washers are illustrated and named in Figs. 51 and 52. The Dardelet thread mentioned in Art. 26 is self locking.

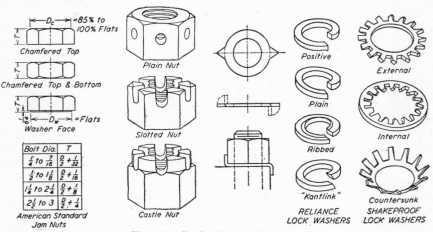

FIG. 51. Lock Nuts and Devices.

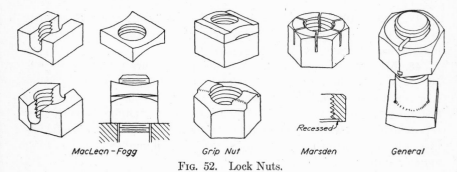

FIG. 52. Lock Nuts.

46. Miscellaneous Bolts.—Several forms of bolts are illustrated and named in Figs. 53 and 54. They are typical of many kinds used for special conditions.

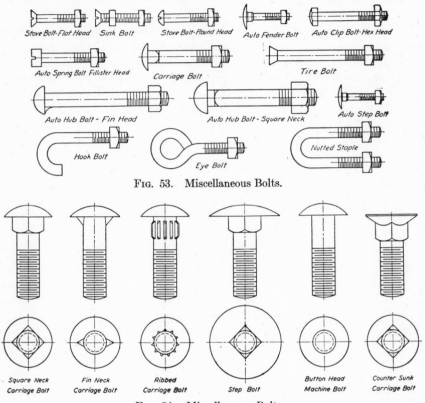

Fig. 53. Miscellaneous Bolts.

Fig. 54. Miscellaneous Bolts.

47. Track bolts are made to American Standards. Some information is given in Fig. 55. Either American Standard or Harvey Grip threads may be used. (See Art. 26 and Fig. 28.)

48. Miscellaneous Screws.—A number of screws are shown in Fig. 56. The common wood screw is made with different forms of heads. Lag screws are used for somewhat heavy wood constructions and for fastening machines or parts of machines to wood. Different methods of representing screws are indicated in the figure. Screws are specified by their diameter, length and form of head. The diameter is generally by gauge number.

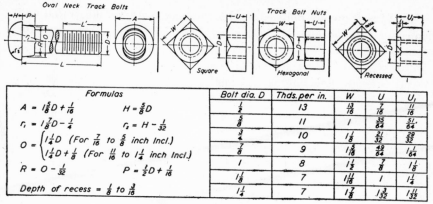

Oval Neck Track Bolts

Track Bolt Nuts

Square   Hexagonal   Recessed

Formulas		Bolt dia. D	Thds. per in.	W	U	U_1
$A = 1\frac{5}{8}D + \frac{1}{16}$ $H = \frac{5}{8}D$		$\frac{1}{2}$	13	$\frac{13}{16}$	$\frac{7}{16}$	$\frac{11}{16}$
$r_1 = 1\frac{7}{8}D - \frac{1}{4}$ $r_2 = H - \frac{1}{32}$		$\frac{5}{8}$	11	1	$\frac{35}{64}$	$\frac{51}{64}$
$O = \begin{cases} 1\frac{1}{4}D \text{ (For } \frac{7}{16} \text{ to } \frac{5}{8} \text{ inch Incl.)} \\ 1\frac{1}{4}D + \frac{1}{8} \text{ (For } \frac{11}{16} \text{ to } 1\frac{1}{4} \text{ inch Incl.)} \end{cases}$		$\frac{3}{4}$	10	$1\frac{1}{8}$	$\frac{21}{32}$	$\frac{29}{32}$
		$\frac{7}{8}$	9	$1\frac{5}{16}$	$\frac{49}{64}$	$1\frac{1}{64}$
$R = O - \frac{1}{32}$ $P = \frac{1}{2}D + \frac{1}{16}$		1	8	$1\frac{1}{2}$	$\frac{7}{8}$	$1\frac{1}{8}$
		$1\frac{1}{8}$	7	$1\frac{11}{16}$	1	$1\frac{1}{4}$
Depth of recess = $\frac{1}{8}$ to $\frac{3}{16}$		$1\frac{1}{4}$	7	$1\frac{7}{8}$	$1\frac{3}{32}$	$1\frac{11}{32}$

FIG. 55.   Track Bolts.

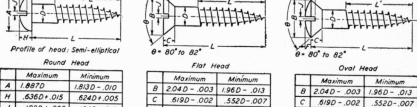

Flat Head   Fillister Head   Drive Screw

Oval Head   Round Head   Lag Screw

FIG. 56.   Miscellaneous Screws.

49. American Standard wood screws are shown in Fig. 57, with some formulas for proportions.   Sizes of wood screws are given in Table 10.

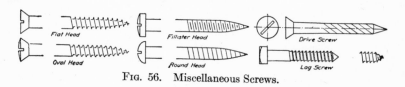

Profile of head: Semi-elliptical $\theta = 80°$ to $82°$ $\theta = 80°$ to $82°$

Round Head

	Maximum	Minimum
A	1.887D	1.813D - .010
H	.636D + .015	.624D + .005
J	.182D + .020	.164D + .010
T	.362D + .017	.268D + .013

Flat Head

	Maximum	Minimum
B	2.04D - .003	1.96D - .013
C	.619D - .002	.552D - .007
J	.182D + .020	.164D + .010
E	.288D - .002	.192D - .002

Oval Head

	Maximum	Minimum
B	2.04D - .003	1.96D - .013
C	.619D - .002	.552D - .007
J	.182D + .020	.164D + .010
F	.304D + .003	.268D - .001
G	.556D - .003	.460D - .003

FIG. 57.   American Standard Wood Screws.

TABLE 10

Screw No.	0	1	2	3	4	5	6	7	8
Dia.	.060	.073	.086	.099	.112	.125	.138	.151	.164
Screw No.	9	10	11	12	14	16	18	20	24
Dia.	.177	.190	.203	.216	.242	.268	.294	.320	.372

50. Drafting room procedure for bolted flanges is indicated in Arts. 51 to 55, for convenience in making allowances for bolts and studs. For design calculations under various conditions books on Machine Design and Strength of Materials should be consulted.

51. Flanges and Bolting.—A method of finding the diameter of bolt circle and diameter of flange is illustrated in Fig. 58. For through bolts the explanation applies to conditions shown at I and II. Draw the desired fillet at r_1. This may be taken at about $t/4$. Lay off X, equal to one-half distance across flats of bolt head, and Y equal to one-half distance across corners of nut. The diameter of the bolt circle, D_B, may now be found by laying a scale on the drawing and selecting a dimension. This will be equal to or greater than, $d + 2 (t + r_1 + X)$, and may be taken at the nearest larger $\frac{1}{8}$th inch. The flange diameter may then be obtained by laying out the distance Y, as indicated, and using the scale to find a dimension equal to, or greater than $D_B + 2 (Y + r_2)$. The radius r_2 may be taken at $\frac{1}{8}$th to $\frac{1}{16}$th the thickness of the flange.

When studs are used, the diameters D_B and D_F may be very much decreased as at III. The distance C should be about equal to t, although if necessary it can be made equal to one-half the diameter of the bolt.

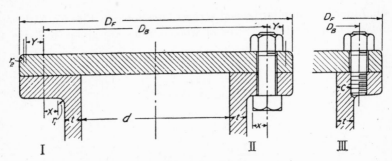

I   II   III

Fig. 58. Circle of Drilling and Flange Diameter.

52. Strength and Number of Bolts.—The strength of a bolt is tension is the strength of the root area. The tensile strength of Am. Standard threads is given in Table 11. When the load is applied as at I, Fig. 59 the stress is found by the formula $S = P/A$. This is direct tension with no initial stress. At II the bolt is used for holding a cover plate or cylinder where a ground joint is used. If the bolt lengthens under pressure the joint will open. The nuts must be screwed up so that the stress in the bolt will be equal to or greater than the stress due to pressure against the plate. At III an elastic packing material is used. When the nut is tightened the packing is compressed. The pressure against the plate will lengthen the bolts and relieve them of some of the stress due to the packing which is less compressed.

TABLE 11

TENSILE STRENGTH OF AMERICAN STANDARD COARSE THREAD SERIES

Diameter	Threads per Inch	Total Strength of One Bolt for Unit Stresses of		
		4000	5000	6000
$1/4$	20	105	135	160
$5/16$	18	180	225	270
$3/8$	16	270	340	405
$7/16$	14	370	465	555
$1/2$	13	500	625	750
$9/16$	12	650	810	970
$5/8$	11	805	1010	1210
$3/4$	10	1200	1500	1800
$7/8$	9	1680	2100	2520
1	8	2200	2750	3300
$1 1/8$	7	2770	3460	4160
$1 1/4$	7	3120	3900	4680
$1 1/2$	6	5120	6400	7680
$1 3/4$	5	7040	8800	10560
2	$4 1/2$	9200	11500	13800
$2 1/4$	$4 1/2$	12075	15095	18115
$2 1/2$	4	14840	18550	22260
$2 3/4$	4	18480	23100	27720
3	4	22400	28000	33600

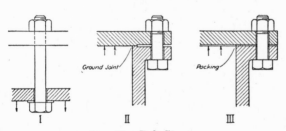

FIG. 59. Bolt Stress.

S = stress in lbs., per sq. in. P = load, lbs. A = area, sq. ins.

53. The total stress in the bolts may be that due to tightening plus that due to pressure. This may be further increased by the twisting stress by an amount equal to 10 per cent. or more of the load stress. The stress due to tightening may be equal to the load stress.

54. To figure the load on bolts for cover plates or cylinder heads divide the total pressure by the number of bolts. The size is often found by using a low value for the working stress.

55. To figure the number of bolts, divide the total pressure by the working strength of the size of bolt selected. To maintain a tight joint under pressure requires careful judgment in selecting size of bolt, location of drilling and distance between bolts. The distance X between bolts should not generally exceed 4 or 5 times their diameter, Fig. 60. For plain joints either full or ring gaskets, Fig. 61 may be used.

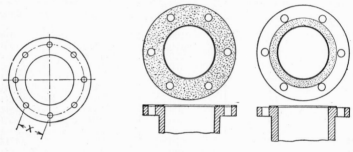

Fig. 60.   Fig. 61. Full and Ring Gaskets.

CHAPTER IIA

WELDED AND RIVETED CONSTRUCTION

56. Welding methods provide an efficient kind of fastening for an increasing field of applications. Machine frames, bases, jigs and fixtures, piping, and parts of machines as well as structures of all kinds can be built or put together by welding. Tanks and sheet metal containers of all sizes can be made by welding plates together. Plates, rods, and structural shapes can be used in the design of machines and parts. Welding instructions are given on drawings by symbols and notes.

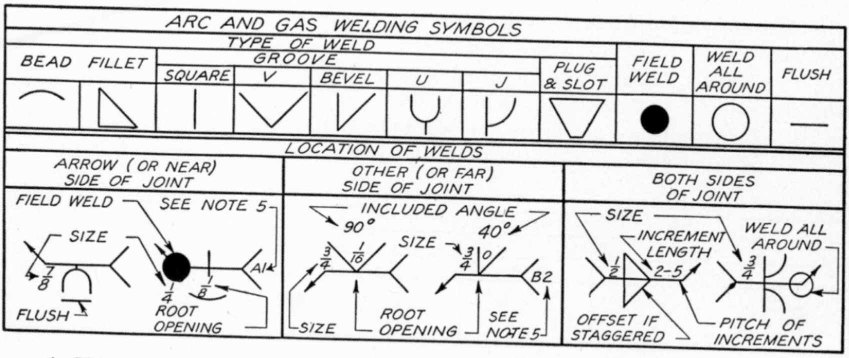

1. The side of the joint to which the arrow points is the arrow (or near) side.
2. Both-sides welds of same type are same size unless otherwise shown.
3. Symbols apply between abrupt changes in direction of joint or as dimenisoned (except where all-around symbol is used).
4. All welds are continuous and of user's standard proportions, unless otherwise shown.
5. Tail of arrow used for specification reference (tail may be omitted when reference not used).
6. Dimensions of weld sizes, increment lengths and spacings in inches.

Fig. 62.   Arc and Gas Welding Symbols.

57. The latest edition of "*Welding Symbols and Instructions for Their Use,*" published by the American Welding Society, New York, should be available for study and reference. The basic symbols shown in this chapter for two systems of welding are from the above publication.

(1) *Resistance welding* is a method in which the parts are pressed together and fused by passing an electric current through them. (2) *Arc welding* and gas (fusion) welding are methods in which a space is provided into which a metal rod or filler is melted to the metal parts. An electric arc or an acetylene torch is used for this purpose.

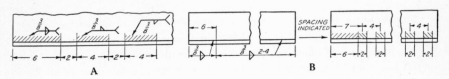

A   B

FIG. 63.   Some Applications of Fig. 62.

58. Arc and gas welding symbols are given in Fig. 62 and two brief quotations which apply to Fig. 63 are as follows:

A. "When it is desired to show extent of welds by hatching, use one type of hatching with definite end lines" as shown at **A** in Fig. 63.

B. "Increments and not spaces assumed to be at ends of all intermittent welds and overall length dimensions govern to ends of those increments" as shown at **B** in Fig. 63.

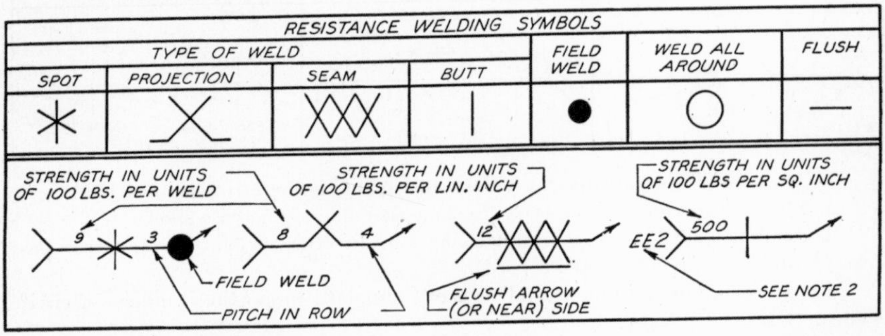

RESISTANCE WELDING SYMBOLS						
TYPE OF WELD				FIELD WELD	WELD ALL AROUND	FLUSH
SPOT	PROJECTION	SEAM	BUTT			
✳	✕	XXX	|	●	◯	—

STRENGTH IN UNITS OF 100 LBS. PER WELD — STRENGTH IN UNITS OF 100 LBS. PER LIN. INCH — STRENGTH IN UNITS OF 100 LBS PER SQ. INCH

9 ✳ 3 ●   8 ✕ 4   12 XXX   EE2 ⟩ 500

FIELD WELD   PITCH IN ROW   FLUSH ARROW (OR NEAR) SIDE   SEE NOTE 2

1. Symbols apply between abrupt changes in direction of joint or as dimensioned (except where all-around symbol is used).

2. Tail or arrow used for specification reference (tail may be omitted when reference not used).

3. All spacings in inches.

FIG. 64.   Resistance Welding Symbols.

59. Resistance welding symbols are given in Fig. 64 and a few brief quotations which apply to Fig. 65 are as follows:

" (a) Center resistance welding symbols for spot and seam welds on reference line because these symbols have no arrow side or other side (near and far side) significance: (see Fig. 64) but do not center projection welding symbols because the latter have such significance."

" (b) Designate resistance welds by strength rather than sign (because of impracticability of determining latter)."

A. "Spot and seam weld symbols may be used directly on drawings, thus; but projection weld symbols should not: 'as at A in Fig. 65.'"

B. "When not used on lines of drawing, connect reference line to center line of welds or rows of welds with arrow, thus: 'as at B in Fig. 65.'"

C. "Show welds of extent less than between abrupt changes in direction of joint, thus: 'as at C in Fig. 65.'"

D. "When the weld encircles the joint but there is no abrupt change in the direction of the joint or parts of the joint (changes in the direction of rolled structural sections are considered abrupt even though there are fillets in the corners), the all-around symbol may or may not be used as desired, thus: 'as at D in Fig. 65.'"

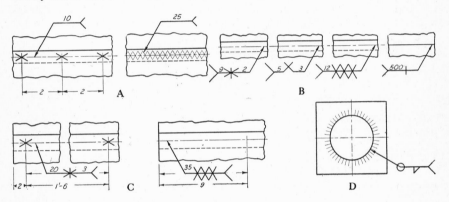

FIG. 65.   Some Applications of Fig. 64.

The location of welding information is indicated in Fig. 66.

The Tee-joint of Fig. 67 is described by the American Welding Society publication as follows:

"Double-fillet-welded, partially-grooved, double-J, tee-joint with incomplete penetration. (Type of joint shown by drawing.) Grooves of standard proportions (which are 1/2 in. R, 20° included angle, edges in contact before welding 3/4 in. deep for other (or far) side weld and 1 1/4 in. deep for arrow (or near) side weld. 3/8 in. continuous other (or far) side fillet weld and 1/2 in. intermittent arrow (or near) side fillet weld with increments 2 in. long, spaced 6 in. center-to-center. All fillets standard 45° fillets. All welding done in field in accordance with welding specification number A2 (which requires that weld be made by manual D.C. shielded metal-arc process using high-grade, covered, mild steel electrode; that root be unchipped and welds unpeened but that joint be preheated before welding)."

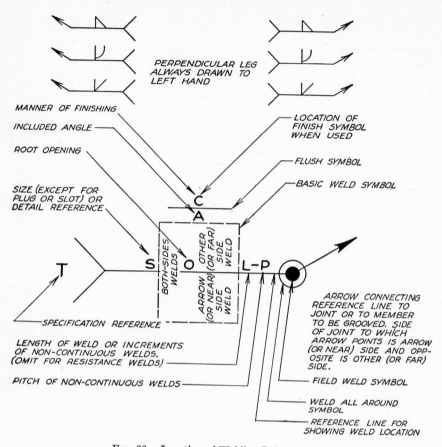

Fig. 66. Location of Welding Information.

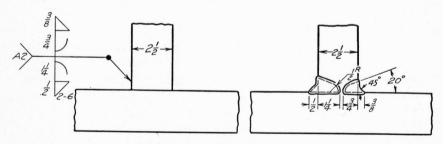

Fig. 67. Tee Joint Information.

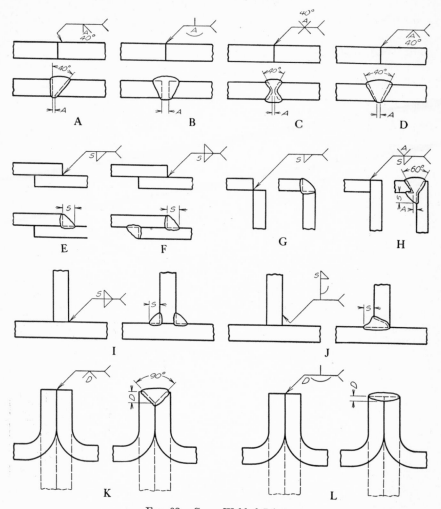

Fig. 68. Some Welded Joints.

60. Some typical welded joints are indicated in Fig. 68 which shows the symbols and the sections as follows: (The letters A, D, and S are used to indicate dimensions). **A.** Butt joint, 40° bevel groove, arrow side. **B.** Butt joint, open, square, bead, arrow side. **C.** Butt joint, 40° double V-groove, both sides. **D.** Butt joint, U-groove, arrow side. **E.** Lap joint, fillet weld, arrow side. **F.** Lap joint, fillet weld, both sides. **G.** Corner joint, bead on arrow side. **H.** Corner joint, single V, on arrow side, bead on other side. **I.** Tee-joint, fillet weld, both sides. **J.** Tee-joint, single-fillet, single-*J*, other side. **K.** Edge joint, *V*-groove. **L.** Edge joint, bead weld.

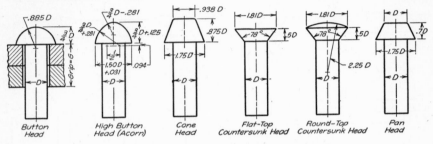

FIG. 69. American Standard Large Rivet Heads.

61. Riveting.—Machines or structures composed entirely or in part of sheet metal may be fastened together by rivets. Boilers, tanks, steel structures, machine frames, etc., are often fastened together permanently in this way. Rivets for such purposes are generally made of mild steel. They have a head on one end and sufficient length to allow forming a head on the other end after being put into place. They are driven hot (at a red heat).

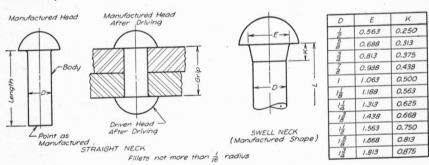

D	E	K
$\frac{1}{2}$	0.563	0.250
$\frac{5}{8}$	0.688	0.313
$\frac{3}{4}$	0.813	0.375
$\frac{7}{8}$	0.938	0.438
1	1.063	0.500
$1\frac{1}{8}$	1.188	0.563
$1\frac{1}{4}$	1.313	0.625
$1\frac{3}{8}$	1.438	0.668
$1\frac{1}{2}$	1.563	0.750
$1\frac{5}{8}$	1.668	0.813
$1\frac{3}{4}$	1.813	0.875

FIG. 70. American Standard Large Rivets.

62. Rivet Heads.—A rivet is a metal rod with a head on one end. Some basic proportions of rivet heads for large rivets (nominal diameters of $1/2''$ to $1^3/4''$) are given in Figs. 69 and 70, and for small rivets (nominal diameters of $7/16''$ and under) are given in Fig. 71. For dimensions and complete information see A.S.A. standards.[1]

[1] Large Rivets B18.4; Small Rivets B18a.

63. Rivet Holes.—The holes for rivets may be either punched or drilled. As punching injures the metal, drilled holes are better for pressure work and are required for steam boiler work. The injury due to punching may be removed by annealing or the hole may be punched small and reamed to size. Holes are made $1/16''$ larger than the rivets used in them. Thus a rivet for a $1''$ hole is $15/16''$ diameter before driving.

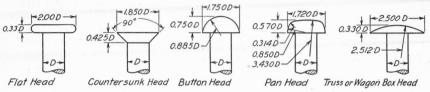

Flat Head   Countersunk Head   Button Head   Pan Head   Truss or Wagon Box Head

Fig. 71. American Standard Small Rivet Heads.

64. Calking.—For many purposes rivets must make a leaktight joint as well as hold the plates together. To assist in this a blunt chisel is used to force or pound the edge of one of the plates down against another. This is called calking and makes a steam or watertight joint between the plates. The bevel of about 75° to 80° shown in Fig. 72 at **A** is to make calking easier.

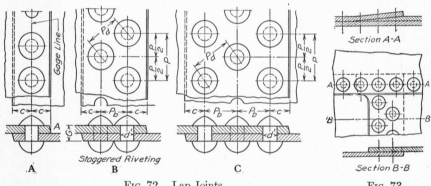

Staggered Riveting

A   B   C.

Fig. 72. Lap Joints.   Fig. 73.

65. Riveted Joints.—The nomenclature of riveted joints includes *gage line*, pitch (P), back pitch (P_b), diagonal pitch (P_d), marginal distance (c), and chain and staggered riveting, all of which are illustrated in Figs. 72 to 74. For a given joint the pitch is the maximum spacing (Fig. 74 at **B**). The *grip* (G) is equal to the thickness of the plates through which the rivet passes. The diameter of a rivet is (d). After driving it is (d'), the diameter of the rivet hole.

A classification of riveted joints for tanks, boilers, and pressure vessels in general includes:

1. Lap joints
     a. Single-riveted (Fig. 72 at **A**).
     b. Double-riveted (Fig. 72 at **B**).
     c. Triple-riveted (Fig. 72 at **C**).

2. Butt joints
     a. Single-riveted (Fig. 74 at **A**).
     b. Double-riveted (Fig. 74 at **B**).
     c. Triple-riveted ⎱
     d. Quadruple-riveted ⎰ not illustrated.
     e. Quintuple-riveted ⎰

66. A method of arranging a lap joint for three plates is indicated in Fig. 73. A butt joint uses one or two butt-straps as illustrated in Figs. 74

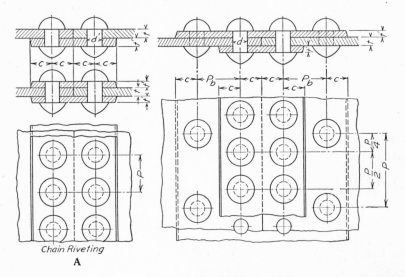

Chain Riveting
A

FIG. 74. Butt Joints.

at **A** and **B**. In general, lap joints are used for girth or circumferential seams, and butt joints for longitudinal seams, except for pressure less than 100 lbs. per sq. in. and for diameters less than 36 in. For the design of riveted joints refer to *Machine Design* by Berard and Waters, and for boiler construction refer to the codes of the American Society of Mechanical Engineers.

67. Miscellaneous Connections.—Methods of making connections are shown in Fig. 75A. Angles may be used as at I and IV or one of the plates may be bent as at II and III. In this case the radius of curvature r can be made about two and one-half times the thickness of the plate. Also note that a short straight part x is provided to allow easy calking.   When drawing to small scale, thin sections are sometimes blacked in as shown in Fig. 75B at I and II, which also illustrates methods of closing the ends of

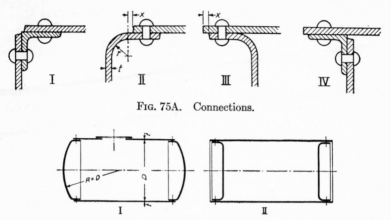

Fig. 75A.   Connections.

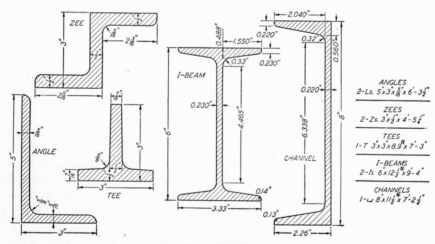

Fig. 75B.   Cylindrical Tanks.

cylindrical tanks.   With rounded ends the radius of curvature can be taken equal to the diameter of the tank.

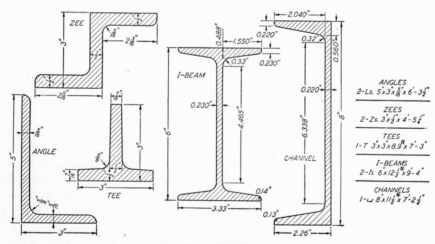

Fig. 76A.   Steel Shapes.

68. Rolled Steel Shapes.—For many constructions, rolled steel shapes are used.   The dimensions and weights as well as other information can

MACHINE DRAWING

best be obtained from the handbooks issued by the steel companies. The names of a few of the common sections are given in Fig. 76A.

The pitch of rivets for structural purposes may be taken at from three to six inches. The distance from the center of the rivet to the edge of the

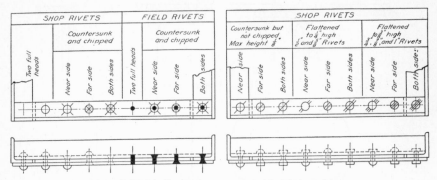

Fig. 76B. American Standard Rivet Symbols.

plate should be about two times the rivet diameter. The pitch for various sizes of rivets is given below.

MINIMUM RIVET SPACING

Diameter of rivet in inches	$^1/_4$	$^3/_8$	$^1/_2$	$^5/_8$	$^3/_4$	$^7/_8$	1
Pitch in inches	$^3/_4$	$1^1/_8$	$1^1/_2$	$1^7/_8$	$2^1/_4$	$2^5/_8$	3

The American Standard conventional representation of rivets is shown in Fig. 76B.

69. Aluminum aircraft rivets are made with four shapes of heads and of aluminum and aluminum alloys. Standard head markings are used for alloy identification as indicated in Fig. 77A.

Type A is made of 2S aluminum and requires no heat treatment before using.

Type D is made of 17ST aluminum alloy and must be heat-treated before using. Min. shear, 30,000# /sq.in.

Type AD is made of A17S-T aluminum alloy and must NOT be heat-treated before using. Min. shear 25,000# /sq.in.

Type DD is made of 24S-T aluminum alloy and must be heated before using. Min. shear, 35,000# /sq. in.

Code: AN425-4-6 means type A with countersunk head, $^1/_8''$ diameter and $^3/_8''$ long (the first dash number is the number of 32nds diameter ($^4/_{32}$ diam.) and the last number is the length in 16ths ($^6/_{16}$ long)). In like manner: AN430D-8 means round head, $^3/_{32}$ inch diam., $^1/_2$ inch long; AN442AD4-10 means flat head $^1/_8$ inch diam., $^5/_8$ inch long; AN442DD6-12 means brazier head, $^3/_{16}$ inch diam., $^3/_4$ inch long.

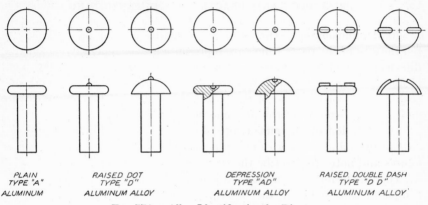

PLAIN TYPE "A" ALUMINUM   RAISED DOT TYPE "D" ALUMINUM ALLOY   DEPRESSION TYPE "AD" ALUMINUM ALLOY   RAISED DOUBLE DASH TYPE "D D" ALUMINUM ALLOY

FIG. 77A.   Alloy Identification for Rivets.

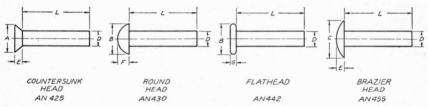

COUNTERSUNK HEAD AN 425   ROUND HEAD AN430   FLATHEAD AN442   BRAZIER HEAD AN455

FIG. 77B.   Aircraft Rivets.

Explosive rivets, Fig. 77C, are used for blind riveting. After the rivet is inserted as at A, a tiny charge in the end of the rivet is exploded to form a blind head as at B.

FIG. 77C.   Explosive Rivet.

ALUMINUM AND ALUMINUM ALLOY AIRCRAFT RIVETS (FIG. 77B)

Dash No.	D	A	B	C	E	F	G
−2	$^1/_{16}$	.117	$^1/_8$	$^5/_{32}$	$^1/_{32}$	.047	.025
−3	$^3/_{32}$	.168	$^3/_{16}$	$^{15}/_{64}$	$^3/_{64}$	.070	.038
−4	$^1/_8$	.226	$^1/_4$	$^5/_{16}$	$^1/_{16}$	.094	.050
−5	$^5/_{32}$	.282	$^5/_{16}$	$^{25}/_{64}$	$^5/_{64}$	.117	.062
−6	$^3/_{16}$	.339	$^3/_8$	$^{15}/_{32}$	$^3/_{32}$	.141	.075
−8	$^1/_4$	.452	$^1/_2$	$^5/_8$	$^1/_8$	.188	.100
−10	$^5/_{16}$	.565	$^5/_8$	$^{25}/_{32}$	$^5/_{32}$	.234	.125
−12	$^3/_8$	.678	$^3/_4$	$^{15}/_{16}$	$^3/_{16}$	.281	.150

CHAPTER III

PRINCIPLES AND PRACTICE OF DIMENSIONING

70. Dimensioning.—Dimensions are figures placed on drawings to tell the size of the parts which are represented. As generally considered, dimensioning also includes specification as to degree of accuracy, kind of finish, materials, number of parts, etc. To dimension a drawing successfully the construction of the patterns, methods of machining, fitting and putting together of the machine must be studied.

71. Notation of Dimensioning.—The notation of dimensioning consists of lines and symbols used on a drawing to show the application of figures and notes to describe the size of a machine or part.

The dimensioning of a drawing is never started until all the views are complete, thus finishing the description of shape. Following this, extension and dimension lines are drawn to indicate the location of dimensions. Finally the arrow points, figures and notes are put on, using a lettering pen.

A *dimension line*, Fig. 78, indicates a distance, the amount of which is shown by a figure placed in a space left in the dimension line.

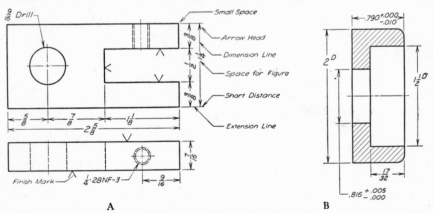

Fig. 78. Notation of Dimensioning.

Arrow-heads or *points* are used at the ends of a dimension line to show the extent of a dimension. An arrow point very much enlarged is shown in Fig. 79. Note that it is two and one-half times as long as it is wide and that the two sides are slightly curved.

Extension lines are used to extend lines of a view when a dimension line is placed outside of the view.   A small space is always left between an extension line and the object line, Fig. 78.   The extension line extends a small distance beyond the arrow-head.

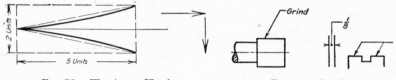

FIG. 79.   The Arrow-Head.   FIG. 80.   Leaders.

Pointing or *leading* lines are fine, full lines drawn from a figure or note to show the part of the drawing to which the figure or note applies. Straight, ruled lines terminated with an arrow-head are preferred, Fig. 80.

72. Surfaces which are machined are said to be "finished" and are indicated on a drawing by marking the line which represents the edge view of the surface with a symbol "*f*" shown enlarged in Fig. 81, or a 60 deg. "V" touching the line (Am. Std.).   The kind and quality of finish is designated by a letter or symbol [1] placed in the opening of the "V" and listed on the drawing.

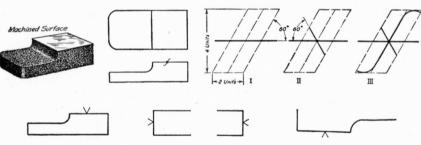

FIG. 81.   The Finish Mark.

Feet are indicated by the mark (') and inches by (") as 5'-3".   When all dimensions are given in inches the inch marks are often omitted.

It has been almost universal practice in the past to place the dimensions to read "in line" with the dimension lines so as to read from the lower and right-hand edges of the sheet.   Such an aligned system is used in Fig. 78 at **A**.   This practice is followed in most engineering work. However, the aircraft industry places all the dimensions so as to read from the bottom of the sheet except when conditions make it undesirable. Such a unidirectional or one direction system is used in Fig. 78 at **B**.   This system is being adopted to some extent in certain other industries.

73. Elements of Dimensioning.—A definite method of dimensioning consists of separating construction into elementary parts. These parts

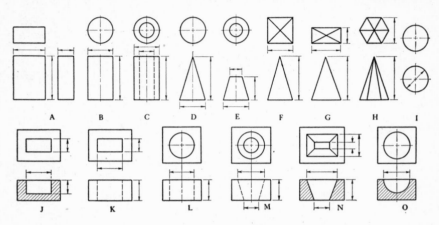

Fig. 82. Elementary Size Dimensions.

can then be divided into geometrical shapes. Each shape can then be dimensioned and the relation of one to another fixed by location dimen-

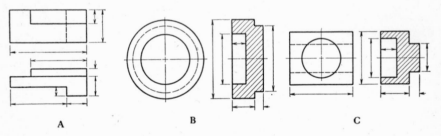

Fig. 83. Size Dimensions.

sions. Thus there are two kinds of dimensions to be considered:

1. Size dimensions.
2. Location dimensions.

74. Size Dimensions.—The elementary cases include the type solids, which may be either positive or negative (Fig. 82) such as the following:

For a prism give the dimension parallel to the edges and the other necessary dimensions on the other view.

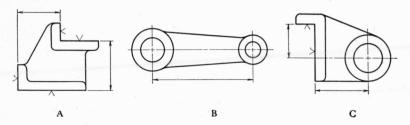

A   B   C

FIG. 84.   Location Dimensions.

For a pyramid the dimensions may be on one or two views depending upon the shape of the base.

For a right circular cylinder give the diameter and length on one view.

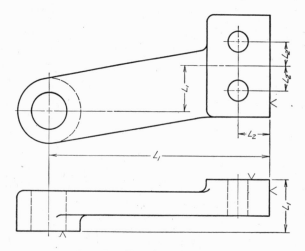

FIG. 85.   Location Dimensions.

For a right circular cone give both dimensions on one view.   For a frustum give the three dimensions on one view.

For a sphere give the diameter.

For other shapes give dimensions based upon the methods of forming or the practical requirements of manufacture.

Size dimensions for prisms are shown at **A** in Fig. 83, for cylinders at **B**, and for cylinders and prisms at **C**.

75. Location dimensions are used to position the elementary parts in relation to each other or from primary locating references such as base lines, axes, and finished or contact surfaces. Prisms are located by surfaces, by axes, or both. Cylinders are located by axes and bases.

Location dimensions are illustrated in Fig. 84 which shows *surface to surface* dimensions at **A**, *center to center* dimensions at **B**, and *surface to center* dimensions at **C**.

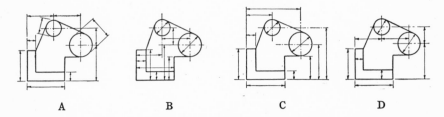

A   B   C   D

FIG. 86.   Placing Dimensions.

There are two principal kinds of location dimensions, primary and secondary. Primary location dimensions (marked L_1 on Fig. 85) are from main axes or positioning surfaces. Secondary location dimensions (marked L_2 on Fig. 85) are derived from the elementary parts which make up the piece. They are often mating dimensions and must be given from the same reference line on the mating pieces.

76. Location of Dimensions.—Facility in manufacture should be a motto in dimensioning. The figures must be so placed as to be easily found and perfectly clear in their meaning when found. Consider the effect of location upon ease of reading the drawing. It is very seldom necessary to repeat dimensions. Drilling is generally best located in the view where it shows in plan, that is, in the view where it is laid out. The drilling for flanges is dimensioned by giving the diameter of the bolt circle and the size of bolt holes. The holes are understood to be equally spaced unless otherwise noted.

It is generally preferable to place the dimensions outside of the view as at **A** in Fig. 86, as this separates the size from the shape and allows the details to be clearly seen.

Dimensions may be placed inside of a large simple view when it is desirable to preserve the outline. It is not generally desirable as it produces confusion due to crossing of lines and crowding of figures (Fig. 86 at **B**).

Dimensions may be given from reference or base lines as at **C** in Fig. 86. This is particularly adapted to plate work and laying out, where holes or other details must be accurately located.

A combination of the methods of **A, B,** and **C** in which dimensions are placed outside of the views whenever conveniently possible is shown at **D**. This method is the one generally used.

Dimension lines must be kept away from other lines and from each other. The clear distance between lines should be from $^{3}/_{16}''$ to $^{5}/_{16}''$, estimated. If there are several parallel lines they should be the same distance apart. Larger dimensions should be kept outside of smaller ones. In the interest of clearness there should be as few lines as possible crossing each other. Similar pieces should be dimensioned in exactly the same way.

77. When a slanting dimension line must be used, the figure reads in line with the slant, either from the left or right as in Fig. 87 where the limiting angle is shown as 45°.

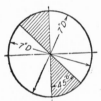

FIG. 87.   Slanting Dimension Lines.

When a dimension line is made continuous for several successive dimensions, as in Fig. 88, it is said to be " continuous."

When the dimension lines for several successive dimensions are not continuous, they are said to be " staggered," Fig. 89.

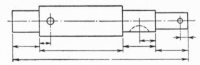

FIG. 88.   "Continuous" or "Chain"
Dimensions

FIG. 89.   "Staggered" Dimensions.

78. Methods of Finishing.—Kinds of finished surfaces should be indicated by a note as in Fig. 90. The meaning of the different shop

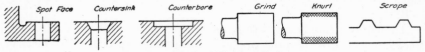

FIG. 90. Kinds of Finished Surfaces.

operations involved should be found by consulting a good shop handbook. Holes should be marked according to how they are to be formed or treated as: Core; Drill; Bore; Punch; Ream; Tap; Counterbore; Countersink; etc. Surfaces should be marked to tell the shop operations to be performed as: Finished; Rough Finish; Chipped; Spot Faced; Scraped; Ground; Polished; Filed; etc.

The kind of fit is sometimes marked as Loose Fit; Running Fit; Driving Fit; Forced or Pressed Fit; Shrink Fit; etc. The tendency of present practice is to give the tolerance or limits of accuracy required.

79. Dimensioning Arcs and Curves.—A number of cases of dimensioning arcs and curves are illustrated in Fig. 91. If a complete circle

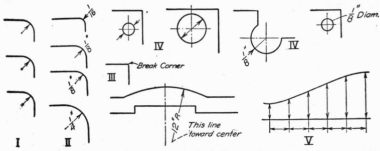

FIG. 91. Arcs and Curves.

is shown, give the diameter in preference to the radius. For arcs and fillets give the radius. If desired, the center for a radius may be indicated by one of the methods shown at I. For a very small radius the figure may be placed as at II. The note " break corner " at III means that the sharp corner is to be removed so that it will be slightly rounded. The dimension line for an arc should always take a direction which would pass through the center as shown in the figures. The methods at IV may be used for small diameters. For other curves a templet may be called for, or shown full size on the sheet. Another method is to give a number of parallel dimensions and the distance between them as at V.

80. Dimensioning Angles and Tapers.—Angles are generally dimensioned by giving the number of degrees included between the two sides. Three methods of dimensioning angles are shown in Fig. 92. For many

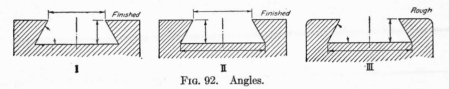

FIG. 92.   Angles.

purposes standard tapers are used, in which the name and number of the taper is given in a note. This fixes all necessary dimensions as given in tables for B. & S. (Brown & Sharpe); Morse; Read Lathe Center; Jarno, and Sellers Tapers. Sometimes a note is employed giving the taper per inch or per foot of length, as $3/4''$ *per foot*. When the slope is considerable it may be given as a ratio, as 1 : 1, indicating a 45° slope. When fillets or rounds come at the ends of inclined lines the methods of Fig. 93 at I,

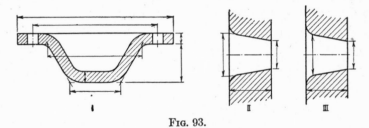

FIG. 93.

II, and III are used. The larger diameter at III although located inside gives the same dimension as at II. The dimensions indicate the distances between the sloping lines where they cut the vertical lines.

81. Dimensioning in Crowded Places.—A drawing should be made to a scale sufficiently large to carry most of the dimensions without crowding. It is not always possible to avoid a few somewhat crowded dimensions. Notes and figures may be placed out of their usual positions when necessary. Some methods to use in such cases to preserve clearness are shown in Fig. 94.

82. Dimensioning Shafts and Cylindrical Pieces.—Shafts should be dimensioned by giving the diameters and lengths together with the sizes of keyways and pins and their location, Fig. 95. Often the size dimensions both detail and overall are given below the view and the location dimensions above.

Examples of dimensioning for shafts and similar conditions are shown in Fig. 96. The position of bearings is sometimes shown by diagonal

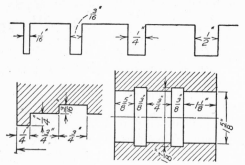

FIG. 94. "Crowded" Dimensions.

lines, either plain or " blacked in." A square section may be shown in a similar way. A note should be used in either case if necessary to make the meaning clear. Positions of pulleys, gears, etc., are located by center lines as in the drawing, Fig. 205.

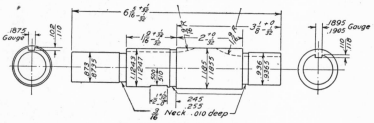

FIG. 95. A Shaft Drawing.

83. Dimensioning Wood Constructions.—Such wood constructions as the engineer has to do with seldom require such close dimensions as are common for metal machinery. Timbers are located by centers, and are dimensioned by note as 2 x 4; 4 x 6; etc. Sometimes with the

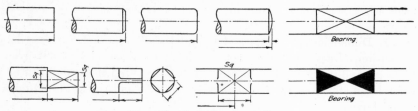

FIG. 96. Shaft Representations.

length added as 2″ x 8″—6′-10″. Boards are specified by note as 1″ x 10″; ³/₄″ x 6″, etc. Such sizes are nominal rather than exact as a 2″ x 4″ piece measures 1⁵/₈″ x 3⁵/₈″, etc. General overall dimensions should be given and any other dimensions which must come to a required figure. Wood foundation timbers; crib work; shelves; wall and ceiling planks to support or hold machines, pulleys, etc., and similar mechanical uses of wood must be drawn and dimensioned by the mechanical draftsman, Fig. 97. Nails, screws, bolts, etc., are specified in notes.

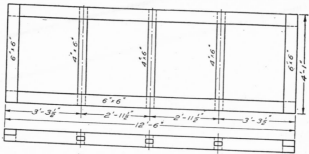

FIG. 97.   Dimensioning Wood.

Nails are specified by a number followed by the letter d.   8 d means 100 nails weigh 8 lbs., and is read 8 penny.

84. Dimensioning for Interchangeable Manufacture.—The whole question of limits, fits, tolerance, manufacturing equipment of machines, tools, jigs, fixtures, etc., is involved in properly dimensioning a drawing for parts which are to be interchangeable. It is not necessary that limits be given for every dimension but only for those which are required because of the relation of parts. Some dimensions should be given without limits especially when particular accuracy is not required. Giving limits for all dimensions frequently makes the specification ambiguous as where several part dimensions are each given limits and the overall dimension is also given limits as in Fig. 98. The separate dimensions might be within the limits but the overall might not be, as a great number of combinations of part dimensions are possible. Fig. 99 is the correct method where several dimensions are given limits. In such cases take all measurements from the same surface. The dimensioning of drawings for interchangeable manufacture is an important part of design and specification for mass production. It requires both study and experience and a knowledge of the particular company's product and manufacturing facilities.

85. Ordinary dimensions without any indication of accuracy are used to give *nominal sizes*. In such cases the actual measurements may vary slightly from the dimensions which give the nominal size. In general, a large proportion of the dimensions on drawings of castings and forgings are nominal size dimensions. When common fractions are used for machined parts the variation may be taken as not more than $1/128''$ over or under the basic size for dimensions of $1/4''$ or less, and not more than $1/64''$ over or under the basic size for dimensions of more than $1/4''$. Decimals are used when greater accuracy is required. The necessity for accuracy becomes important when it implies accurately fitted mating parts as illustrated in the assembly of a modern machine tool in order that it may be

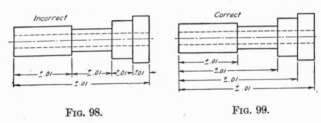

FIG. 98.   FIG. 99.

operated satisfactorily for the purpose for which it was designed. In manufacturing machine parts it is practically impossible to machine them exactly to the specified dimensions. Consequently, in order to have parts fit and mate together properly some definite limitations for these errors must be made. A *basic size*, or theoretically exact basic dimension, is followed by upper (+ plus) and lower (− minus) limits, such as $3.5 \begin{smallmatrix} + .0035 \\ - .0025 \end{smallmatrix}$, which the workman must not exceed. The difference between these limits is called *tolerance;* it represents the amount of error permitted or tolerated when machining to the specified dimension.

When two parts are fitted together the difference between a dimension of one part and the corresponding dimension of the second part is called *allowance*. For a loose fit, such as a shaft turning in a bearing, the allowance is "positive," i.e., there is a small amount of clearance between the parts. For a tight fit, such as a shaft forced into a wheel, the allowance is "negative," i.e., it represents interference which is overcome by stretching the hole or by compressing the shaft as the latter is forced into the hole.

Interchangeable manufacture involves many problems of accuracy in manufacturing equipment such as tools, jigs, and fixtures. Limits should be given for only those dimensions which require them because of the particular relation of fitted parts.

The choice of tolerance and allowance is related to the method of assembly as well as to the purpose of a machine or its parts. The limiting sizes for interchangeable assembly must be such that any given part selected from a quantity of the same kind can be used with any mating part (Fig. 99A).

For selective assembly, limits are fixed but parts are selected which will result in the desired fit, thus: for wring, force, and shrink fits, large shafts are mated with large holes and small shafts with small holes, to give the required interference of metal (Fig. 99-B).

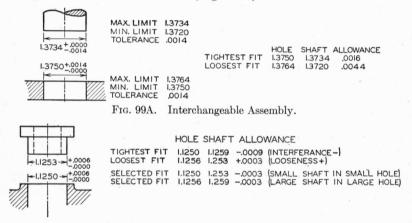

MAX. LIMIT 1.3734
MIN. LIMIT 1.3720
TOLERANCE .0014

1.3734 +.0000 −.0014

1.3750 +.0014 −.0000

MAX. LIMIT 1.3764
MIN. LIMIT 1.3750
TOLERANCE .0014

	HOLE	SHAFT	ALLOWANCE
TIGHTEST FIT	1.3750	1.3734	.0016
LOOSEST FIT	1.3764	1.3720	.0044

FIG. 99A.   Interchangeable Assembly.

	HOLE	SHAFT	ALLOWANCE	
TIGHTEST FIT	1.1250	1.1259	−.0009	(INTERFERANCE −)
LOOSEST FIT	1.1256	1.253	+.0003	(LOOSENESS +)
SELECTED FIT	1.1250	1.253	−.0003	(SMALL SHAFT IN SMALL HOLE)
SELECTED FIT	1.1256	1.259	−.0003	(LARGE SHAFT IN LARGE HOLE)

1.1253 → +.0006 −.0000

1.1250 → +.0006 −.0000

FIG. 99B.   Selective Assembly.

86. General Rules.—Some rules and practice not included in the preceding articles are here collected.

For a complete drawing: give sizes of pieces for the patternmaker; give sizes and finish for the machinist; give assembly dimensions; give office dimensions; give notes where needed.

Always dimension similar parts in the same way.

Give dimensions from finished surfaces or to center lines. When a

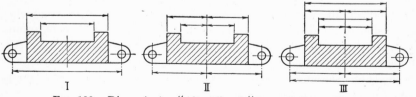

I   II   III

FIG. 100.   Dimensioning "About" and "Across" Center Lines.

piece is symmetrical, the dimension is given "about" or across the center line, as at I, Fig. 100. Methods shown at II and III are sometimes used.

Place dimensions so that other dimensions or lines do not cross them or crowd them. Where a number of dimension lines are parallel do not place the figures under each other but locate as in Fig. 101.

"Overall" dimensions should be given when necessary as at I, Fig. 102. For the piece shown at II, *do not* give overall dimension but give "center to center" dimension.

When most of the dimensions are in inches, they may all be given in inches and the mark (″) omitted.

When feet and inches are used, always indicate by the mark (′) and (″) or by (ft.) and (in.). Decimals may have the point emphasized by writing thus 1.″05.

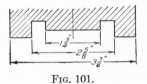

FIG. 101.

Center lines and object lines have only one purpose and should never be used as dimension lines.

On structural drawings, dimension lines are made continuous and the figure is placed above the line.

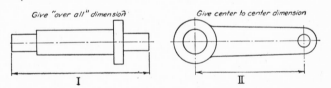

I   II

FIG. 102. "Overall" and "Center to Center" Dimensions.

Where clearness is not sacrificed, parts can sometimes be defined in one view by using a note to give missing dimensions or to specify diameters, etc.

Small details which are standardized do not have to be completely dimensioned. This is true for bolts and screws, standard tapers, piping, wire, sheet metal, rope, chain, pins, rolled steel shapes, etc. See "Machinery" or "American Machinist" Handbooks. The names, terms, and methods of specifying sizes of materials and supplies used should be consulted in the company's standards and in manufacturers' lists.

Do not put notes within views if it can be avoided. Keep notes clear of all lines. In general, put all notes referring to the same piece together and near the view of that piece.

Use leaders or pointing lines to show where notes apply.

The dimension for a diameter should be followed by the letter D (unless evident on the drawing). The dimension for a radius should be followed by the letter R.

87. Checking Drawings.—The checking of a drawing is one of the important duties of most draftsmen. Whenever possible it should be done by someone who has not worked on the drawing. In the drafting room the regular procedure is to make a "check print" from the tracing. This print is used to check the views, dimensions, notes, and other items. A light blueprint or a positive print may be used. Sometimes colored pencils are used, one color for what is OK and another to make corrections or changes. For school drawings a soft lead pencil is satisfactory.

The first thing to do is to see if the drawing can be used without unnecessary difficulty, and to see if the parts are such as will fit together and operate successfully.

There must be sufficient views to completely determine the parts.

All necessary dimensions for making the patterns, machining and erecting must be given and properly located.

Details and dimensions must be shown without crowding. This requires proper choice of scale.

All figures must be checked for correctness by use of the scale and by computation.

Notes containing the same meaning should be worded in the same way.

The materials of which the parts are made should be specified.

The construction of the patterns, cores, and methods of machining must be considered.

All finished surfaces must be indicated. The kind of finish and accuracy required must be specified.

Limits or tolerance, must be given for dimensions where necessary.

Basic or starting surfaces and center lines must be located.

There must be clearance for moving parts.

The name of each piece and the number required for a single machine or unit should be given on detail drawings.

Manufacturing methods and the selection of sizes must be checked for conformity with company. practice. The drawings should call for the use of standard tools available and not special sizes. Special and difficult operations should be avoided to permit regular methods of manufacture.

CHAPTER IV

MACHINE DRAWING

88. Working Drawings.—Any drawing used to give information and directions for doing work is a working drawing.

Such drawings are made by architects and civil, mechanical, and electrical engineers, for buildings, bridges, power plants, machine shops and all kinds of industrial work. This book treats of present practice in machine drawing.

89. There are two general classes of machine drawings—assembly drawings and detail drawings. These have been listed as follows:

A. Assembly drawings in outline or section. Design lay-out drawings. Erection drawings. Skeleton or diagram drawings.

B. Assembly working drawings. Part assembly working drawings. Location drawings to show relation of parts with dependent dimensions and fits for two or more details. Tool, jig and fixture drawings.

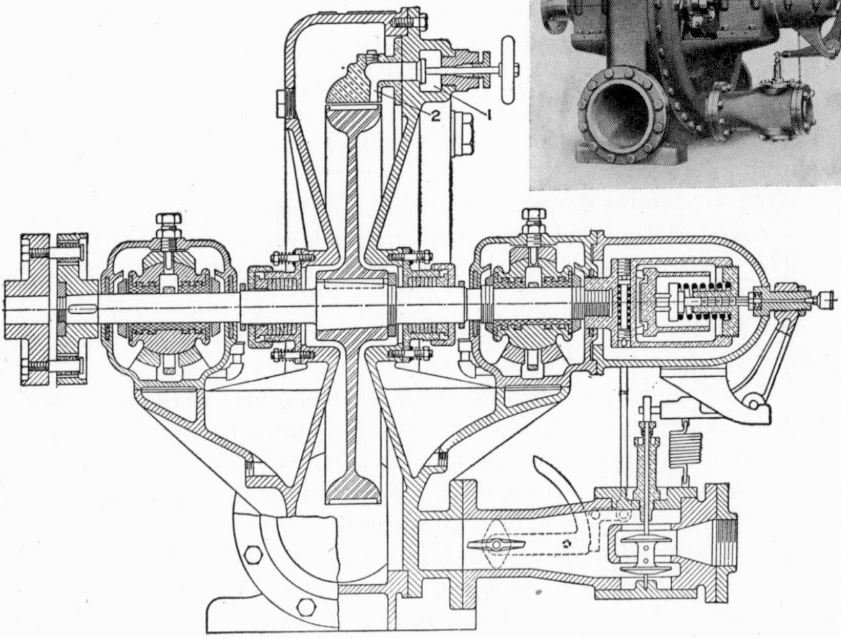

Fig. 103. Main Assembly Drawing.

C. Detail working drawings.   General purpose drawings.   Pattern drawings.   Machine drawings.   Forging drawings, etc.

90. A main assembly drawing of a B. F. Sturtevant Co., Type 6, Steam Turbine is shown in Fig. 103.

"Steam enters an annular steam chamber in the casing of the turbine through a balanced throttle valve (1).   From this chamber it passes through nozzles (2) to the rotor or bucket wheel.   These nozzles expand the steam to a pressure equal to the exhaust pressure in the turbine casing, so that the steam leaves the nozzles at a very high velocity.

"At this high velocity the steam then impinges against the semi-circular rotor buckets, imparting full impulse to the rotor, and leaves the buckets in the reverse direction.   As it leaves the rotor, the steam enters the semi-circular reversing buckets, which are cast in one piece with the nozzles, which again reverse the direction of the steam and drive it back into the rotor.   The steam enters and leaves the rotor in a circular motion several times before its kinetic energy is absorbed and its velocity dropped to that of the rotor.   It then passes out into the exhaust."

91. Detail Drawings.—A detail drawing, Fig. 104, is one which contains the necessary views of each single piece, completely dimensioned and with specifications as to material, machining, etc.

1. Choose views which will completely describe the shape of the piece.
2. Do not draw unnecessary views.

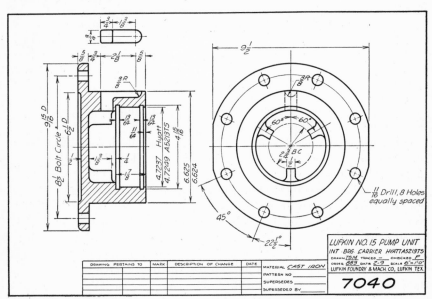

FIG. 104.   A Detail Drawing.

3. Views should carry dimensions without crowding.

4. Choose a scale that will show the piece clearly.

5. Choose a scale that will not require crowding of dimensions.

6. Detail drawings are made full size, half size, quarter size or eighth size.

7. Avoid the use of different scales on same sheet when possible.

8. Arrange detail parts in the same position and order that they will have in the assembled machine when this is possible.

9. Keep views of each part near together but do not crowd them.

10. Leave a space between views of *different* pieces.

11. When possible, details that are closely related mechanically should be kept on the same sheet.

12. Make detail drawings so complete that no additional information will be required for duplicating the parts shown.

13. Small parts may be grouped together as: small castings; bronze and composition castings; forgings; bolts and screws, etc.

14. Standard small parts such as pressure gauges, oil and grease cups, lubricators, valves, ball bearings, etc., which can be described by notes can be drawn in outline or not at all.

15. If special or extra views of any kind are used, they must be defined by explanatory notes.

92. Making a Detail Drawing.—There are three major considerations when starting a detail drawing.

> (a) Choice of Views,
> (b) Treatment of Views,
> (c) Choice of Scale.

A freehand layout sketch is very convenient and helpful, especially when standard size drawing sheets must be used.

First locate the main *center* and *base lines* for all views. Then draw the *preliminary blocking in* lines for all views. Finally work out the shape of the object.

93. Consider the object shown in Fig. 105. Two base lines and two center lines have been drawn at I in the order shown by the numbers. Note that the front view is located by the two base lines and that the top and end views are each located by one center line and one base line. At II the preliminary " *blocking in* " lines have been drawn very lightly, while at III, three of the final lines drawn distinctly have been added as their length is fixed. The " blocking in " is completed at IV. The details have been drawn at V and the preliminary lines have been gone over to give them the character of the other final lines.

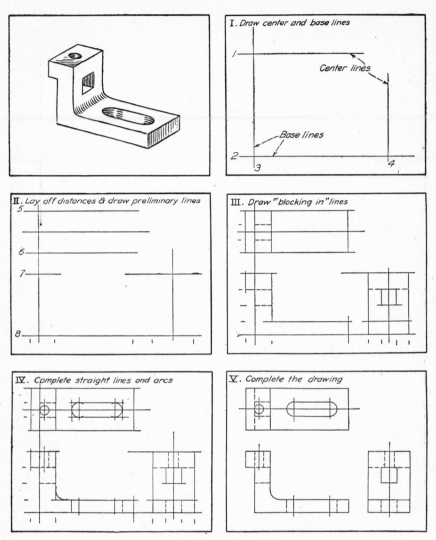

Fig. 105.   Penciling a Detail Drawing.

The general procedure for pencil drawings is to block in with straight lines and large circles.   The small circles and fillets are drawn last.   If the drawing is not to be inked or traced, the dimension, extension, and section lines should be drawn very lightly and the figures and notes added.

94. Drawings are not often inked on paper as good pencil work serves just as well and requires less time. If many copies are wanted, tracing cloth is used. The ink will work better on the dull side, especially if it is first dusted with powdered chalk. For erasing either pencil or ink, use a pencil eraser. Pencil tracings are often made on tracing paper or cloth. If a thin bond paper is used, blue prints can be made from pencil drawings. The dimensions are often put on in ink. The order of inking is shown in Fig. 106, where fine lines are used to represent the pencil drawing.

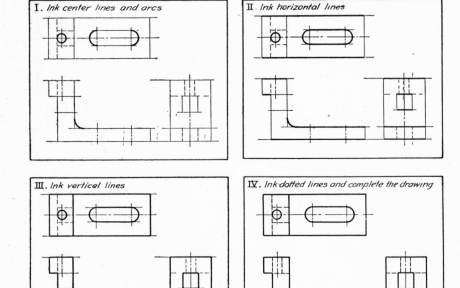

I. Ink center lines and arcs

II. Ink horizontal lines

III. Ink vertical lines

IV. Ink dotted lines and complete the drawing

Fig. 106. Inking a Detail Drawing.

95. The order of inking on either paper or cloth is:

1. Center lines.
2. Small circular arcs and circles.
3. Large circular arcs and circles.
4. Irregular curved lines.
5. Straight horizontal lines.
6. Straight vertical and slant lines.
7. Dotted circles and arcs.
8. Dotted straight lines.
9. Extension and dimension lines.
10. Dimensions, notes, title.
11. Section lining.

All inking except arrow points, figures and lettering must be done with the instruments and the order given must be followed if good drawings are to be made. Use Gillott's 404 pen for lettering, arrows etc.

96. Reproduction of Drawings.—The usual method of making copies of drawings is by direct contact printing. The drawing on tracing paper or cloth is placed with the drawing side against glass. Paper with a "light sensitive" coating is held in contact with the drawing while light is supplied through the glass.

If blueprint paper is used it is removed and washed in water. The result is a white line drawing on a blue ground. Other papers may be used to obtain prints with blue, black, brown, red, etc., lines on a light ground. Development may be wet (using the proper solutions) or dry (using vapors) according to the particular paper used. Electric printing machines (Fig. 107), with equipment to give finished prints, are used. Enlarged, reduced, or same size copies (photostats) are made with the Photostat (a specially designed camera).

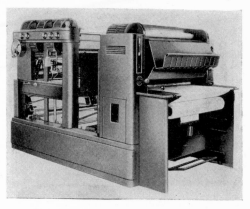

FIG. 107. Blueprinting Machine with Washer and Dryer.
(*The C. F. Pease Company.*)

Other methods of reproduction include the offset printing process, the hectograph, and the mimeograph.

97. Assembly Drawings.—As already indicated, assembly drawings may be made for almost any purpose. For showing the general appearance of a machine and giving center and overall dimensions an outline assembly such as Fig. 108 is used.

It is sometimes desirable to give all the dimensions on an assembly drawing so that the machine can be built from it. This gives an assembly working drawing. A part or group assembly drawing shows a group of parts in their relation to each other. If dimensioned, no detail drawings are needed.

Piping or wiring diagrams are assembly drawings made to show the sizes, location and arrangement of pipes and wires. When drawn to scale and completely dimensioned, they are called piping or wiring drawings.

Erection drawings show the order of putting parts together, dimensions for center distances, location of oil holes, valves, switches, etc.

98. Making an Assembly Drawing.—The purpose for which the drawing is desired must first be considered, after which the proper selection of views must be made. The next step is to determine the position of the views on the sheet and the scale to be used. The detail drawings are then collected ready for reference.

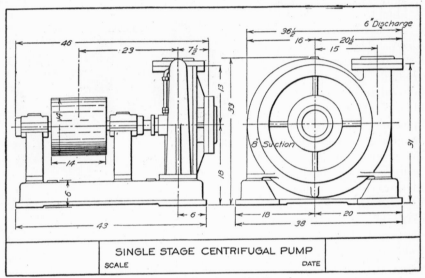

SINGLE STAGE CENTRIFUGAL PUMP

SCALE   DATE

Fig. 108.   Outline Assembly Drawing.

Locate the main center and base lines for the complete machine. Locate the center and base lines of the larger details of which the machine is composed. Draw the larger stationary parts in the different views. Determine limiting positions of moving parts if there are any. After this the smaller parts may be drawn very much in the same order as though assembling the actual machine. Since a small scale is often used, judgment must be exercised as to the amount of detail to be drawn. The character of the machine must show in the completed drawing. Maximum distances for stationary or moving parts, positions for foundation bolts, location of shafts, pulleys, piping and other dimensions having to do with erection or connecting up must be checked and are often given on the drawing.

99. Identification, Record, Etc.—For commercial engineering work, clean cut drawings having a definite character and containing all essential information are required. Extra views or notes, " fancy " lettering, complete detailing of standard parts to exact scale, confusion of dotted lines, and other non-essential work add to the cost of the drawing and to the cost of using the drawing.

Every piece drawn should have a name and a number so that it can be identified. The same name should always be used for a given part. The identification number for a part is generally put in a circle near the name of the part or the views representing it.

When a drawing is started the date and draftsman's name should be written on it. When the tracing is completed it should be signed either in full or by initials, by all who have worked on it, as draftsman, tracer, and checker, and by those responsible for its approval. Abbreviations lead to mistakes and should not be used when they can be avoided.

MATERIAL LIST

Part Number	Name of Part	No. Reqd.	Mat'l.	Pattern No.	Remarks
1	Emergency Valve	1	C.I.	M-932	
2	Valve Stem	1	Steel		
3	Stuffing Box Gland	1	C.I.	M-933	
4	Gland Stud	2	Steel		
5	Valve Liner	1	Tool Steel		
6	Bell Crank	1	Tool Steel		
7	Stud for No. 6	1	Steel		
8	Split Pin for No. 1	2	Steel		$\frac{3}{16}" \times 2"$

FIG. 109.   Bill of Material.

When used the possibility of misunderstanding must be considered and a standard form adopted. When changes are made on a drawing they should be indicated. This is often done by enclosing a letter in a circle

BOLT LIST FOR 5"x6" STEAM ENGINE

No.	Name	No. Reqd	Diam	Lgth.	Lgth. of Thread	Material	No. Nuts	Location
1	Stud - Hex Nut	6	$\frac{5}{8}$	$2\frac{3}{8}$	$\frac{7}{8}$	Steel	6	Cyl. Hd. to Cyl.
2	Bolt - Hex Hd.	6	$\frac{5}{8}$	$2\frac{1}{2}$	$\frac{7}{8}$	Steel	—	Cyl. to Frame
3	Stud - Hex Nut	8	$\frac{5}{8}$	$2\frac{3}{8}$	$\frac{7}{8}$	Steel	8	Cover to Stm. Chest
4	Set Screw	2	$\frac{5}{8}$	$1\frac{1}{4}$	$1\frac{1}{4}$	Steel	—	Eccentric to Shaft
5	Bolt-Hex Hd & Nut	2	$\frac{1}{2}$	$4\frac{3}{4}$	$1\frac{1}{2}$	Steel	4	Eccentric

FIG. 110.   Bolt List.

placed near the change and recorded in the title or record strip with statement of change and the date when made.

Part lists should be complete, and numbers for patterns, tools and dies or other necessary information for identification or record should be placed on the drawing and recorded on filing cards or in record books. Every drawing should have a number and be recorded so as to be easily found. Systems of filing, numbering, recording, transmitting and keeping track of drawings vary with the kind of work, and the extent to which the drawings are used. Some forms are shown in Figs. 109, 110 and 111.

PIPE AND FITTINGS LIST

Size	Pipe Feet	Number of Valves	Number of Fittings	Threads	Material	Make
$\frac{1}{2}$	365			R	W.I.	
$1\frac{1}{4}$	185			R	W.I.	
$1\frac{1}{4}$		8 Globe		R	Brass	T-Z Co.
$1\frac{1}{4}$			21 Ells	R	C.I.	
$1\frac{1}{4}$			7 Tees	R	C.I.	
$1\frac{1}{4}$			5 Couplings	R & L	C.I.	

Fig. 111.   Pipe and Fittings List.

100. Idioms of Drawing.—The basis for all working drawings is orthographic projection. For simple parts the regular views are used and all lines both full and dotted are drawn. There are many cases however when such representations might make it difficult to read the drawing, or require a long time to make the drawing. In the practical application of drawing it has been found necessary to depart from true projection under some conditions and to use special or idiomatic representations. Such conventional representations may be full views or sectional views, either partial or complete. A view of an object is not a picture and is

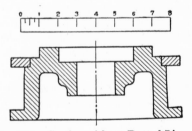

Fig. 112.   Section without Dotted Lines.

not to be regarded as such, still we should be careful not to convey a false impression of an object or its construction. It is to avoid the possibility of such false impressions that various conventional representations have been developed. In the practice of engineering, time has ever been an important element, and conventions or representations of the more common parts of machinery have been devised to save time. The true projection of a screw thread would involve drawing a helix and when the frequency with which screw threads occur is considered, the necessity for using idioms or " engineering shorthand " can be understood. There are many other conditions where conventional treatment is desirable.

101. Treatment of Sectional Views.—It is not necessary to include all dotted lines beyond the plane of a section if they tend to confuse rather than help. In some cases only the sectioned surfaces and the full lines beyond them are shown, Fig. 112. Whenever dotted lines tend to confuse, they should be left out, compare Figs. 113 and 114.

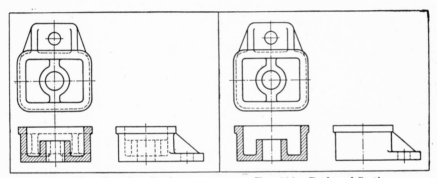

FIG. 113.   Complete Section.   FIG. 114.   Preferred Section.

When a sectional view is used in place of an exterior view, all of the full lines beyond the plane of the section are generally drawn. In cases where the shape of the sectioned surface is the important feature or when the full lines beyond the cut surface require a great deal of time to draw without adding to the usefulness of the drawing, they should be left out as in Fig. 115, where several " sliced " sections are shown.

A view should serve the purpose for which it is intended without unnecessary or confusing lines. Extra or part views are often sufficient.

102. It is sometimes desirable to show both the exterior and section in one view. This can be done when the view is the same on both sides of a center line by drawing one half in section and the other half in full as in Fig. 116. All or most all of the dotted lines are often omitted from

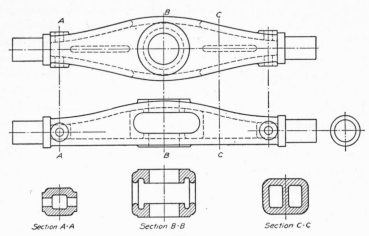

FIG. 115.   "Sliced" Sections.

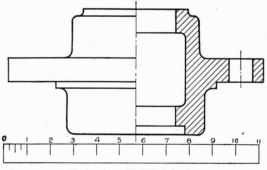

FIG. 116.   Half Section.

both halves.   The planes of the section form a right angle and cut away one quarter of the object.   If two " half sectional " views are used they should be cut by planes which will bring the two half sections toward each other as shown, Fig. 117.

103.   When different pieces are shown in a section they are indicated by changing the direction of the cross hatching.   The width of spacing between section lines is determined by the area to be sectioned, smaller areas having them closer together than larger ones.   Different materials are sometimes indicated by different forms of section lining.   Fig. 118 gives some forms proposed for use as American recommended practice. The spacing of lines shown will be found satisfactory for most areas.   All

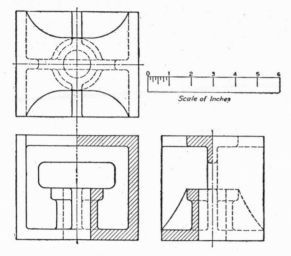

Fig. 117. Two Half Sections.

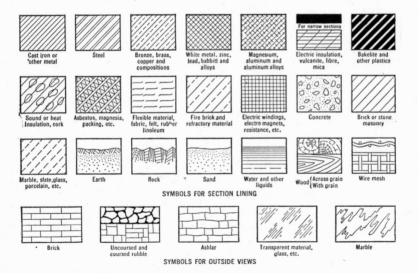

Fig. 118. American Standard Symbols for Materials.

lines must be fine, of uniform width and uniformly spaced. The character of sectioning must not be depended upon to tell the material and a note should always be added when the materials are not perfectly evident. Their chief value is to make it easier to distinguish different pieces.

104. Common Uses and Treatments of Sections.—There are many cases where parts of a view are not sectioned. Such parts as shafts, bolts, nuts, screws, rivets, keys, pulley arms, gear teeth, etc., are not sectioned even though the rest of the view is in section. This saves time and in many cases makes the drawing easier to read, Fig. 119.

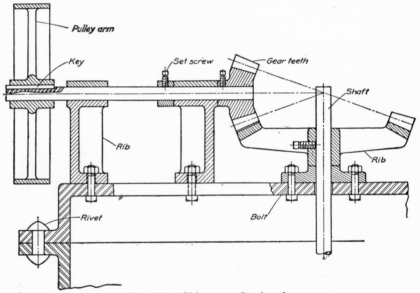

FIG. 119.   Objects not Sectioned.

A larger scale can often be used by " breaking " the piece, and moving the parts together. The manner of breaking generally indicates the shape of the cross section and the material as in Fig. 120. This method cannot be used unless the cross section is uniform in shape, generally shown by a " set in " or revolved section. The true taper is drawn when a long tapering piece is represented by the above method, Fig. 121.

105. Treatment of Ribs and Special Sections.—When a sectional view gives a false impression of solidity it is often modified. Ribs, pulley arms, etc., are not sectioned for this reason, Fig. 122. Good practice

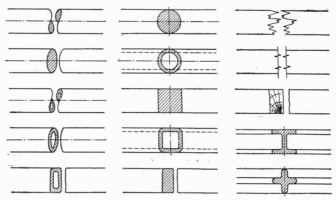

FIG. 120.   Revolved Sections.

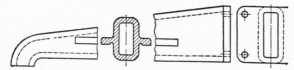

FIG. 121.   Tapered Piece with Section.

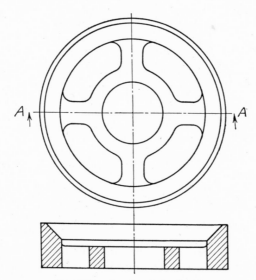

FIG. 122.   Section through Rib.

requires the arms, ribs, etc., to be shown in their true length rather than as they would project. Fig. 123 at I is a true projection but better practice is shown at II.

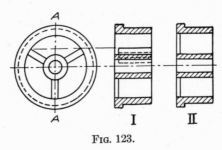

Fig. 123.

When a rib occurs on a plane of a section in such a way that it is necessary to call attention to it, alternate sectioning can be used as in Fig. 124. Note the use of the dotted line to show the extent of the rib. This method can be used to advantage on one-view drawings.

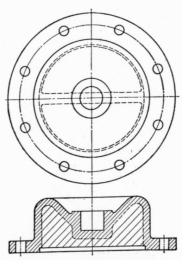

Fig. 124. "Alternate" Sectioning.

106. When small areas are sectioned the surfaces may be " blacked in " as in Fig. 125. When large areas are sectioned the surfaces may be indicated by short lines following the contour lines, Fig. 126, sometimes

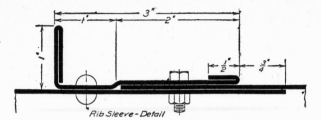

Rib Sleeve - Detail

FIG. 125. "Blacked in" Section.

FIG. 126. "Herring bone" Section.

called " herring bone " sectioning. Dotted sections are in the nature of " phantom views " as shown in Fig. 127 where dotted section lines are used on a full view to distinguish different pieces. This treatment sometimes saves an extra view.

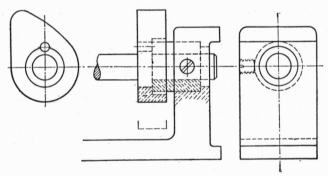

FIG. 127. Dotted or "Phantom" Section.

A " developed section " is shown in Fig. 128, where the true length of each part of the cutting plane shows in the sectional view.

107. Contour and Continuity.—The contour or characteristic appearance of an object is often an aid in the quick interpretation of a drawing. This is illustrated in Fig. 129, where the usual treatments for exterior and sectional views are shown at I and II. The true projections

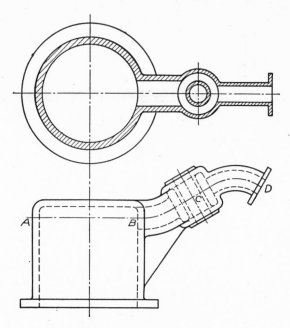

FIG. 128.   Developed Section.

are not only less useful but require more time to draw as indicated at
III and IV.

The representation of a cylinder head in Fig. 130 is a similar case.
A true section on plane *A–A* is shown at I.   At II the section is taken on
B–B and revolved into position of *A–A*.   The bolt holes and lugs are
then located at their true distances from the center.   An alternate method
is shown at III, where the section *C–F* is revolved.

108. Ribs, lugs, ears and other incidental parts are better left in full
when they occur in a sectional view.   The section of an object having an
uneven number of incidental parts or having incidentals " off centers "
is best shown as though there were an even number and near but not
coincident with the plane of the section.   The general rule of continuity
is to section those parts which continue clear around the axis.

It is often desirable to show the contour elements of cylinders and
cones unbroken when openings or attached parts would cause a break
if shown in true projection.   This treatment is illustrated in Fig. 131
in which the true section is shown at I and the conventional treatment
at II.

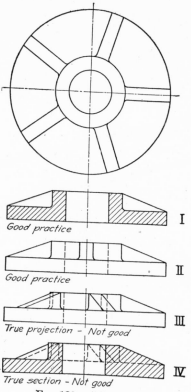

I

Good practice

II

Good practice

III

True projection – Not good

IV

True section – Not good

FIG. 129. "Contour."

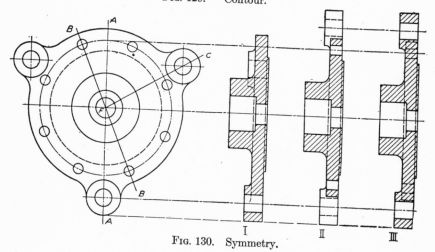

I   II   III

FIG. 130. Symmetry.

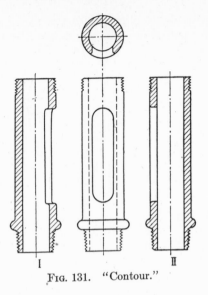

FIG. 131. "Contour."

109. There are many cases where true projection is departed from in the interest of simplicity and clearness.

The section or edge view of a flange shows the centers of the bolt holes a distance apart equal to the diameter of the circle of drilling, regardless of their true projection. In such cases the intermediate holes are not drawn as they add nothing to the information conveyed by the drawing. Several treatments for drilled flanges are indicated in Fig. 132.

110. Special Views.—When an object has one part at an angle the two views do not have to project if a better representation may be ob-

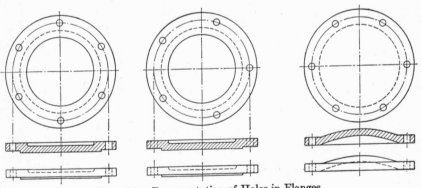

FIG. 132. Representation of Holes in Flanges.

tained by revolving or developing one of the views or part of a view. In Fig. 133 the top view shows the true angle and the front view the

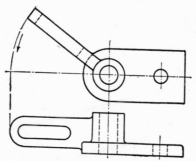

FIG. 133.   "True Length" View.

true shape of the left hand part of the object, by revolving it parallel to the vertical plane.   Auxiliary views or parts of views are often convenient. Some studies in representation are given in Figs. 134 to 138 which show both exterior and sectional treatments.   The line marked in Fig.

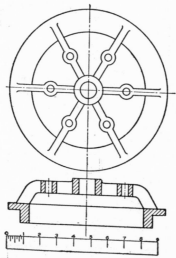

FIG. 134.   Conventional Treatment.

138 is not an actual line but is useful for reading the drawing.   Special views and idiomatic representations have come about in the practical use of drawing as an engineering language.   They have been adopted

through custom because they convey the idea more clearly and exactly, or more quickly than strict conformity to the rules of projection would do.

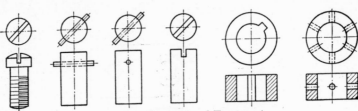

FIG. 135. Conventional Treatment.

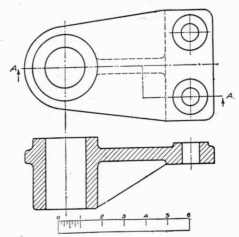

FIG. 136. Non-continuous Section.

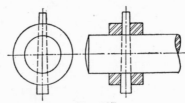

FIG. 137.

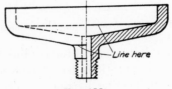

FIG. 138.

CHAPTER V

MACHINE SKETCHING

111. Sketches have many uses for engineering and other purposes. This has resulted in a variety of ideas as to what is meant by a sketch. A sketch may be anything from a few lines to suggest an idea to a complete working sketch, carefully proportioned and as fully dimensioned as a drawing made with drafting tools. Sketching is the engineering language of the executive as well as a convenient and quick means of representation for the draftsman. The views are worked out in much the same way as on regular drawings except that the views are carefully proportioned by eye and the lines are drawn freehand. The idioms of drawing, treatment of sectional views, dimensioning, and the general principles of machine drawing are used in making engineering sketches.

112. Kinds of Sketches.—Sketches may be orthographic views more or less complete, pictorial views, diagrams, charts or any graphical method of representation. They may be made on plain paper, or for some purposes on one of the many varieties of ruled papers. In every case the sketch must be definite as to its purpose and include all information necessary for that purpose.

" Thinking sketches " are used for developing or working out an idea or an arrangement. " Working sketches " are used in place of working drawings or to give information for making working drawings. Choice of views, treatment of views, size of views, dimensions, notes, etc., are important considerations in making a working sketch. " Diagram sketches " for indicating positions of wiring, piping, shafting, etc., form an important class of sketches. Notes and computations should be included. " Location sketches " for positioning machinery and apparatus are used for layout and efficiency studies.

The importance of clean lines, definite detail, correct position, and accuracy of representation and dimensioning cannot be over emphasized when making sketches.

113. Elements of Sketching.—The materials for sketching consist of a medium or H drawing pencil, eraser and paper. The pencil should be kept well sharpened to a long round point. Views are composed of straight lines and curves. Straight lines may be sketched by marking points as at *A*, Fig. 139, and sketching from one to the other as at *B*.

Another method is to make a succession of short straight lines as at C.
Keep the point of the pencil in sight. Hold the pencil about $3/4''$ or $1''$

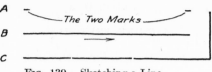

A
B   The Two Marks
C

FIG. 139. Sketching a Line.

from the point and sketch from left to right for horizontal lines as illustrated in Fig. 140. Vertical lines are sketched downward as shown in
Fig. 141. To sketch a circle " block in " a square made up of four

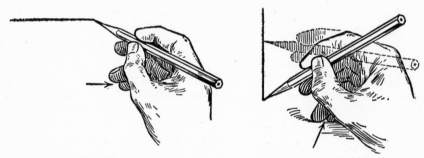

FIG. 140. Horizontal Line.   FIG. 141. Vertical Line.

smaller squares and sketch one fourth of the required circle in each of
them as shown in stages in Fig. 142. Another method is to draw center
lines at right angles, space off radii and complete the circle as shown in
stages in Fig. 143.

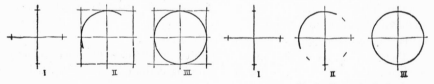

FIG. 142. Circle, First Method.   FIG. 143. Circle, Second Method.

114. Orthographic Sketches.—There are a number of progressive
stages in making the orthographic views of a working sketch for a machine
part as indicated in Fig. 144. For a complete working sketch the
procedure is as follows:

1. Examine the part.
2. Determine the views necessary to describe its shape.
3. Sketch center and preliminary lines.
4. "Block in" the views.

5. Sketch lines necessary to define the views.
6. Put on dimension lines.
7. Put on the dimensions.
8. Note materials, finish and any other necessary information.

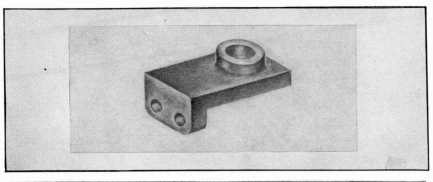

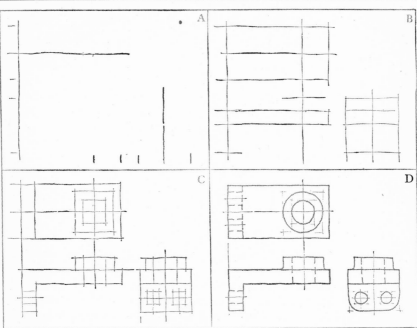

FIG. 144.   Making a Sketch.

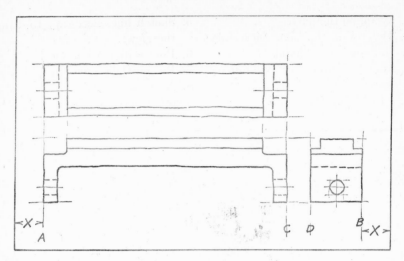

Fig. 144A. View Proportions.

For a piece such as Fig. 144A, the size of the views is determined by the end spaces at X as the three views taken together are longer in proportion to the width than the space available. In Fig. 14B the size of the views is determined by the top and bottom distances Y and Z. A complete sketch is shown in Fig. 145.

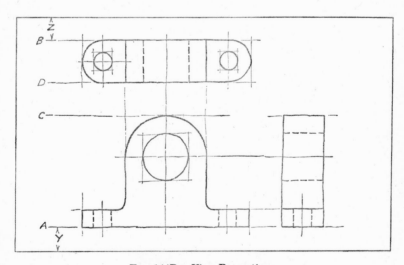

Fig. 144B. View Proportions.

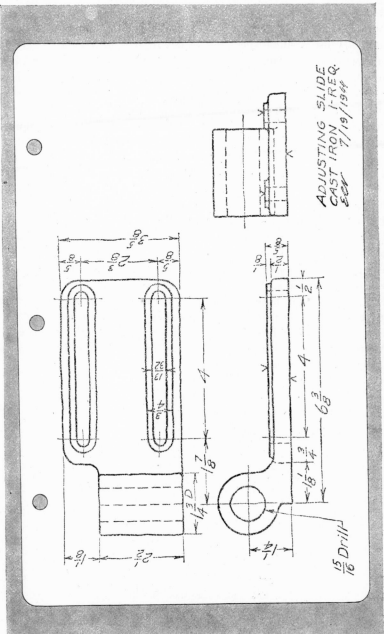

FIG. 145. A Complete Detail Sketch.

115. Proportioning Views.—Engineering sketches must be carefully proportioned and large enough to show details and dimensions clearly. If necessary use a single sheet for a view or part of a view. There are several ways of securing proportion. Distances may be estimated in inches and lines drawn on the sketch to agree with the estimated lengths. One-half, one-quarter or other proportional part of the estimated distances may be used. Squared paper is sometimes convenient. A general method is to estimate the proportions of the views and then select a part of the object as a unit from which to proportion the details and parts of the views.

116. General Rules.—Some considerations to be kept in mind when making sketches are included in this article.

Use part views to show special features or details.

Use notes freely but not as a substitute for necessary views.

Use surface shading sparingly if it will be of value in bringing out the shape of parts not easily understood.

Use a note or otherwise indicate the location of a machine in reference to building features if such information has any possibility of being useful.

Use one view and notes or revolved sections to represent rods, bolts, shafts, bars, and long pieces of uniform shape of cross section.

Use a part view and note when it will serve as well as a full view.

A circular object with lugs is shown in Fig. 146. The word diameter will often save an extra view.

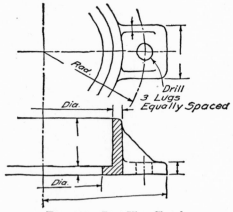

Fig. 146.　Part View Sketch.

Use sections rather freely on sketches, especially if it is desirable to give prominence to a view.

It is often desirable to make a separate outline sketch without dotted lines in connection with a sectional drawing of a part or machine, especially when the sketches must be hastily made, as the two sketches result in less confusion than when combined in one view.

Use templets whenever in doubt as to curves, location of drilling, etc. Note finished surfaces and kinds of finish.

Note materials of which the machine or parts are made.

Note identification marks, and mark parts to facilitate putting together and for fixing relative positions.

Most machines and some parts of machines will carry the manufacturer's name and identification mark, sometimes stamped into the machine and sometimes on a name plate. The information given in this manner should always be noted on a sketch.

Sometimes parts are " right " hand or " left " hand, and this fact should be noted.

117. Dimensioning.—The theory of dimensioning as explained in Chapter III applies to sketches as well as drawings. The procedure is as follows:

1. Analyze the construction into its elementary parts—prisms, cylinders, etc.

2. Identify or fix the locating axes and surfaces.

3. Put on dimension lines for all location dimensions to fix the position of each part.

4. Put on dimension lines for all size dimensions.

5. Put on the dimensions.

6. Put on notes to tell material, methods of working, kinds of finish, accuracy, quantities, or other necessary information.

7. Put on title, date, and initials or name of the one who made the sketch.

118. Measurements are not taken until the views are complete and all dimension lines in place. A scale and a pair of calipers will suffice in many cases. Other tools such as the depth gage, hook gage, screw-thread gage, micrometer calipers, protractor, straight edges, surface plates, etc., are often convenient or necessary for obtaining accurate measurements.

The question of accuracy in taking measurements will arise frequently. The finished or machined parts should be measured as accurately as the means at hand will allow. In general, take measurements as accurately as time and instruments permit; make corrections or changes only on the finished mechanical drawing—never on the sketch. If a distance cannot be measured directly, record the measurements from which it is calculated. Do not assume that distances or pieces are alike because they look alike or because they go together. Shafts or sliding blocks, or wherever a fit is involved should be measured with the micrometer or similar accurate means. Rough castings of small or medium size may be measured to the nearest $1/16''$, while larger ones may be near enough when measured to $1/8''$ or even $1/4''$. In all cases judgment must be exercised.

Where the parts being sketched are for repairs or replacement, very accurate measurements are often required, and in the case of a fit, allowance for wear must be made. If a whole new machine or construction is to be built much time can often be saved by less accurate measurements, as the parts will be dimensioned to go together when the final drawing is made. In the taking of measurements, ingenuity and common sense are the primary requisites. Curved outlines may be obtained by offset measurements, Fig. 147, by rubbing an outline on paper, or by making a templet.

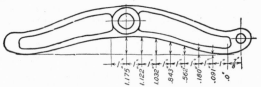

FIG. 147.   Offset Dimensions.

119. Duplicating Sketches.—Extra copies of sketches can be made in a variety of ways, some of which will be mentioned. If fairly thin paper is used, blue prints can be made. A piece of carbon paper used with the coated side against the back of the sketch paper will insure good printing qualities. If only a few copies are needed carbon paper can be used. The Photostat is a convenient means of making copies. For some purposes, the hectograph, mimeograph, etc., may be used, especially when a number of copies are required.

120. Pictorial Sketches are based upon the principles of pictorial drawing as explained in Chapter XXII of Svensen's "Drafting for Engineers," D. Van Nostrand Co., N. Y. Freehand pictorial representations save time and are effective in describing or explaining shapes and working out ideas. Dotted lines are seldom drawn on pictorial sketches but may be used sparingly when they will make a detail clear or save an extra view. Pictorial sketches can be modified by giving them a perspective effect when parallelism is objectionable.

121. Isometric Sketches.—The isometric cube and some positions of the axes are shown in Fig. 148. All distances are estimated along or

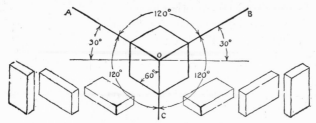

FIG. 148. The Isometric Axes.

parallel to the axes. Circles appear as ellipses on isometric views, Fig. 149. Note the direction of the long axis of the ellipse in each of the three

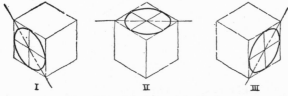

I   II   III

FIG. 149. The Isometric Circle.

cases. Always block in " isometric squares " before sketching isometric circles. The usual positions of the axes are given in Fig. 148. For sketching purposes they may have other positions as indicated in Fig. 150. While small angles with the horizontal give a more pleasing picture, artistic effect is less important than definite and complete representation. Note that the view at I in Fig. 150 shows the square depression and the round hole, while the view at IV gives much less information. In some cases a sectional view can be used to advantage. The best rule is to select the position of the axes and the method of representation best suited to the piece or construction to be described.

The first step in making an isometric sketch is to locate the three axes. Then estimate distances along and parallel to the axes. Block in prisms and details, using straight lines as at I in Fig. 151. The curves and final lines of the object may then be sketched in as at II in Fig. 151. Dimensions

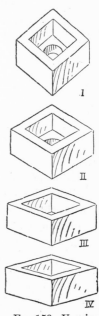

FIG. 150. Varying Positions of the Axes.

may be placed on pictorial sketches when required, Figs. 271 and 272.

In most cases, isometric or other axonometric methods should be used for objects having circles or curves in more than one plane and for objects having more or less " box like " form with incidental parts such as lugs, bosses, etc.

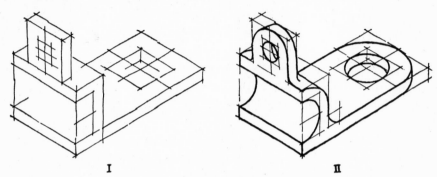

I   II

FIG. 151.   Making an Isometric Sketch.

122. Oblique Sketches.—Oblique views are obtained by using projecting lines which are oblique to a plane instead of perpendicular as in orthographic projection. The oblique cube and some positions of the axes are shown in Fig. 152. The axis OB may make any desired angle

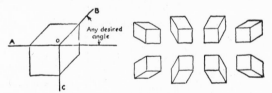

FIG. 152.   The Oblique Axes.

with the horizontal, either left or right. If most of the curves, circles and irregular outlines of an object are parallel to the same plane, they can be shown in their true shape on that plane. Circles on the faces of an oblique sketch of a cube are shown in Fig. 153. Sometimes distances

FIG. 153.   The Oblique Circle.

on the oblique axis are shortened to improve the appearance of the picture.   This is illustrated in Fig. 154 where the full distances are used at I and shorter distances at II, III and IV as three-fourths, one-half and

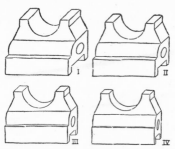

FIG. 154.   Varying Lengths of Oblique Axes.

one-third respectively.   Too much distortion of shapes on the oblique surfaces must be avoided as definite and complete representation are more important than pleasing effects.

The first step in making an oblique sketch is to locate the axes. Select an angle for the oblique axis that will show the shape of the part to advantage.   Then estimate distances along and parallel to the axes. Place the irregular outlines parallel to the vertical plane.   Block in prisms and details, using straight lines as at I in Fig. 155.   The curves and final lines of the object may then be sketched as at II in Fig. 155.

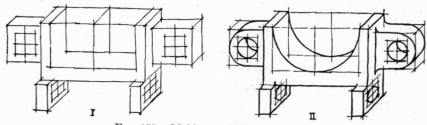

FIG. 155.   Making an Oblique Sketch.

CHAPTER VI

MACHINE DETAILS

123. Machine details include many standard and commercial parts such as threaded fastenings (Chapter II), gears and cams (Chapter X), and a large number of elements used for a variety of purposes on different machines. The steam engine, Fig. 156, illustrates the use of a combination of stationary parts, sliding parts, and rotating parts, typical of many machines. The names of some of the principal parts are listed.

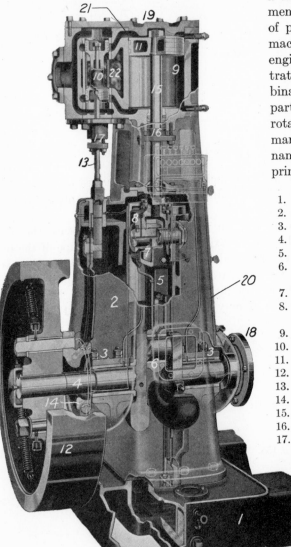

1. Base
2. Panel
3. Pillow Block Cap
4. Main Shaft
5. Connecting Rod
6. Crank Pin End Conn. Rod (and crank pin)
7. Crosshead End
8. Crosshead Connecting Rod
9. Cylinder
10. Piston Slide Valve
11. Piston
12. Flywheel
13. Valve Rod
14. Eccentric
15. Piston Rod
16. Piston Rod Stuffing Box
17. Valve Rod Stuffing Box
18. Coupling
19. Cylinder Head
20. Frame
21. Steam Port
22. Exhaust Port

Fig. 156. A Vertical Steam Engine.

Steam is admitted to alternate sides of the piston by means of the piston valve which is actuated by the eccentric through the eccentric rod. The piston transmits the pressure of the steam through the piston rod, crosshead, and connecting rod to the crank. The crank causes the shaft to revolve, and with it the flywheel from which power may be transmitted by means of a belt or the power may be taken off by means of a direct connection through the coupling. Such parts as cylinders, rods, links, guides, pulleys, flanges, etc., are used for similar purposes on different kinds of machines and have many features which are common to all such parts. In order for a machine to have "character" or "style" it is necessary for the designer to have a knowledge of what has been done by other designers and to be familiar with the ordinary standard details and how they are used on machines.

124. The parts of machines which come from the foundry, forge, or rolling mill, generally require finishing such as machining to size, drilling and tapping of holes, etc., before they can be assembled in the machine where they are to be used. A knowledge of what is involved in the processes of machining is important to the machine draftsman.

The principal operations are turning, drilling, boring, planing, and milling. The machines used are lathes, drills, boring mills, planers, shapers, milling machines, etc. At least one book on machine shop practice should be studied while pursuing a course in machine drawing. The advertising pages of such magazines as "Machinery" and "American Machinist" are further sources of information which should not be neglected. Every opportunity should be taken to observe and study work as it is carried out in the pattern shop, forge, foundry, machine shop, and welding shop. Such knowledge is invaluable and will often enable the draftsman to reduce the expense of production by simplifying or adapting his designs.

There are many details which are used on a great variety of machines. Parts which are used for similar purposes on different kinds of machines have many features that are common to all such parts. In order for a machine to have "character" it is necessary for the designer to have a knowledge of what has been done by other designers and to be familiar with the ordinary standard details of machines. Other standards which should be considered include company standards, AN and AC and other government standards, American Standards, S.A.E., and other technical society standards of various kinds according to the kind of work to be done and the products of the company.

125. Graphical Data and Dimensions.—So much information is now given by graphical diagrams that their use must be understood by those who have to do with engineering matters.   Charts serve to present information and to work out information as to power, forces, motions, and dimensions.   Formulas and tables are often put into graphical form. When the curve is a straight line its slope can be figured from the equation for a straight line, $y = mx + b$, in which y is the ordinate, x is the abscissa, m is a ratio and b is a constant.   Other equations may be worked out from curved lines if formulas are desired.   Sometimes the dimensions

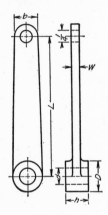

Fig. 157.

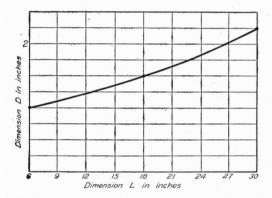

Fig. 158.   Dimensions from Curve.

for two or three sizes of a machine part will be figured and plotted and the dimensions for other sizes within the range of the curve obtained from the graphical chart.   This is illustrated in Figs. 157 and 158.   The dimensions for three sizes of the lever are known as follows:

L	6	18	30
h	$^3/_4$	$^3/_4$	$^3/_4$
d	$^1/_2$	$^3/_4$	$1^1/_8$
D	1	$1^1/_2$	$2^1/_4$
W	$^1/_4$	$^1/_4$	$^1/_4$
b	$^3/_4$	$^3/_4$	$^3/_4$

Plot values of D for the three values of L and draw a curve as shown. Values of D for other values of L may be taken from the curve.   Thus for 27″ length the value of $D = 2″$ and since $d = D/2$ we have $d = 1″$. The other dimensions are constant for all sizes.

126. Pistons are used in many kinds of machines and vary accordingly. A one-part piston is shown in Fig. 159. The names of the parts for a follower type piston are given for Fig. 160 as follows: 1, Piston Body; 2, Follower; 3, Follower Bolts; 4, Bull Ring; 5, Packing Rings. To prevent loss of pressure by leakage past the piston some form of packing ring is used. Pistons are generally made of cast iron, as are the rings. The rings are turned to a slightly larger diameter than the cylinder, a piece is then cut out, and the rings sprung into place. They are often

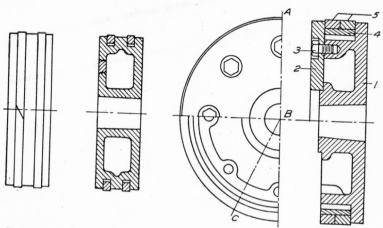

FIG. 159.   One-Part Piston.   FIG. 160.   Piston and Follower.

made with eccentric diameters Fig. 161 with the cut on the thin side. The cut may be diagonal or lap, as in the figure.

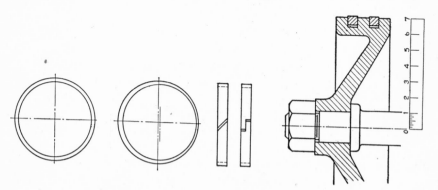

FIG. 161.   Piston Rings.   FIG. 162.   Locomotive Piston.

A form of locomotive piston is shown in Fig. 162.   It is a steel casting for lightness and of conical form for strength.   A gas engine piston is illustrated in Fig. 163.

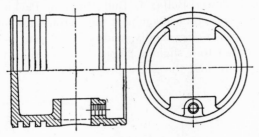

FIG. 163.   Gas Engine Piston.

127. Crossheads are used on steam engines, pumps, air compressors and many other machines.   Two types of crossheads are shown in Figs. 164 and 165, with the names of the parts.   The body of the cross-

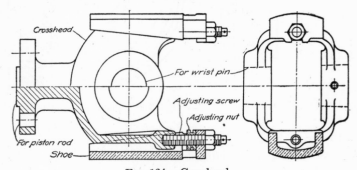

FIG. 164.   Crosshead.

head is made of cast iron or steel and the gib or shoe of brass or may be babbitted.

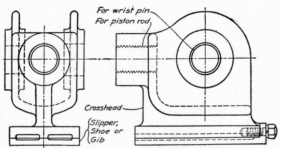

FIG. 165.   Crosshead.

128. A connecting rod is used to connect a sliding part of a machine with a rotating part. They are made of wrought iron, steel, and brass. Forms vary greatly. The ends may be solid or open. Some provision

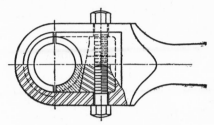

Fig. 166. Connecting Rod End.

is generally made for adjusting the distance between the centers of the ends. The rod itself may have a circular, elliptical, rectangular, I-shape,

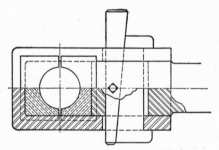

Fig. 167. Connecting Rod End.

or other form of cross section. Types of connecting rod ends are shown in Figs. 166, 167 and 168.

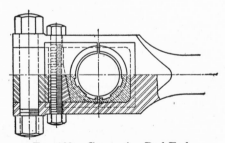

Fig. 168. Connecting Rod End.

129. An eccentric is a circular disc which rotates about an axis which does not pass through its center, Fig. 169. An eccentric as made for

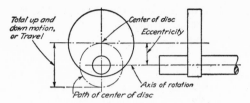

FIG. 169. Eccentric.

use on a steam engine to move the steam valve is shown in Fig. 170. It consists of the eccentric, eccentric straps and bolts. The eccentric is secured to a shaft which causes it to rotate and so move the eccentric rod, which is attached to the straps.

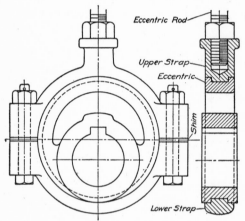

FIG. 170. Eccentric Parts.

130. A crank is a machine part which rotates about an axis near one end. It may be a part of the shaft or made separate and secured in place. A crank disc, over-hung crank, and center crank, are shown in Fig. 171, where some general proportions are indicated.

$$A = D \text{ to } 1^1/_2 D \qquad F = {}^3/_4 D \text{ to } 1^1/_2 D \qquad H = {}^3/_4 d$$

$$B = 2 D \qquad G = {}^3/_4 d \text{ to } 1^1/_2 d \qquad J = d \text{ to } 2 d$$

$$C = 2 d \qquad\qquad\qquad\qquad\qquad K = d \text{ to } 1^1/_4 d$$

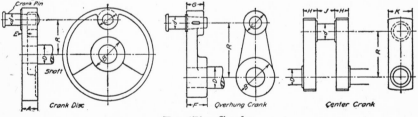

FIG. 171. Cranks.

131. Levers, Handles, Etc.—Levers, handles and similar parts are used on a great variety of machines and are made in forms to suit their purpose, Fig. 172.

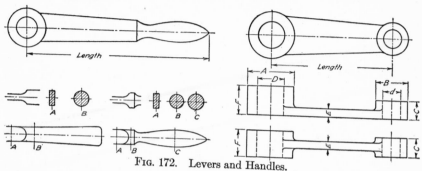

FIG. 172. Levers and Handles.

The length of a lever is from center to center of holes or an equivalent distance as illustrated.

The three classes of levers are shown in Fig. 173. In each case the

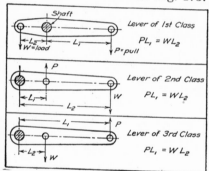

FIG. 173. Classes of Levers.

values for the loads or distances can be figured from the formulas.

$$PL_1 = WL_2 \quad P = \frac{WL_2}{L_1} \quad L_1 = \frac{WL_2}{P} \quad W = \frac{PL_1}{L_2} \quad L_2 = \frac{PL_1}{W}.$$

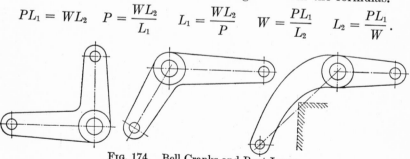

FIG. 174. Bell Cranks and Bent Lever.

When the load and force act at an angle some form of bell crank is used, Fig. 174. Bent levers are used when it is necessary to avoid a stationary part as shown. The length of a bent lever is the shortest distance between the two centers.

Handles are designed to suit a given position and so as to be convenient for getting hold of and operating. Several forms of machine tool handles are shown in Figs. 175 and 176 with standard dimensions as manufactured by the Cincinnati Ball Crank Co. (Tables 16 and 17).

TABLE 16

Machine Handles and Two Ball Levers

(Cincinnati Ball Crank Co.)

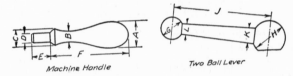

Machine Handle   Two Ball Lever

Fig. 175. Machine Handles.

Size	A	B	C	D	E	F	G	H	J	K	L
000......	$7/16$	$3/16$	$5/16$	.252 .253	$7/16$	$1^9/32$	.....	.....	.....	.....	.....
00......	$5/8$	$5/16$	$5/8$	.252 .253	$7/16$	$1^{15}/32$	.....	.....	.....	.....	.....
0......	$3/4$	$3/8$	$9/16$	.3145 .3155	$7/16$	$1^{23}/32$	.....	.....	.....	.....	.....
$1/2$....	$13/16$	$5/16$	$1/2$	.3145 .3155	$7/16$	2	.....	.....	.....	.....	.....
1......	$7/8$	$3/8$	$9/16$	.377 .378	$9/16$	$2^1/8$	$3/4$	$1^1/8$	$2^9/16$	$1/2$	$3/8$
$1^1/2$......	.....	.....	.....	.....	.....	.....	$13/16$	$1^1/4$	$2^{15}/16$	$9/16$	$7/16$
2......	1	$7/16$	$11/16$	.4395 .4405	$11/16$	$2^3/8$	$15/16$	$1^3/8$	$3^{11}/32$	$9/16$	$7/16$
3......	$1^1/8$	$7/16$	$11/16$	.4395 .4405	$11/16$	$2^3/4$	1	$1^1/2$	$3^3/4$	$11/16$	$15/32$
4......	$1^3/16$	$1/2$	$3/4$	.4395 .4405	$11/16$	$3^7/32$	1	$1^1/2$	$4^1/4$	$3/4$	$1/2$
5......	$1^3/16$	$1/2$	$3/4$	.4395 .4405	$13/16$	$3^7/16$	.....	.....	.....	.....	.....
6......	$1^1/4$	$1/2$	$7/8$	.503 .504	$15/16$	$3^5/8$	1	$1^3/4$	$5^1/8$	$3/4$	$1/2$
7......	$1^3/8$	$1/2$	$15/16$	.503 .504	$15/16$	$4^1/16$	1	$1^3/4$	$5^5/8$	$25/32$	$1/2$
8......	$1^1/2$	$5/8$	$1^1/8$	.628 .629	$1^3/16$	$4^9/16$	1	$1^3/4$	$6^1/8$	$13/16$	$17/32$
10......	.....	.....	.....	.....	.....	.....	$1^1/8$	$1^3/4$	$7^1/16$	$13/16$	$19/32$
11......	.....	.....	.....	.....	.....	.....	$1^3/16$	$1^3/4$	$7^{17}/32$	$7/8$	$5/8$

TABLE 17

BALL CRANK AND COMPOUND REST HANDLES

(Cincinnati Ball Crank Co.)

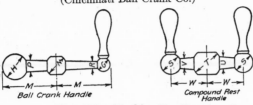

Ball Crank Handle

Compound Rest Handle

FIG. 176. Machine Handles.

Size	Size of Handle		G	H	M	N	P	R	S	T	U	V	W
	Ball Crank	Compound Rest											
0...	00	1	$5/8$	1	$1 1/2$	$7/8$	$1/2$	$3/8$	$5/8$	$13/16$	$3/8$	$5/16$	$15/16$
1...	0	....	$3/4$	$1 1/8$	$1 3/4$	1	$1/2$	$3/8$	$3/4$	$1 1/16$	$13/32$	$13/32$	$7/8$
$1 1/2$	$1/2$	....	$13/16$	$1 1/4$	2	$1 1/8$	$9/16$	$7/16$	....	....	....		
2...	1	2	$15/16$	$1 3/8$	$2 1/4$	$1 1/4$	$9/16$	$7/16$	$3/4$	$1 1/16$	$13/32$	$13/32$	$7/8$
3...	2	2	1	$1 1/2$	$2 1/2$	$1 5/16$	$11/16$	$15/32$	$3/4$	$1 1/16$	$13/32$	$13/32$	$7/8$
4...	2	....	1	$1 1/2$	$2 3/4$	$1 5/16$	$23/32$	$1/2$	$3/4$	$1 1/16$	$7/16$	$3/8$	$1 1/8$
5...	3	2	1	$1 5/8$	3	$1 3/8$	$3/4$	$1/2$	$3/4$	$1 1/16$	$7/16$	$3/8$	$1 1/8$
6...	4	2	1	$1 5/8$	$3 1/4$	$1 3/8$	$3/4$	$1/2$	$3/4$	$1 1/16$	$7/16$	$3/8$	$1 1/8$
7...	4	....	1	$1 3/4$	$3 1/2$	$1 7/16$	$25/32$	$1/2$	$3/4$	$1 1/16$	$7/16$	$13/32$	$1 3/8$
8...	4	3	1	$1 3/4$	$3 3/4$	$1 1/2$	$25/32$	$17/32$	$3/4$	$1 1/16$	$7/16$	$13/32$	$1 3/8$
9...	4	3	$1 1/16$	$1 3/4$	4	$1 1/2$	$27/32$	$17/32$	$3/4$	$1 1/16$	$7/16$	$13/32$	$1 3/8$
10...	5	....	$1 1/8$	$1 3/4$	$4 1/4$	$1 9/16$	$13/16$	$19/32$	$7/8$	$1 3/16$	$17/32$	$7/16$	$1 9/16$
11...	5	4	$1 3/16$	$1 3/4$	$4 1/2$	$1 5/8$	$7/8$	$9/16$	$7/8$	$1 3/16$	$17/32$	$7/16$	$1 9/16$
12...	7	4	$1 1/4$	2	$5 1/2$	$1 13/16$	$31/32$	$5/8$	$7/8$	$1 3/16$	$17/32$	$7/16$	$1 9/16$
13...	7	....	$1 1/4$	2	$6 1/2$	$1 15/16$	$1 1/32$	$23/32$	$1 1/16$	$1 3/8$	$5/8$	$1/2$	$1 11/16$

132. Stuffing Boxes.—Common forms of gland stuffing boxes and screw stuffing boxes are shown in Figs. 177 and 178.

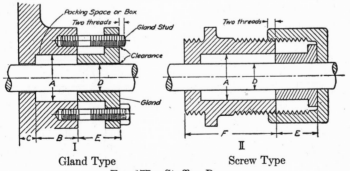

Gland Type

Screw Type

FIG. 177. Stuffing Boxes.

The gland stuffing box is used for rods $1\frac{1}{2}''$ and more in diameter. The names of the parts are given on Fig. 177. The box should be deep enough for at least four strands of packing and the gland proportioned so

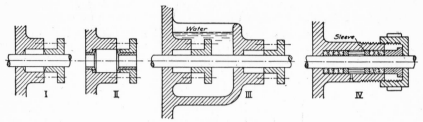

FIG. 178. Stuffing Boxes.

as to compress it to about one-half its original length. The box and gland may be either flat or bevelled. If lined with composition the lining should be at least $\frac{3}{16}''$ thick, but for small rods (less than $2''$ diameter) it is generally advisable to make the gland either all brass or cast iron. The gland is moved by turning the nuts on the studs.

For rods $1\frac{1}{4}''$ diameter or less the common screw stuffing box is much used. It is made of brass or composition except on very cheap work where cast iron is used.

Some general proportions for use with Fig. 177 are as follows: $A = 1.4\,D + .4''$, $B = .8\,D + .8''$, $C = \frac{1}{4}\,D + \frac{1}{4}''$ or more, $E = .8\,D + .8''$, $F = 2.5\,D + 1''$.

These are the common types, but the student should investigate and make sketches of some of the metallic packings as they are much used in good designs.

133. Fillets, Rounds, Arcs, Etc.—The suggestions which follow are to facilitate the drafting part of design and are not rules which must be strictly adhered to.

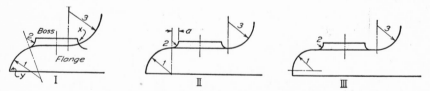

FIG. 179. Limiting Radii, Fillets and Rounds.

Fillets and rounds are so common that they should be understood. A part of a machine is shown at Fig. 179. The centers and radii are indicated. All the radii at I are too large, particularly those marked

1 and 2. Radius 1 gives a point at *y*. Radius 2 is so large that it cannot be used for the complete circumference of the boss indicated at *x*. Of course a changing radius of fillet might be used, but this would not be as good design.

The limiting radii are indicated at II while a much better design is shown at III. Note that the radii 1 and 2 are less than the thickness of

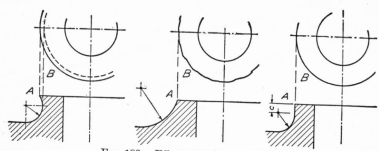

Fig. 180. Effect of Different Fillets.

the flange and boss respectively. The effect of a quarter circle is obtained by this method in which the flange and boss each start with a straight line.

The effect of different fillets is shown in Fig. 180. At I there is an undercutting, at II the radius is too large, giving an irregular outline to the top view, while the correct design is shown at III.

When arcs and straight lines are used the faults shown at *a*, Fig. 181, should be avoided. Do not run an arc past the tangent point. The correct methods are shown at *b*.

134. Flanges.—Flanges for two bolts or nuts may take a variety of

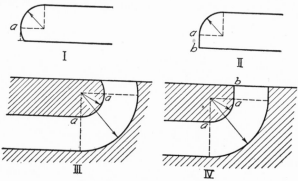

Fig. 181. Tangent Points.

MACHINE DRAWING

outlines other than circular as shown in Fig. 182. After locating the centers of the bolt holes the extent of the flange may be found by adding

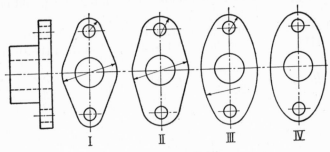

FIG. 182.   Flange Outlines.

twice the bolt diameter to the distance between bolt centers. The outline is often obtained as at I where the radius is equal to the diameter of the hole, with center as shown. A better design is to use a radius of one and one-half the bolt hole diameter as at II. Either straight, circular or elliptical lines may be used to complete the outline.

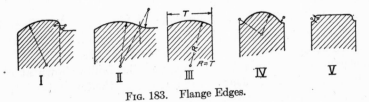

FIG. 183.   Flange Edges.

The edges are often finished with curves so as to avoid machining as indicated in Fig. 183.

CHAPTER VII

BEARINGS

135. Bearings.—The motion of machine parts is generally either translation or rotation. Supports for moving parts are called bearings when the parts rotate. For translatory motion the supports are called guides.

The simplest form of support for a rotating member is a hole through a piece of metal. The rotating member is called a shaft or journal. A solid journal box or bearing is shown at **A** in Fig. 184 and a step bearing for a vertical shaft is shown at **B**. Thrust bearings are made to take loads parallel to the axis of the shaft.

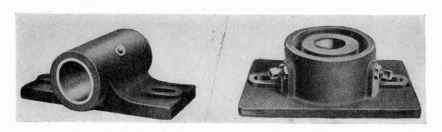

A   **B**

Journal Box.   Adjustable Step Bearing

Fig. 184. Bearings. (*T. B. Wood's Sons Company.*)

Bearings may be of solid metal, may be lined with babbitt metal, may have bushings, may have divided shells or boxes, may be composed of balls, or may be composed of rolling cylinders or cones.

Smoothness of surfaces is only relative. Moving surfaces in contact wear rapidly so that it is necessary to provide for lubrication and for taking up wear. For this reason plain bearings are generally made in two parts.

105

136. Bearing Metals.—For very low pressures cast iron may be used. If there is much of a load or much speed, it is liable to "seize" as the heat cannot be dissipated fast enough. For this reason babbitt and

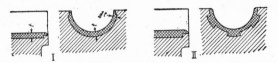

Fig. 185. Babbitted Boxes.

other metals are used, such as brass, bronzes, and various other metals. Babbitt metal is softer than brass, flows more easily under pressure, and if overheated will melt without seizing. Its frictional resistance is low

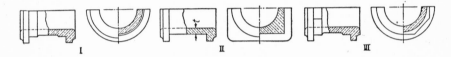

Fig. 186. Bearing Boxes.

but it is too weak to support a load and so has to be held in place and anchored, Fig. 185. The babbitt may be melted and poured into place, using the shaft to mould it to the size. For better work a smaller shaft

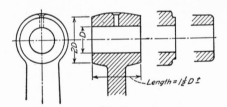

Fig. 187. Solid Bearing.

is used and the babbitt is peaned into firm contact with the containing member after which it is bored and scraped to size. The thickness t may be made about $(d + 1)/12$ where d equals diameter of shaft.

Various forms of brass and white metal boxes or shells are suggested in Fig. 186. The thickness t may be made about $(d + 1.5)/12$ where d equals diameter of shaft.

137. Simple Bearings.—For a simple solid bearing the proportions of Fig. 187 may be used. Some dimensions for a babbitted bearing, Fig. 188 are given in Table 18. A split babbitted bearing is given in Fig. 189 with some dimensions in Table 19. The data in tables 18 to 22 are from the Royersford Foundry and Machine Company.

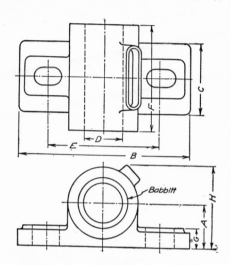

FIG. 188. Solid Babbitted Bearing.

TABLE 18 (FIG. 188)

SOLID BABBITTED BEARING

Size of Shaft, Inches	A	B	C	E	F	G	H	Bolts	
								No.	Size
$^{15}/_{16}$ and 1	$1^1/_8$	5	2	$3^3/_8$	3	$^9/_{16}$	$2^1/_8$	2	$^1/_2$
$1^3/_{16}$ and $1^1/_4$	$1^3/_8$	$5^1/_2$	$2^1/_4$	$3^5/_8$	$3^3/_8$	$^5/_8$	$2^3/_4$	2	$^1/_2$
$1^7/_{16}$ and $1^1/_2$	$1^1/_2$	6	$2^9/_{16}$	4	$3^7/_8$	$^{11}/_{16}$	$2^3/_4$	2	$^1/_2$
$1^{11}/_{16}$ and $1^3/_4$	$1^{13}/_{16}$	$6^1/_2$	$2^3/_4$	$4^3/_8$	$4^1/_4$	$^5/_8$	$3^3/_8$	2	$^5/_8$
$1^{15}/_{16}$ and 2	$1^{11}/_{16}$	7	3	$4^3/_4$	$4^1/_2$	$^7/_8$	$3^7/_8$	2	$^5/_8$
$2^3/_{16}$ and $2^1/_4$	$2^1/_8$	$7^5/_8$	$3^1/_4$	$5^1/_4$	$4^{11}/_{16}$	$^7/_8$	4	2	$^5/_8$
$2^7/_{16}$ and $2^1/_2$	$2^1/_8$	8	$3^1/_2$	$5^3/_4$	$5^7/_{16}$	$^{13}/_{16}$	$4^1/_4$	2	$^5/_8$
$2^{11}/_{16}$ and $2^3/_4$	$2^3/_8$	$9^3/_8$	$3^5/_8$	$6^1/_2$	$5^3/_4$	$^{15}/_{16}$	$4^3/_4$	2	$^3/_4$
$2^{15}/_{16}$ and 3	$2^1/_2$	$10^1/_2$	4	$7^3/_8$	$6^1/_8$	1	$4^7/_8$	2	$^3/_4$

138. Hangers.—Bearings for line shafting are supported by some form of hanger with provision for adjusting the position of the bearing. The general appearance and some proportions are shown in Fig. 190 (Table 20). A section of a ring oiled babbitted box for shafting is shown in Fig. 190A. A rigid post box is illustrated in Fig. 191 (Table 21).

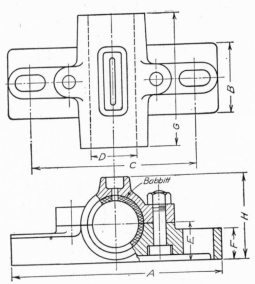

FIG. 189.   Split Babbitted Bearing.

TABLE 19 (FIG. 189)

SPLIT BABBITTED BEARING

Size of Shaft, Inches	A	B	C	E	F	G	H	Bolts	
								No.	Size
$^{15}/_{16}$ and 1	$4^3/_4$	$1^3/_4$	$3^{11}/_{16}$	$1^1/_8$	$^3/_4$	$2^1/_2$	$2^1/_4$	2	$^3/_8$
$1^3/_{16}$ and $1^1/_4$	$5^3/_8$	2	$4^3/_{16}$	$1^1/_4$	$^3/_4$	$3^5/_8$	$2^9/_{16}$	2	$^3/_8$
$1^7/_{16}$ and $1^1/_2$	$6^3/_8$	$2^3/_8$	$4^{15}/_{16}$	$1^1/_2$	$^{15}/_{16}$	$4^3/_8$	3	2	$^1/_2$
$1^{11}/_{16}$ and $1^3/_4$	$7^1/_4$	$2^3/_4$	$5^{11}/_{16}$	$1^5/_8$	$1^1/_{16}$	$5^1/_8$	$3^1/_2$	2	$^1/_2$
$1^{15}/_{16}$ and 2	$8^1/_4$	$3^1/_4$	$6^1/_2$	2	$1^1/_4$	$5^3/_4$	$3^7/_8$	2	$^5/_8$
$2^3/_{16}$ and $2^1/_4$	$9^1/_2$	$3^1/_2$	$7^{11}/_{16}$	$2^1/_4$	$1^3/_8$	$6^5/_8$	$4^1/_2$	2	$^5/_8$
$2^7/_{16}$ and $2^1/_2$	$10^5/_8$	4	$8^3/_{16}$	$2^1/_2$	$1^1/_2$	$7^3/_8$	5	2	$^3/_4$
$2^{11}/_{16}$ and $2^3/_4$	$11^5/_8$	$4^3/_8$	$9^1/_8$	$2^3/_4$	$1^5/_8$	$8^1/_8$	$5^3/_8$	2	$^3/_4$
$2^{15}/_{16}$ and 3	$12^5/_8$	$4^1/_4$	$9^9/_{16}$	$3^1/_8$	$1^{11}/_{16}$	$8^{15}/_{16}$	6	2	$^7/_8$
$3^3/_{16}$ and $3^1/_4$	$13^5/_8$	$5^1/_8$	$10^{15}/_{16}$	$3^1/_4$	$1^3/_4$	$9^1/_2$	$6^1/_8$	2	$^7/_8$
$3^7/_{16}$ and $3^1/_2$	$14^3/_4$	$5^1/_2$	$11^7/_8$	$3^1/_2$	2	$10^1/_4$	$6^5/_8$	2	$^7/_8$
$3^{11}/_{16}$ and $3^3/_4$	$15^7/_8$	6	$12^7/_8$	$3^7/_8$	$2^1/_4$	11	$7^1/_4$	2	1
$3^{15}/_{16}$ and 4	$17^5/_8$	$6^1/_2$	$13^7/_8$	4	$2^1/_4$	$11^3/_4$	$7^3/_4$	2	$1^1/_8$

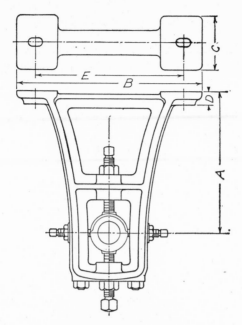

Fig. 190.
Hanger Bearing.

TABLE 20 (Fig. 190)
Universal Ring Oiling Hangers

Size of Shaft, Inches	Drop A	L'ng'h of Boxes	B	C	D	E	F	Bolts No.	Bolts Size
$^{15}/_{16}$ and 1	10 to 12	$4^3/_4$	$13^1/_4$	4	1	$9^7/_8$	......	2	$^1/_2$
$1^3/_{16}$ and $1^1/_4$	14 to 16	$5^{13}/_{16}$	17	$4^3/_4$	1	$13^3/_8$	......	2	$^5/_8$
$1^7/_{16}$ and $1^1/_2$	14 to 16	$6^5/_8$	17	$4^3/_4$	1	$13^3/_8$	......	2	$^5/_8$
$1^{11}/_{16}$ and $1^3/_4$	16 to 18	$7^{13}/_{16}$	20	5	1	16	......	2	$^5/_8$
$1^{15}/_{16}$ and 2	16 to 18	$8^3/_8$	20	5	1	16	......	2	$^5/_8$
$2^3/_{16}$ and $2^1/_4$	18 to 20	$9^5/_8$	$22^1/_2$	6	$1^1/_4$	$18^1/_4$	......	2	$^3/_4$
$2^7/_{16}$ and $2^1/_2$	18 to 20	$10^5/_{16}$	$22^1/_2$	6	$1^1/_4$	$18^1/_4$	......	2	$^3/_4$
$2^{11}/_{16}$ and $2^3/_4$	18 to 20	$11^1/_2$	$23^1/_4$	7	$1^1/_2$	$18^3/_8$	......	2	1
$2^{15}/_{16}$ and 3	18 to 20	12	$23^1/_4$	7	$1^1/_2$	$18^3/_8$	......	2	1
$3^3/_{16}$ and $3^1/_4$	22 to 24	$13^1/_2$	$28^1/_2$	$10^3/_8$	$1^3/_4$	$23^1/_4$	$4^3/_4$	4	$^3/_4$
$3^7/_{16}$ and $3^1/_2$	22 to 24	$14^1/_2$	$28^1/_2$	$10^3/_8$	$1^3/_4$	$23^1/_4$	$4^3/_4$	4	$^3/_4$
$3^{11}/_{16}$ and $3^3/_4$	22 to 24	$15^1/_4$	$28^1/_2$	$10^1/_2$	$1^7/_8$	$22^1/_2$	$4^1/_4$	4	$^7/_8$
$3^{15}/_{16}$ and 4	22 to 24	$16^3/_8$	$28^1/_2$	$10^1/_2$	$1^7/_8$	$22^1/_2$	$4^1/_4$	4	$^7/_8$

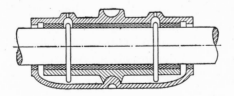

Fig. 190A.
Section of Box.

TABLE 21 (FIG. 191)

RIGID POST BOXES

Size of Shaft, Inches	A	B	C	I	E	F	H	G	Bolts	
									No.	Size
$^{15}/_{16}$ and 1	$3^7/_8$	$7^5/_{16}$	3	$^5/_8$	5	$1^7/_8$	$3^7/_8$	$3^1/_8$	3	$^1/_2$
$1^3/_{16}$ and $1^1/_4$	$3^7/_8$	$8^1/_2$	$3^1/_4$	$^5/_8$	$6^1/_8$	$2^1/_4$	$4^7/_8$	$3^3/_4$	3	$^1/_2$
$1^7/_{16}$ and $1^1/_2$	$3^7/_8$	10	$3^5/_8$	$^5/_8$	$7^1/_2$	$2^1/_2$	$5^7/_8$	$4^1/_2$	3	$^1/_2$
$1^{11}/_{16}$ and $1^3/_4$	$5^7/_8$	$11^3/_8$	4	$^5/_8$	$8^3/_4$	$2^5/_8$	$6^7/_8$	$5^1/_4$	3	$^1/_2$
$1^{15}/_{16}$ and 2	$5^7/_8$	13	$4^3/_4$	$^3/_4$	10	3	$7^7/_8$	6	3	$^5/_8$
$2^3/_{16}$ and $2^1/_4$	$5^7/_8$	$14^3/_4$	$5^1/_4$	$^3/_4$	$11^1/_8$	$3^1/_4$	$8^7/_8$	$6^3/_4$	3	$^5/_8$
$2^7/_{16}$ and $2^1/_2$	$5^7/_8$	$16^1/_4$	$5^3/_4$	$^7/_8$	$12^1/_4$	$3^1/_2$	$9^7/_8$	$7^1/_2$	3	$^3/_4$
$2^{11}/_{16}$ and $2^3/_4$	$5^7/_8$	$16^3/_4$	$6^5/_8$	$^7/_8$	$12^3/_4$	$3^3/_4$	10	$8^1/_4$	3	$^3/_4$
$2^{15}/_{16}$ and 3	$5^7/_8$	$19^1/_4$	7	1	15	4	$11^3/_4$	9	3	$^3/_4$

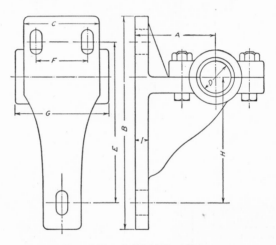

FIG. 191. A Rigid Post Box.

139. Ball bearings reduce friction to a very small amount, have no increase in friction when starting, have negligible wear, and are easily lubricated. Radial bearings, Fig. 192A, are used for loads perpendicular to the axis of the shaft. Radial-thrust bearings, Fig. 192B, are used for combined radial and thrust loads. Thrust bearings, Fig. 192C, are used for axial loads. Ball bearings are made in light, medium, and heavy series to meet the requirements of different load and speed requirements. For details and dimensions see A.S.A. B3 or S.A.E. Handbook, and manufacturers' catalogs.

The methods of installation of ball bearings necessarily vary to meet the requirements of the purpose for which they are used and the design features of the machine. There must be provision for lubrication, pro-

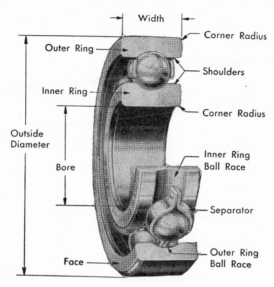

FIG. 192A.   Radial Ball Bearing.

(*New Departure Division, G. M. C.*)

FIG. 192B.   Radial-Thrust Ball Bearing.

(*The Fafnir Bearing Company.*)

FIG. 192C.   Thrust Ball Bearing.

(*SKF Industries, Inc.*)

MACHINE DRAWING

tection of the bearing, arrangements for inspection or removal, etc. A single-row radial bearing at the end of a shaft is shown at **A** in Fig. 192D and with the shaft extending through the cover at **B**. Note the felt

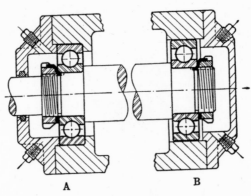

A   B

FIG. 192D.   Single Row Radial Ball Bearing.

(*The Fafnir Bearing Company.*)

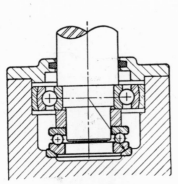

FIG. 192E.   Thrust Bearing in Combination with Single Row Radial Ball Bearing.   Self Aligning.

(*The Fafnir Bearing Company.*)

FIG. 193A.   Roller Bearing.

(*SKF Industries, Inc.*)

seal at **B**. A thrust bearing in combination with a single-row radial bearing (self-aligning) is shown in Fig. 192E.

140. Roller bearings use rolling cylinders or cones instead of balls. They are adapted for more severe load conditions than ball bearings. A SKF radial bearing with rolling cylinders is shown in Fig. 193A. The Timken bearings illustrated in Figs. 193B and 193C use tapered rollers (cones) which roll between an inner race or cone, and an outer race or cup. A cage is used to space the rollers properly and retain them around the cone.

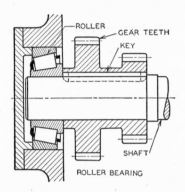

FIG. 193B. Roller Bearing. (*The Timken Roller Bearing Company.*)

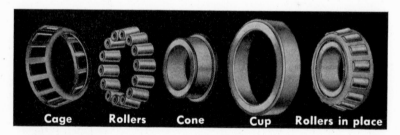

FIG. 193C. Roller Bearing. (*The Timken Roller Bearing Company.*)

The Wood's machine or unit mount pillow block shown in Fig. 193D (with dimensions in the Table) consists of the inner housing of the Wood's-Timken self-aligning, straight sleeve, roller bearing pillow block. Such units may be fitted into different machines. A roller bearing pillow block (two bolt) is illustrated in Figs. 193E and 193F. Some installation dimensions are given in the Table with Fig. 193F.

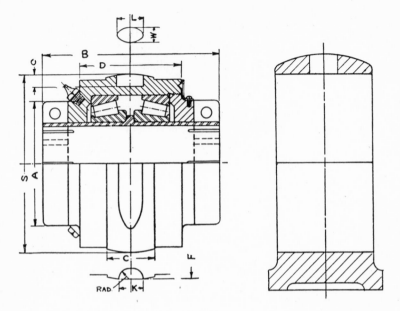

Fig. 193D. Unit Mount Pillow Block. (*T. B. Wood's Sons Company.*)

Shaft Sizes	A	B	C	D	F	K	L	O	S	W	Rad.
$1^{13}/_{16}$–2	$3^5/_8$	$5^3/_4$	$1^1/_4$	3	$2^5/_8$	$7/_8$	1	$3/_8$	$5^1/_8$	$9/_{16}$	$5/_{16}$
$2^1/_{16}$ –$2^1/_4$	$4^1/_8$	6	$1^1/_2$	$3^1/_4$	$2^3/_4$	$7/_8$	1	$3/_8$	$5^3/_4$	$9/_{16}$	$3/_8$
$2^5/_{16}$ –$2^1/_2$	$4^7/_{16}$	$6^1/_2$	$1^3/_4$	$3^5/_8$	$2^{15}/_{16}$	$7/_8$	1	$3/_8$	$6^1/_8$	$9/_{16}$	$3/_8$
$2^9/_{16}$ –$2^3/_4$	5	$7^3/_8$	2	$4^1/_4$	$3^7/_{16}$	1	$1^1/_8$	$1/_2$	$7^1/_8$	$5/_8$	$7/_{16}$
$2^{13}/_{16}$–3	5	$7^3/_8$	2	$4^1/_4$	$3^7/_{16}$	1	$1^1/_8$	$1/_2$	$7^1/_8$	$5/_8$	$7/_{16}$
$3^1/_8$ –$3^1/_2$	$5^3/_4$	8	$2^1/_4$	$4^7/_8$	$3^{13}/_{16}$	$1^1/_4$	$1^1/_8$	$1/_2$	$7^3/_4$	$5/_8$	$1/_2$
$3^5/_8$ –4	$6^3/_4$	$8^7/_8$	$2^1/_2$	$5^3/_4$	$4^5/_8$	$1^3/_8$	$1^1/_4$	$9/_{16}$	$9^1/_2$	$3/_4$	$9/_{16}$
$4^1/_8$ –$4^1/_2$	$7^3/_4$	10	3	$6^1/_4$	$5^1/_4$	$1^3/_8$	$1^1/_2$	$3/_4$	$10^3/_4$	$7/_8$	$9/_{16}$
$4^5/_8$ –5	$8^3/_4$	$10^3/_4$	4	$6^3/_4$	$5^7/_8$	$1^1/_2$	$1^1/_2$	$3/_4$	$12^1/_4$	$7/_8$	$5/_8$

FIG. 193E. Roller Bearing Pillow Block. (*T. B. Wood's Sons Company.*)

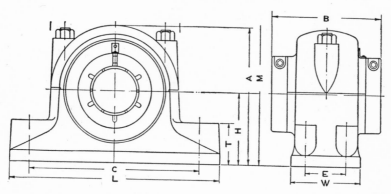

FIG. 193F. Roller Bearing Pillow Block. (*T. B. Wood's Sons Company.*)

Shaft Sizes	A	B — Straight Sleeve Type	C	E	H	L	T	W	2 Bolts	4 Bolts
1¹³/₁₆-2	6³/₈	5³/₄	8¹/₂		3¹/₄	11	2¹/₄	3¹/₂	⁵/₈	
2¹/₁₆-2¹/₄	7¹/₄	6	9¹/₄		3³/₄	11³/₄	2⁵/₈	4	⁵/₈	
2⁵/₁₆-2¹/₂	7³/₄	6¹/₂	10¹/₄	2¹/₂	4	13	2³/₄	4¹/₄	³/₄	⁵/₈
2⁹/₁₆-2³/₄	9	7³/₈	11¹/₂	2³/₄	4³/₄	14¹/₄	3	4³/₄	³/₄	⁵/₈
2¹³/₁₆-3	9	7³/₈	11¹/₂	2³/₄	4³/₄	14¹/₄	3	4³/₄	³/₄	⁵/₈
3¹/₈-3¹/₂	10	8	13	3¹/₄	5¹/₄	16	3	5¹/₂	⁷/₈	³/₄
3⁵/₈-4	12¹/₈	8⁷/₈	15¹/₂	3¹/₄	6³/₈	19	3¹/₂	6¹/₂		⁷/₈
4¹/₈-4¹/₂	13³/₈	10	16¹/₄	3¹/₂	7	19³/₄	4	7		⁷/₈
4⁵/₈-5	14³/₄	10³/₄	18³/₄	3³/₄	7¹/₂	23	4¹/₄	8		1

CHAPTER VIIA

PULLEYS, BELTS, ETC.

141. Pulleys.—The forms and proportions of pulleys are dependent upon their use. For belt drives pulleys of cast iron, wood, or steel are used with flat belts made of leather, cotton, rubber, and other flexible materials.

FIG. 194. Cast Iron Pulleys.

Cast iron pulleys are illustrated in Fig. 194 where a solid pulley is shown at **A**, a split pulley at **B**, and a double-arm split pulley at **C**. The split construction is convenient for handling and for putting on or removing from the shaft. The diameter of a pulley is measured at the center or at the highest point of the "crown."

Pulleys may be secured on the shafts by plain keys, set screws, or in the case of split pulleys by the clamping effect of bolting the two halves together.

Rim speed for solid cast iron pulleys is limited to about 5000 ft. per min., and for split pulleys to about 4500 ft. per min. Steel split pulleys may be run at any speed that is practicable for regular double leather belts.

142. Proportions for Cast Iron Pulleys.—The face width should be at least equal to the width of the belt or $3/8''$ to $1/2''$ or more wider. Small pulleys up to 6″ or 8″ diameter may have a web or plate instead of pulley arms. Diameter 6″ or 8″ up to 12″ or 18″ diameter may have four arms, larger diameters usually have six arms. Wide face pulleys are made with double arms.

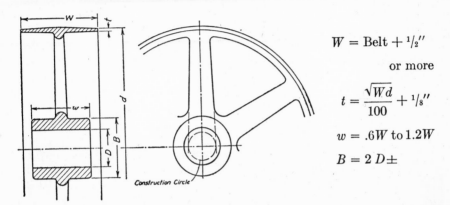

$$W = \text{Belt} + 1/2''$$
$$\text{or more}$$
$$t = \frac{\sqrt{Wd}}{100} + 1/8''$$
$$w = .6W \text{ to } 1.2W$$
$$B = 2\,D\pm$$

FIG. 195A. Pulley Proportions.

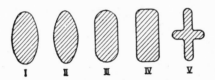

FIG. 195B. Pulley Arms.

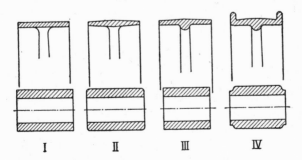

FIG. 195C. Rims and Hubs.

Some proportions for cast iron pulleys are given in Fig. 195A. Note the construction circle for the pulley arms. The taper of the arms may be $1/4''$ to $3/8''$ per foot on each side. In the left-hand view the taper may be about half as much. Pulley arms are commonly made elliptical

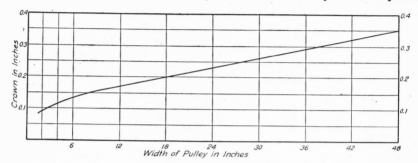

FIG. 195D. Crowning Chart.

in section although other sections are sometimes used, Fig. 195B. Several forms of rims and hubs are indicated in Fig. 195C. In order to prevent the belt from slipping off, the face of the pulley may be provided with flanges as at IV, Fig. 195C. The usual method, however, is to make the rim "crowned" as at II and III. The belt tends to "ride" the highest part of the pulley. The amount of crowning varies greatly but may be taken from Fig. 195D. Keyseat dimensions are given in Fig. 195E.

Diameter of Shaft, Inches	W	T	Diameter of Shaft, Inches	W	T
$15/16$—$1\,1/8$	$1/4$	$1/8$	$3\,7/16$—$3\,5/8$	$7/8$	$7/16$
$1\,3/16$—$1\,3/8$	$5/16$	$5/32$	$3\,11/16$—$3\,7/8$	$15/16$	$15/32$
$1\,7/16$—$1\,5/8$	$3/8$	$3/16$	$3\,15/16$—$4\,1/8$	1	$1/2$
$1\,11/16$—$1\,7/8$	$7/16$	$7/32$	$4\,3/16$—$4\,5/8$	$1\,1/8$	$1/2$
$1\,15/16$—$2\,1/8$	$1/2$	$1/4$	$4\,11/16$—$5\,3/8$	$1\,1/4$	$1/2$
$2\,3/16$—$2\,3/8$	$9/16$	$9/32$	$5\,7/16$—$5\,5/8$	$1\,3/8$	$1/2$
$2\,7/16$—$2\,5/8$	$5/8$	$5/16$	$5\,11/16$—$6\,7/8$	$1\,1/2$	$5/8$
$2\,11/16$—$2\,7/8$	$11/16$	$11/32$	$6\,15/16$—$7\,7/8$	$1\,3/4$	$3/4$
$2\,15/16$—$3\,1/8$	$3/4$	$3/8$	$7\,15/16$—$8\,7/8$	2	$3/4$
$3\,3/16$—$3\,3/8$	$13/16$	$13/32$			

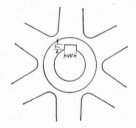

FIG. 195E. Keyseats for Pulleys and Rope Sheaves.

143. Velocity Ratio.—The r.p.m. (revolution per minute) of the driving pulley is to the r.p.m. of the driven pulley as the diameter of the driven pulley is to the diameter of the driving pulley, or in Fig. 196 at A, N_1 = r.p.m. of driver, N_2 = r.p.m. of driven, D_1 = diam. of driver, D_2 = diam. of driven. Then $\dfrac{N_1}{N_2} = \dfrac{D_2}{D_1}.$

For a compound drive, Fig. 196 at **B**, the ratio is: $\dfrac{N_1}{N_6} = \dfrac{D_2 \times D_4 \times D_6}{D_1 \times D_3 \times D_5}$.

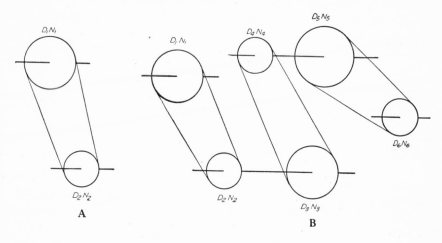

Fig. 196. Velocity Ratio.

144. Quarter-Twist Drive.—When the pulley shafts are not parallel they may be at right angles to each other (called quarter-twist or quarter-turn drive) or they may be at any other angle. The condition which must exist for any drive is stated in Unwin's Machine Design: "the point at which the belt is delivered from any pulley must be in the plane of the other pulley." This is illustrated for a quarter-turn drive in Fig. 197 at **A**, which indicates the line from the center of the face of the driven pulley to the center of the face of the driving pulley. This drive is not reversible. To reverse the drive the pulleys would have to be arranged as indicated in Fig. 197 at **B**.

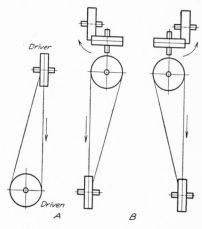

Fig. 197. Quarter-Twist Drive.

145. Horsepower Transmitted by Belts.—Power is transmitted by a belt because one side is tigher than the other. The difference in pull on the two sides depends upon the tightness of the belt, the friction between the belt and the pulley and the arc of contact or wrap of the belt around the pulley. The tight side of a belt should come on the bottom so that any sagging of the belt will increase the arc of contact as at I, Fig. 198, where T_1 is the tension in the tight side and T_2 in the slack side.

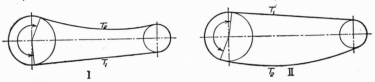

FIG. 198.   Belt Tension.

The power transmitted by a belt is determined by the difference in tensions and the speed of the belt. The horsepower transmitted is equal to the effective pull times the speed divided by 33,000 which may be written as a formula.

$$\frac{(T_1 - T_2)\, V}{33,000} = \text{HP},$$

$T_1 =$ Tension on tight side in lbs.,
$T_2 =$ Tension on slack side in lbs.,
$V =$ Speed in feet per minute.

The value of T_1 may be taken at 35 to 50 lbs. per inch of width for single belts and 60 to 90 lbs. per inch of width for double belts. The value of V should be less than 2,000 feet per minute when this formula is used.

For higher speeds the effect of centrifugal force must be considered. (See Machinery's Handbook or Mark's Handbook.)

Common empirical rules often used are:

$$1\ \text{HP} = \frac{W\,V}{1000}\ \text{for single belts}$$

and

$$1\ \text{HP} = \frac{W\,V}{600}\ \text{for double belts.}$$

146. Belt Length.—The length of a belt for a pair of pulleys is best obtained by direct measurement, using a steel tape. For open belts, Fig. 199 at I, the length of belt may be calculated from the formula,

$$L = 1.57(D_1 + D_2) + \sqrt{4\,X^2 - (D_1 - D_2)^2} + \frac{(D_1 - D_2)^2}{2\,X}$$

For crossed belts as at II, the formula is:

$$L = 1.57(D_1 + D_2) + \sqrt{4\,X^2 - (D_1 + D_2)^2} + \frac{(D_1 + D_2)^2}{2\,X}$$

All dimensions must be in the same units, either feet or inches.

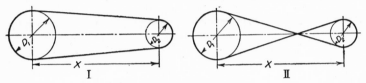

FIG. 199. Length of Belt.

A graphical method of finding the length of belt for cone pulleys is given in the American Society of Mechanical Engineers Transactions, Vol. X. Given R_1 and R_2 and distance between centers C, Fig. 200.

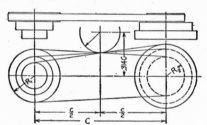

FIG. 200. Cone Pulley Radii.

Draw circles with radii R_1 and R_2 and a line tangent to them. At middle point of C erect a perpendicular and locate a point on it, .314 C above center line. With this point as a center, draw an arc tangent to the belt line. Lines tangent to this arc will determine diameters of other pulleys requiring the same belt length.

When crossed belts are used, the sum of the diameters of each pair of pulleys must be equal to the sum of the diameters of every other pair.

147A. V-Belt drives use sheaves with V-grooves, Fig. 201. A separate belt is used for each groove. They may be used on very short centers. They are smooth and quiet in starting and operation, have high gripping characteristics, and are flexible. V-belts are made in sizes ranging from $1/2''$ x $11/32''$ to $1\tfrac{1}{2}''$ x $1''$ to meet power transmission requirements.

147B. Rope drives use grooved pulleys or sheaves. There are two systems, the English system which uses a separate rope for each groove, and the American system which uses a single rope wound around the

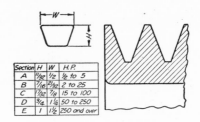

Section	H	W	H. P.
A	$^{11}/_{32}$	$^1/_2$	$^1/_2$ to 5
B	$^7/_{16}$	$^{21}/_{32}$	2 to 25
C	$^{17}/_{32}$	$^7/_8$	15 to 100
D	$^3/_4$	$1\,^1/_4$	50 to 250
E	1	$1\,^1/_2$	250 and over

FIG. 201. Vee Belt Grooves.

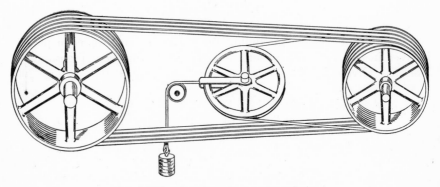

FIG. 202A. American System Rope Drive.

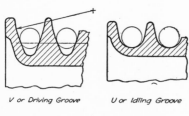

V or Driving Groove   U or Idling Groove

FIG. 202B. Rope Drive Grooves.

driving and driven sheaves to make as many turns as are required to transmit the power. The American system, Fig. 202A, is favored in this country. Rope drives can be used to transmit greater powers and over longer distances than are practical for belt drives. Grooves for manila rope are illustrated in Fig. 202B.

147C. Chain drives use sprocket wheels designed to accommodate the kind of chain used. Chain drives in general run at lower speeds than belts (link chains under 700 ft. per min.; roller chains under 1000 ft. per min.; silent chains made up of a series of steel leaves of link, under 1600 ft. per min.).

CHAPTER VIII

SHAFTING AND COUPLINGS

148. Shafting.—Shafting is made from various grades of wrought iron and steel. Cold finished shafting is much used. This is shafting which has been cleaned of scale and rolled under pressure. It can be used for many purposes without machining to size and is considerably strengthened by the surface which comes from the rolling process.

Hot rolled shafting is "black" and must be turned to size before using. Actual diameters are $^{1}/_{16}''$ less than nominal diameters.

149. Standard Sizes.—American standard diameters and lengths for cold-finished shafting are as follows:

Transmission Shafting Diameters
$^{15}/_{16}''$; $1^{3}/_{16}''$; $1^{7}/_{16}''$; $1^{11}/_{16}''$; $1^{15}/_{16}''$; $2^{3}/_{16}''$; $2^{7}/_{16}''$; $2^{15}/_{16}''$; $3^{7}/_{16}''$; $3^{15}/_{16}''$; $4^{7}/_{16}''$; $4^{15}/_{16}''$; $5^{7}/_{16}''$; $5^{15}/_{16}''$.
Machinery Shafting Diameters
Size intervals extending to $2^{1}/_{2}$ in., by sixteenth inches; from $2^{1}/_{2}$ in., to 4 in. inclusive by eighth inches; and from 4 in., to 6 in., by quarter inches.
Standard stock lengths are 16, 20 and 24 feet.

150. Special Shafts.—Special shafts have to be forged of steel suitable for the particular purpose. Shafts for machine tools and power machinery are made with varying diameters and must be completely dimensioned as indicated in Fig. 95.

151. To Compute the Diameter of a Shaft.—The diameter of a shaft for a given purpose will depend upon the material, the speed, and the character of the load. If a force is applied at a distance from the center of a shaft it will tend to twist the shaft, Fig. 203. The measure of this

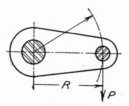

Fɪɢ. 203.

115

twisting tendency is called the twisting moment and is equal to $M_t = PR$ in which P = pounds and R = inches.   The moment of the stress within the shaft must equal this twisting moment, or

$$M_t = PR = \frac{S'J}{r},$$

in which S' = shearing stress in pounds per square inch, r = radius of shaft in inches, and J = polar moment of inertia.

For a solid shaft $J = \pi d^4/32$ in which d = diameter of shaft.

Then $PR = S'\pi d^3/16$ or solving the equation for d this becomes

$$d = \sqrt[3]{\frac{16PR}{\pi S'}},$$

which is the formula for figuring the size of a solid shaft.

For a hollow shaft

$$PR = \frac{S'\pi(d_1{}^4 - d_2{}^4)}{16 d_1},$$

in which d_1 = outside diameter and d_2 = inside diameter.

152. Horse Power Transmitted.—To figure a shaft for a given horse power let H.P. = horse power = 33,000 ft. lbs. per minute and N = number of revolutions per minute.

$$\text{H.P.} = \frac{PR2\pi N}{12 \times 33,000}.$$

Substitute the value $S'\pi d^3/16$ for PR and the equation may be put into the form

$$d = \sqrt[3]{\frac{321,000 \text{ H.P.}}{S'N}}.$$

This formula may be written

$$d = k\sqrt[3]{\frac{\text{H.P.}}{N}}.$$

Values of k for different values of S' are given in Table 23.

TABLE 23

S'	k	S'	k
3,000.........	4.75	7,000.........	3.57
4,000.........	4.31	8,000.........	3.42
5,000.........	4.00	9,000.........	3.29
6,000.........	3.77		

For main shafts S' may be taken at 3,000 to 4,000. For line shafts with pulleys, etc., use $S' = 5,000$. For countershafts and other short shafts the value of S' may be from 7,000 to 9,000.

153. The formula $d = k \sqrt[3]{(\text{H.P.}/N)}$ may be solved for the horse power and written in the form

$$\text{H.P.} = \frac{d^3 N}{\text{Constant}}.$$

TABLE 24

VALUES OF $d^3 N$

Dia. of Shaft in In.	Revolutions per Minute							
	100	125	150	175	200	250	300	350
	$d^3 N$	$d^3 N$	$d^3 N$	$d^3 N$	$d^3 N$	$d^3 N$	$d^3 N$	$d^3 N$
$1/2$	12.50	15.66	18.75	21.88	25.00	31.32	37.50	43.76
$5/8$	24.41	30.51	36.62	42.72	48.82	61.02	73.23	85.44
$3/4$	42.19	52.74	63.30	73.83	84.38	105.5	126.6	147.6
$7/8$	66.99	83.74	100.5	117.3	134.0	167.1	201.0	234.0
1	100.0	125.0	150.0	175.0	200.0	250.0	300.0	350.0
$1^1/8$	142.4	178.0	213.6	249.2	284.8	356.0	427.2	498.4
$1^1/4$	195.3	244.1	293.0	341.8	390.6	488.2	585.9	683.6
$1^3/8$	260.0	325.0	390.0	455.0	520.0	650.0	780.0	910.0
$1^1/2$	337.5	421.9	506.3	590.6	675.0	843.8	1013.	1181.
$1^5/8$	429.1	536.4	643.7	750.9	858.2	1073.	1287.	1501.
$1^{11}/16$	480.6	600.8	720.9	841.0	961.2	1202.	1442.	1682.
$1^{15}/16$	727.3	909.1	1091.	1273.	1455.	1818.	2182.	2546.
$2^3/16$	1047.	1309.	1571.	1832.	2094.	2618.	3141.	3664.
$2^1/4$	1139.	1424.	1709.	1993.	2278.	2848.	3417.	3986.
$2^5/16$	1237.	1546.	1856.	2165.	2474.	3092.	3711.	4330.
$2^7/16$	1448.	1810.	2172.	2534.	2896.	3620.	4344.	5068.
$2^{11}/16$	1941.	2426.	2912.	3397.	3882.	4852.	5823.	6794.
$2^{15}/16$	2535.	3169.	3803.	4436.	5070.	6338.	7605.	8872.
$3^7/16$	4062.	5078.	6093.	7110.	8124.	10160.	12190.	14200.
$3^{15}/16$	6105.	7631.	9158.	10680.	12210.	15260.	18320.	21360.
$4^1/2$	9113.	11390.	13670.	15950.	18226.	22780.	27340.	31900.
5	12500.	15630.	18750.	21880.	25000.	31260.	37500.	43760.
$5^1/2$	16640.	20800.	24960.	29120.	33280.	41600.	49910.	58240.
6	21600.	27000.	32400.	37800.	43200.	54000.	64800.	75600.

Values of this constant, as given by the B. F. Sturtevant Co., follow.

Turned steel shafting, head shafts, well supported.   Constant = 125.
Cold rolled shafting, head shafts, well supported.   Constant = 100.
Turned steel shafting, line shafts, bearings 8 ft. apart.   Constant = 90.
Cold rolled shafting, line shafts, bearings 8 ft. apart.   Constant = 70.
Turned steel shafting, countershafts, bearings not over 8 ft. apart.   Constant = 50.
Cold rolled shafting, countershafts, bearings not over 8 ft. apart.   Constant = 40.

Values of $d^3 N$ are given in Table 24.

154. Shaft for Bending and Twisting.—When a shaft carries a heavy flywheel or is otherwise subject to bending as well as twisting we must allow for both stresses.   This is done by finding a moment equivalent to the bending and twisting moments together using the formula

$$M_e = M + \sqrt{M_t^2 + M^2}.$$

in which M_e = equivalent moment. M = bending moment and M_t = twisting moment.

The formula for diameter then is

$$d = \sqrt[3]{\frac{16 M_e}{\pi S'}}.$$

155. Shaft Details.—Methods of dimensioning shafts and other details are given in Chap. III.   Square and filleted shoulders and a shaft collar are indicated in Fig. 204.   The filleted form is, of course, stronger

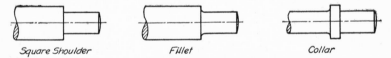

Square Shoulder   Fillet   Collar

Fig. 204.   Square and Filleted Shoulders.

than the square corner shoulder.   A part of a shafting drawing is shown in Fig. 205.   Note the various series of dimensions, the location of bearings, pulleys and other details.

156. Couplings.—Couplings for joining lengths of shafting together are made in many forms.   A solid sleeve or box coupling is a hollow cylinder which holds the ends of the shafts, Fig. 206.   Set screws or keys are used to hold the shafts in place.   Table 25 gives dimensions.*

* Tables 25 to 28 are from the Royersford Foundry and Machine Company, Inc.

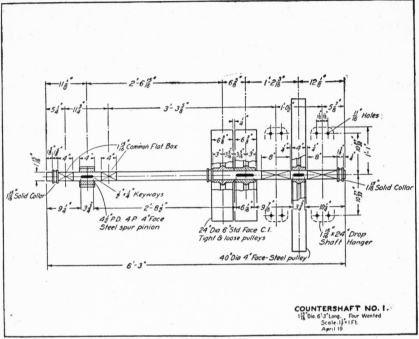

FIG. 205.   A Shafting Drawing.

TABLE 25 (FIG. 206)
* DIMENSIONS OF SOLID SLEEVE COUPLINGS

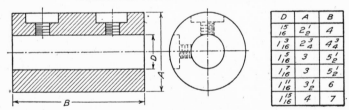

D	A	B
$\frac{15}{16}$	$2\frac{1}{2}$	4
$1\frac{3}{16}$	$2\frac{3}{4}$	$4\frac{3}{4}$
$1\frac{5}{16}$	3	$5\frac{1}{2}$
$1\frac{7}{16}$	3	$5\frac{1}{2}$
$1\frac{11}{16}$	$3\frac{1}{2}$	6
$1\frac{15}{16}$	4	7

FIG. 206.   Solid Sleeve Coupling.

157. The split box or clamp coupling, shown in Fig. 207, is made in halves which are bolted together and are keyed to the two shafts.   Some dimensions are given in Table 26.

158. A simple flange coupling is illustrated in Fig. 208.   Each half is keyed to the end of a shaft and the two halves bolted together.   Some dimensions are given in Table 27.

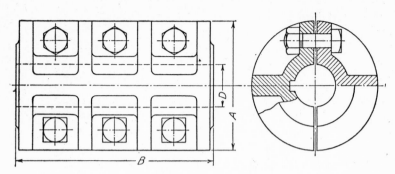

FIG. 207. Clamp Coupling.

TABLE 26 (FIG. 207)

*DIMENSIONS OF CLAMP COUPLINGS

Size of Shaft, Inches	B	A	Size of Keyseat	Bolts No.	Bolts Size
$^{15}/_{16}$ and 1	$5^3/_8$	4	$^1/_4$	4	$^1/_2$
$1^3/_{16}$ and $1^1/_4$	$6^1/_4$	$4^1/_4$	$^1/_4$	4	$^1/_2$
$1^7/_{16}$ and $1^1/_2$	$7^1/_8$	$4^1/_2$	$^3/_8$	6	$^1/_2$
$1^{11}/_{16}$ and $1^3/_4$	$8^1/_4$	$5^1/_8$	$^7/_{16}$	6	$^5/_8$
$1^{15}/_{16}$ and 2	$8^5/_8$	$5^1/_2$	$^1/_2$	6	$^5/_8$
$2^3/_{16}$ and $2^1/_4$	$9^5/_{16}$	$5^3/_4$	$^9/_{16}$	6	$^3/_4$
$2^7/_{16}$ and $2^1/_2$	$9^7/_8$	$6^1/_4$	$^5/_8$	6	$^3/_4$
$2^{11}/_{16}$ and $2^3/_4$	$10^7/_8$	$7^1/_4$	$^{11}/_{16}$	6	$^3/_4$
$2^{15}/_{16}$ and 3	12	$7^1/_4$	$^3/_4$	6	$^7/_8$
$3^3/_{16}$ and $3^1/_4$	$12^7/_8$	$7^7/_8$	$^3/_4$	6	$^7/_8$
$3^7/_{16}$ and $3^1/_2$	$13^1/_2$	8	$^7/_8$	6	$^7/_8$
$3^{11}/_{16}$ and $3^3/_4$	$14^1/_4$	$9^1/_2$	$^7/_8$	6	$^7/_8$
$3^{15}/_{16}$ and 4	$15^1/_2$	$10^1/_4$	1	6	1
$4^3/_{16}$ and $4^1/_4$	$17^1/_2$	$10^1/_2$	1	8	1
$4^7/_{16}$ and $4^1/_2$	$17^1/_2$	11	$1^1/_8$	8	1
$4^{11}/_{16}$ and $4^3/_4$	$18^3/_8$	11	$1^1/_8$	8	1
$4^{15}/_{16}$ and 5	$18^3/_8$	$11^3/_4$	$1^1/_4$	8	$1^1/_8$
$5^3/_{16}$ and $5^1/_4$	$19^1/_4$	$14^1/_4$	$1^1/_4$	8	$1^1/_4$
$5^7/_{16}$ and $5^1/_2$	$19^1/_4$	$14^1/_4$	$1^3/_8$	8	$1^1/_4$
$5^{11}/_{16}$ and $5^3/_4$	20	16	$1^3/_8$	8	$1^3/_8$
$5^{15}/_{16}$ and 6	20	16	$1^1/_2$	8	$1^3/_8$
$6^7/_{16}$ and $6^1/_2$	$22^3/_8$	....	$1^5/_8$	....	....
$6^{15}/_{16}$ and 7	$23^1/_4$	....	$1^3/_4$	....	....

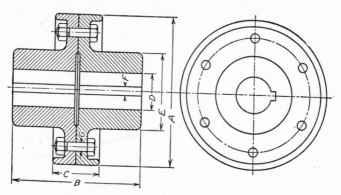

FIG. 208. Flange Coupling.

TABLE 27 (FIG. 208)

*FLANGE COUPLINGS

Size of Shaft, Inches	A	B	C	E	Size of Keyway	Bolts	
						No.	Size
$^{15}/_{16}$ and 1	$4^7/_8$	$3^1/_4$	$1^5/_8$	$1^7/_8$	$^1/_4$	3	$^1/_2$
$1^3/_{16}$ and $1^1/_4$	$6^3/_4$	$4^7/_8$	$2^1/_8$	$2^3/_4$	$^5/_{16}$	4	$^1/_2$
$1^7/_{16}$ and $1^1/_2$	$7^5/_8$	$5^5/_8$	$2^3/_8$	$3^3/_8$	$^3/_8$	5	$^1/_2$
$1^{11}/_{16}$ and $1^3/_4$	$8^3/_8$	$6^1/_2$	$2^1/_2$	4	$^7/_{16}$	5	$^5/_8$
$1^{15}/_{16}$ and 2	9	$7^3/_8$	$2^7/_8$	$4^1/_2$	$^1/_2$	5	$^5/_8$
$2^3/_{16}$ and $2^1/_4$	$9^1/_2$	$8^1/_4$	3	5	$^9/_{16}$	5	$^5/_8$
$2^7/_{16}$ and $2^1/_2$	$10^1/_4$	9	$3^1/_4$	$5^1/_4$	$^5/_8$	6	$^5/_8$
$2^{11}/_{16}$ and $2^3/_4$	$10^3/_8$	10	$3^1/_4$	$6^1/_4$	$^{11}/_{16}$	6	$^3/_4$
$2^{15}/_{16}$ and 3	$10^7/_8$	10	$3^1/_4$	$6^1/_4$	$^3/_4$	6	$^3/_4$
$3^3/_{16}$ and $3^1/_4$	12	$10^7/_8$	$3^3/_8$	$6^3/_4$	$^3/_4$	6	$^3/_4$
$3^7/_{16}$ and $3^1/_2$	$12^1/_4$	$10^7/_8$	$3^3/_8$	$6^3/_4$	$^7/_8$	6	$^3/_4$
$3^{11}/_{16}$ and $3^3/_4$	13	$11^1/_8$	$3^7/_8$	$6^7/_8$	$^7/_8$	6	$^3/_4$
$3^{15}/_{16}$ and 4	13	$11^1/_8$	$3^7/_8$	8	1	6	$^3/_4$
$4^3/_{16}$ and $4^1/_4$	$14^3/_8$	$11^3/_8$	4	8	1	6	$^7/_8$
$4^7/_{16}$ and $4^1/_2$	$14^3/_8$	$11^3/_8$	$4^1/_8$	$8^1/_2$	$1^1/_8$	6	$^7/_8$
$4^{11}/_{16}$ and $4^3/_4$	$16^1/_2$	$13^7/_8$	$5^3/_4$	$10^1/_2$	$1^1/_8$	8	$^7/_8$
$4^{15}/_{16}$ and 5	$16^1/_2$	$13^7/_8$	$5^3/_4$	$10^1/_2$	$1^1/_4$	8	$^7/_8$
$5^3/_{16}$ and $5^1/_4$	$17^3/_4$	$14^3/_4$	6	$10^1/_2$	$1^1/_4$	8	$^7/_8$
$5^7/_{16}$ and $5^1/_2$	$17^3/_4$	$14^3/_4$	6	$10^3/_4$	$1^3/_8$	8	$^7/_8$
$5^{11}/_{16}$ and $5^3/_4$	19	16	$6^1/_2$	11	$1^3/_8$	6	1
$5^{15}/_{16}$ and 6	19	16	$6^1/_2$	$11^1/_4$	$1^1/_2$	6	1

A square jaw clutch coupling is shown in Fig. 209 and dimensions are given in Table 28.

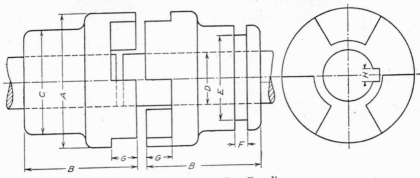

FIG. 209.   Square Jaw Coupling.

TABLE 28 (FIG. 209)

* JAW CLUTCH COUPLINGS

Size of Shaft, Inches	A	B	C	E	F *	G	Size of Keyway
15/16 and 1	......	......	......	......	......	......	5/16
1 3/16 and 1 1/4	3 7/8	3 7/8	3	2 7/16	7/8	7/16	5/16
1 7/16 and 1 1/2	3 7/8	3 7/8	3	2 7/16	7/8	7/16	3/8
1 11/16 and 1 3/4	4 1/4	4 1/4	3 3/4	2 3/4	15/16	1/2	7/16
1 15/16 and 2	4 7/16	5 1/8	4	3 1/4	1	1/2	1/2
2 3/16 and 2 1/4	4 1/2	5 1/2	4 1/4	3 1/4	15/16	9/16	9/16
2 7/16 and 2 1/2	4 3/4	6	4 5/8	3 5/8	1	5/8	5/8
2 11/16 and 2 3/4	5	6 1/2	4 3/4	4	1	5/8	11/16
2 15/16 and 3	5 1/8	7	5 1/4	4 15/16	1	5/8	3/4
3 3/16 and 3 1/4	5 1/4	7 5/8	5 1/2	4 3/4	1 1/16	5/8	7/8
3 7/16 and 3 1/2	5 5/8	8 1/4	6 1/8	5	1 1/16	3/4	7/8
3 11/16 and 3 3/4	......	......	......	......	......	......	......
3 15/16 and 4	7	9 1/2	7	5 1/2	1 1/8	3/4	1
4 7/16 and 4 1/2	7	11	8	6 1/2	1 1/8	3/4	1 1/8
4 15/16 and 5	......	......	......	......	......	......	......
5 7/16 and 5 1/2	......	......	......	......	......	......	......
5 15/16 and 6	......	......	......	......	......	......	......
6 7/16 and 6 1/2	......	......	......	......	......	......	......
6 15/16 and 7	......	......	......	......	......	......	......

The Jones style D (Oldham) coupling shown in Fig. 209-A is suitable for transmitting heavy loads at slow speeds and may be used when the shafts are slightly out of line. The flanged members are of cast iron and the floating center is of steel. Dimensions are given in the Table.

FIG. 209A.   Oldham Coupling.   (*W. A. Jones Foundry & Machine Company.*)

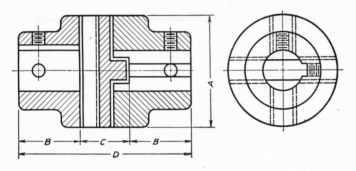

FIG. 209B.   Jones Style D Coupling.

Maximum Bore, Inches	Dimensions, Inches				H. P. at 100 R.P.M.	Maximum R.P.M.	Approx. Weight Pounds
	A	B	C	D			
$1^1/_4$	$3^3/_4$	$1^7/_8$	$1^7/_8$	$5^5/_8$	2.8	1500	12
$1^1/_2$	$4^1/_2$	$2^1/_4$	$2^1/_4$	$6^3/_4$	4.5	1500	20
$1^3/_4$	5	$2^5/_8$	$2^5/_8$	$7^7/_8$	7.0	1500	30
2	$5^1/_2$	3	3	9	10.5	1200	40
$2^1/_4$	6	$3^3/_8$	$3^3/_8$	$10^1/_8$	15.0	1200	55
$2^1/_2$	7	$3^3/_4$	$3^3/_4$	$11^1/_4$	20.0	1200	80
3	8	$4^1/_2$	$4^1/_8$	$13^1/_8$	36.0	1000	130
$3^1/_2$	10	$5^1/_4$	$4^3/_4$	$15^1/_4$	55.0	1000	230
4	12	6	$5^1/_2$	$17^1/_2$	90.0	750	375
$4^1/_2$	14	$6^3/_4$	$6^1/_4$	$19^3/_4$	125.0	750	570
5	16	$7^1/_2$	7	22	172.0	500	820
$5^1/_2$	18	$8^1/_4$	$7^3/_4$	$24^1/_4$	230.0	500	1150
6	20	9	$8^5/_8$	$26^5/_8$	300.0	300	1600

The Jones style double A flexible coupling shown in Fig. 209-C is suitable for high speeds.   The flanged members are semi-steel castings

Fig. 209C.   Flexible Coupling.   (*W. A. Jones Foundry & Machine Company.*)

and the floating disc is of fabric.   The pins are of steel.   A slight mis-alignment can be compensated as the holes are a little larger than the pins.   Dimensions are given in the table.

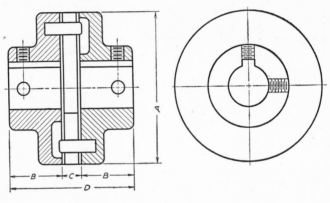

Fig. 209D.   Jones Style Double A Coupling.

Maximum Bore, Inches	Dimensions, Inches				H. P. at 100 R.P.M.	Maximum R.P.M.	Approx. Weight Pounds
	A	B	C	D			
$3/4$	3	$1^1/_4$	$7/_{16}$	$2^{15}/_{16}$	.35	3000	5
1	$3^1/_2$	$1^1/_2$	$1/_2$	$3^1/_2$	.65	2500	7
$1^1/_4$	$4^1/_2$	$1^3/_4$	$9/_{16}$	$4^1/_{16}$	1.3	2000	10
$1^1/_2$	$5^1/_2$	2	$5/_8$	$4^5/_8$	1.8	2000	15
$1^3/_4$	$6^1/_2$	$2^3/_8$	$11/_{16}$	$5^7/_{16}$	3.1	2000	22
2	$7^1/_2$	$2^1/_2$	$3/_4$	$5^3/_4$	5.0	2000	30
$2^1/_4$	$8^1/_4$	$2^3/_4$	$13/_{16}$	$6^5/_{16}$	7.3	2000	42
$2^1/_2$	$9^3/_8$	$3^1/_2$	$15/_{16}$	$7^{15}/_{16}$	12.0	1200	65
3	$10^1/_2$	$4^1/_8$	$1^1/_{16}$	$9^5/_{16}$	16.0	1200	90
$3^1/_2$	$11^3/_4$	$4^7/_8$	$1^3/_{16}$	$10^{15}/_{16}$	22.0	1200	135
4	13	$5^1/_2$	$1^5/_{16}$	$12^5/_{16}$	28.0	1200	190

The Palmer-Bee high-speed flexible coupling shown in Fig. 209E uses a continuous belt which passes under and over the pins. The flexibility of the belt eliminates vibrations due to misalignment and end-wise movement of the shafts. The discs are of cast iron, machined all over, and fitted with turned steel pins. The belt is of a specially treated fabric. Maximum bore sizes are from $3/4''$ to $6\frac{1}{2}''$.

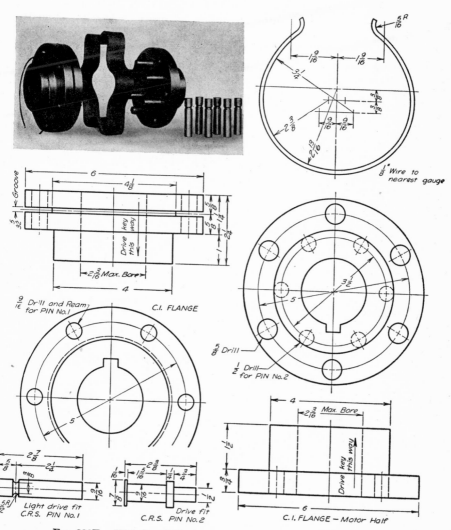

FIG. 209E.   High Speed Flexible Coupling.   (*Palmer-Bee Company.*)

CHAPTER IX

JIGS, FIXTURES AND DETAILS

159. Jigs and Fixtures.—It is not the purpose of this book to discuss the design of jigs and fixtures but a few suggestions bearing upon the drafting of such devices will be given.

Jigs and fixtures, Figs. 210A and 210B, have come into existence through the standardizing of operations necessary for quantity production and interchangeable manufacture.

160. Fixtures.—The terms jigs and fixtures are often used for the same thing. A fixture may be considered as a device to hold work on a machine in the proper position for the different operations and is dependent upon the action of the machine to accomplish its purpose. Fixtures are classified by the machines with which they are used and the method of machining, operating, etc. A milling machine fixture might be considered as typical.

161. Jigs.—A jig may be considered as a device for holding a piece to insure uniformity when a number are to be made. For instance a drilling jig would hold a piece and provide a means for guiding the drill so that each piece would have the holes drilled alike. It is not dependent upon the machine with which it is used. Jigs might be classed as cast iron box jigs, templet type, interchangeable bushing type, etc.

162. Jig and Fixture Drawings.—The general procedure for making drawings of shop devices is similar to any other kind of design drawing.

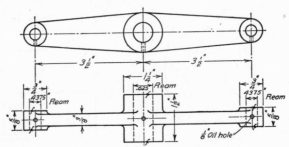

FIG. 210. Simple Beam Detail.

The " production," or part to be machined should be drawn first, using light pencil lines or other distinctive representation, to show its

122D

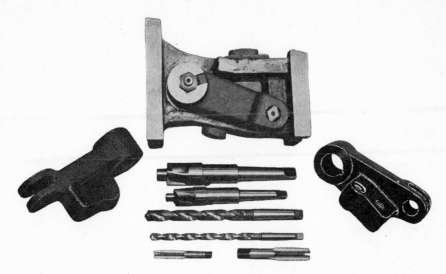

Fig. 210A. Drill Jig for Stop Screw Holes, Shifter Lever. "Work" is shown before and after operations. (*The Lodge & Shipley Machine Tool Co.*)

Fig. 210B. Milling Fixture for Feed Screw Nut. "Work" is shown before and after operations. (*The Lodge & Shipley Machine Tool Co.*)

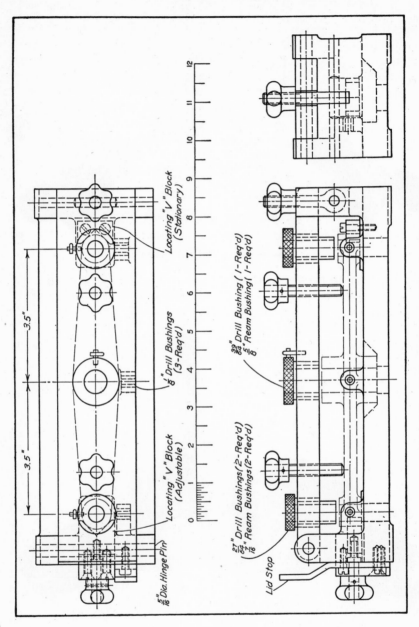

Fig. 211. Jig for Drilling and Reaming Simple Beam.

form after the operations have been completed.   The jig or fixture can then be designed " around " the piece.

The considerations given in Art. 165 should be kept in mind.   Finished surfaces should be indicated and necessary dimensions given.   Limits of accuracy must be specified where required.

163. A typical jig drawing for the *simple beam* of Fig. 210 is shown in position in Fig. 211.   The *work* is shown in position by light dash lines. The work rests upon the finished pads of the *body* and is held by the two screws which pass through the *lid*.   Two " V " *blocks*, one of which is adjustable, fix the work in its horizontal position.   The bushings for drilling and reaming are held in the lid.   The lid is hinged at the left end and clamped at the right end.

164. A fixture drawing for the *arm detail* of Fig. 212 is shown in Fig. 213.   Two swinging blocks are used to locate the arm for the first

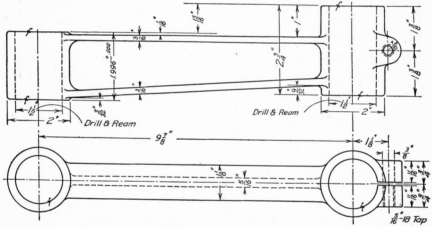

Fig. 212.   Arm Detail.

operation.   These are then dropped down and two large blocks are used to hold the end which has been machined while the second operation is performed.   Figs. 210 to 213 are from drawings kindly supplied by Arthur Brock, Jr., Tool and Manufacturing Works.

165. Fixture Design.—The many forms of jigs and fixtures will not be described here and the reader is referred to the books and articles on this subject.

The Cincinnati Milling Machine Company in their " Treatise on Milling and Milling Machines " * have a chapter on jigs and fixtures

* Published by Cincinnati Milling Machine Co., Cincinnati, O.   Price $1.50.

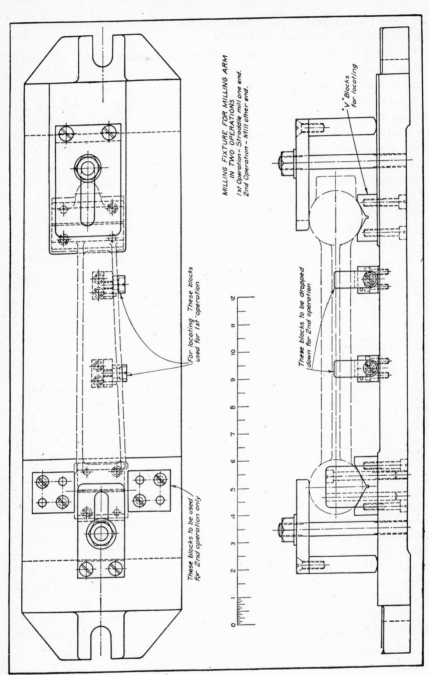

MILLING FIXTURE FOR MILLING ARM
IN TWO OPERATIONS
1st Operation – Straddle mill one end.
2nd Operation – Mill other end.

V Blocks
for locating

For locating. These blocks
used for 1st operation.

These blocks to be dropped
down for 2nd operation

These blocks to be used
for 2nd operation only

Fig. 213. Fixture for Milling Arm.

which has been used in the preparation of these articles including the following, " Axioms for the Fixture Designer."

1. The clamp should be immediately above the supporting point.

NOTE.—Disregard of this leads to springing of the work, or lifting of the work due to support point being transformed into a fulcrum.

2. Three fixed supporting points should be the maximum for any rough surfaces.

3. Supporting points for finished surfaces should be as small in area as is consistent with the pressure to be exerted by the clamps.

4. All supporting points should be set as far apart as the nature of the work will allow.

5. All side clamps should be arranged to press downward.

6. The fixed supporting points should always circumscribe the center of gravity of the work.

7. All supporting points over and above the original three should be sensitive in their adjustment.

8. All clamps and adjusting supports should be operated from the front of the fixture.

9. All clamps and support points that are operated or locked by wrench should have the same size head.

10. Support points should be set so high above the body of the fixture as to minimize the amount of cleaning required.

11. Support points should have provision for easy removing and replacing in the event of breakage.

12. Fixed support points should have provision for adjustments to take care of variations in castings from time to time.

13. Clamps should be arranged so that they can be easily withdrawn from the work.

NOTE.—This is to avoid lengthy unscrewing of the nut in order to give ample clearance between clamp and work.

14. Springs should be used to hold clamp up against clamping nut.

NOTE.—This is to avoid the falling down of the clamp and the consequent loss of time attendant on holding it up while inserting the work beneath.

15. Supporting points and clamps to be accessible to the operator's hand and eye.

16. Adequate provision for taking up end thrust so that this will not be dependent upon friction between work and clamp.

All of the above axioms are applicable to almost every type of fixture.

166. Some considerations in the design of fixtures are given as:

" 1. Rapidity of Clamping.

" 2. Accessibility for Inserting and Removing Work.

" 3. Generous Ducts for the Escape of Chips and Lubricant.

" 4. Removal of the Clamping and Supporting Members from the Cutter Zone. (Safety of Operation.)

" 5. Elimination of Clamping Strains from Table of Machine and Absorption of Same in Fixture.

" 6. Provision of Mass in Excess of Necessary Rigidity to absorb Chatter."

167. Standard Parts for Jigs and Fixtures.—There are certain standard constructions and parts of jigs and fixtures with which the designer must become familiar, especially those used in his own line of work.

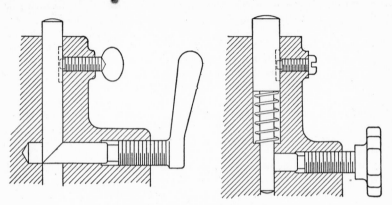

FIG. 214.   Adjustable Support Pins.

Such details as bushings, handles, clamping devices, support pins, setting pieces, etc., might be considered.   A few parts are given in Figs.

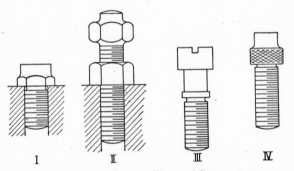

FIG. 215.   Support Pins and Screws.

214 to 216, to which the reader should add sketches of special devices and arrangements.   Dimensions will be found in the various machine handbooks.   Table 29 of standardized bushings is condensed from the data sheet book of the Wright-Fisher Bushing Corporation, who publish very complete tables of dimensions of their standardized bushings, liners, etc. Diameters may be had varying by $1/_{64}''$ and in four standard lengths for each size.

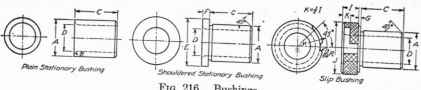

FIG. 216. Bushings.

TABLE 29 (FIG. 216)
DIMENSIONS OF STANDARDIZED BUSHINGS

D	A	B	C	E	F	G	H	I	J
1/8	5/16	1/32	3/8	7/16	1/16	1/16	1/2	1/4	11/16
3/16	3/8	1/32	3/8	1/2	3/32	1/16	17/32	1/4	3/4
1/4	7/16	1/32	3/8	9/16	3/32	1/16	19/32	1/4	7/8
5/16	9/16	1/32	7/16	11/16	3/32	1/16	21/32	7/16	1
3/8	5/8	1/16	1/2	3/4	3/32	1/16	11/16	7/16	1 1/16
7/16	11/16	1/16	9/16	13/16	3/32	1/16	23/32	7/16	1 1/8
1/2	3/4	3/32	9/16	7/8	1/8	1/16	25/32	1/2	1 1/4
9/16	13/16	3/32	5/8	1	1/8	1/16	13/16	1/2	1 5/16
5/8	7/8	3/32	3/4	1 1/8	1/8	1/16	7/8	1/2	1 7/16
11/16	1	1/8	7/8	1 1/4	3/16	1/16	15/16	1/2	1 9/16
3/4	1 1/16	1/8	1 1/8	1 5/16	3/16	3/32	31/32	1/2	1 5/8
13/16	1 1/8	1/8	1 1/4	1 3/8	3/16	3/32	1	1/2	1 11/16
7/8	1 1/4	1/8	1 3/8	1 9/16	1/4	3/32	1 1/16	1/2	1 13/16
15/16	1 5/16	1/8	1 1/2	1 11/16	1/4	3/32	1 3/32	1/2	1 7/8
1	1 3/8	5/32	1 5/8	1 3/4	1/4	3/32	1 1/8	5/8	1 15/16

168. Standard Parts and Details.—When making drawings of machinery it is always desirable and often absolutely necessary to consider the shop facilities available. This means that the designer should know the machines which will be used for making the parts and how they will be used.

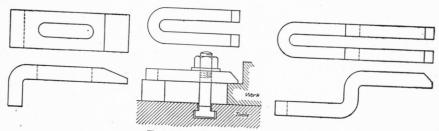

FIG. 217. Common Clamps.

Some of the smaller appliances used about the shop should be familiar to the draftsman. Some usual clamps are shown in Fig. 217. If standard equipment is on hand this is a simple matter that can often be used to advantage when deciding on how to hold a machine part for finishing.

169. The application of holding devices is shown in Fig. 218, and drawings for some " CAD " standardized appliances are shown in Fig.

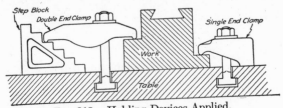

FIG. 218.   Holding Devices Applied.

219.   Drawings and dimensions were furnished by Mr. H. Cadwallader, Jr., of the Standard Shop Equipment Co., Philadelphia, Pa.   Such de-

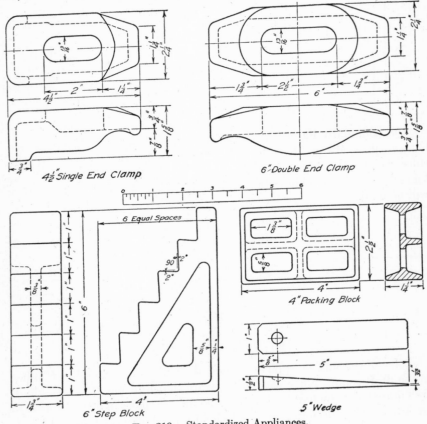

FIG. 219.   Standardized Appliances.

vices can be purchased ready for use in a great variety of sizes and forms and save a great deal of time.

170. The tables and notes which follow will suggest further information which the draftsman should have available in handbooks and note books. Standard T slots are given in Table 30, and "CAD" steel

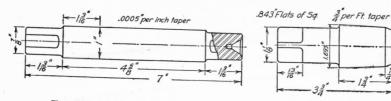

FIG. 220. A Lathe Mandrel.

FIG. 221. Pipe Tap.

TABLE 30

DIMENSIONS OF STANDARD "T" SLOTS

A	$1/4$	$5/16$	$3/8$	$7/16$	$1/2$	$5/8$	$3/4$	$7/8$	1	
B	$1/2$	$5/8$	$11/16$	$13/16$	$15/16$	$1 3/16$	1	$1 1/16$	$1 3/16$	
C	$5/32$	$5/32$	$7/32$	$7/32$	$9/32$	$13/32$	$17/32$	$11/16$	$13/16$	
D	$5/16$	$3/8$	$7/16$	$7/16$	$9/16$	$3/4$	1	$1 1/16$	$1 3/16$	

TABLE 31

DIMENSIONS OF STEEL WASHERS

Bolt. Dia.	$3/8$	$1/2$	$5/8$	$3/4$
A........	$13/32$	$17/32$	$21/32$	$25/32$
B........	$7/8$	1	$1 1/4$	$1 1/2$
C........	$1/8$	$3/16$	$1/4$	$1/4$

TABLE 32

DIMENSIONS OF MACHINE TABLE BOLTS

Bolt Dia......	$3/8$	$1/2$	$5/8$	$3/4$	$7/8$	1
A........	$5/8$	$7/8$	$1 1/16$	$1 3/16$	$1 1/2$	$1 3/4$
B........	$5/32$	$1/4$	$5/16$	$7/16$	$9/16$	$5/8$
B'........	$1/4$	$11/32$	$15/32$	$9/16$	....	

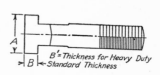

B'= Thickness for Heavy Duty
B = Standard Thickness

washers and machine table bolts in Tables 31 and 32.   Standard tapers such as Jarno, Brown and Sharpe, Morse, etc., are given in full in the American Machinist and Machinery Handbooks. A lathe mandrel is drawn in Fig. 220 and a pipe tap in Fig. 221.

CHAPTER X

GEARS AND CAMS

171. This chapter is intended to give an introductory knowledge of gears and cams so that drawings of them can be made and understood.

For a complete theoretical treatment a good text on mechanism or a special book on gears or cams should be studied.

172. Pulleys and Gears.—Consider two discs or wheels secured on shafts and placed so that the surfaces of the wheels are in contact, Fig. 222. If one of the wheels is turned and there is no slipping, the other

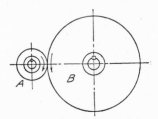

FIG. 222. Friction Wheels.

will turn, but in an opposite direction. If the pulley A has a diameter of 3″ and the pulley B a diameter of 9″, it will be necessary for pulley A to make three revolutions while pulley B makes one revolution. The velocity ratio is 3.

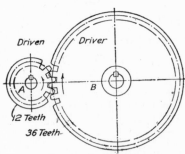

FIG. 223. Pinion and Gear.

If the forces are large or it is necessary to prevent slipping, gear teeth may be added to the two wheels as in Fig. 223. The ratio of velocities or the number of turns for gears is figured by using the number of teeth on each wheel. In the figure gear A has 12 teeth and gear B has 36 teeth, so that gear A must make $36/12 = 3$ turns for one turn of gear B. The smaller of the two gears is called a pinion.

The direction of revolution is indicated. The diameters, or number of teeth, or revolutions may be calculated by the formulas which follow:

T_1 = number of teeth in first gear
N_1 = revolutions per minute of first gear
D_1 = diameter of first gear
R_1 = radius of first gear
T_2 = number of teeth in second gear
N_2 = revolutions per minute of second gear
D_2 = diameter of second gear
R_2 = radius of second gear.

Then

$$\frac{T_1}{T_2} = \frac{N_2}{N_1}, \qquad \frac{D_1}{D_2} = \frac{N_2}{N_1}, \qquad \frac{R_1}{R_2} = \frac{N_2}{N_1}.$$

Toothed gearing is made in a variety of forms some of which are illustrated and named in Fig. 224. The shafts which are connected may be parallel, intersecting, and non-parallel and non-intersecting.

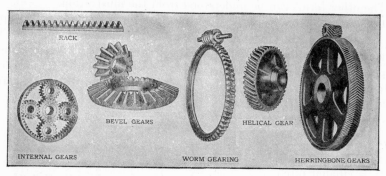

Fig. 224.   Some Types of Gears.   (*Foote Brothers Gear and Machine Co.*)

173. Gear Teeth.—Some of the terms used in gear work and the names of parts of gear teeth are illustrated and named in Fig. 225. The pitch circles are circles having diameters of rolling cylinders which would have the same velocity ratio as the gears which replace them.

The circular pitch as illustrated is the distance from a point on one tooth to the same point on the next tooth measured along the pitch circle.

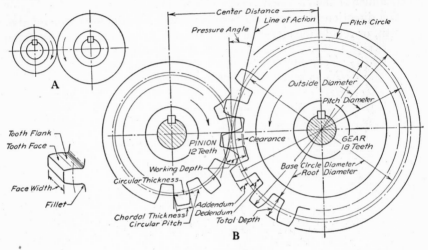

FIG. 225. Gear Terms.

The diametral pitch is the number of teeth per inch of pitch diameter. The other terms can be understood from the illustration.

174. Spur Gears.—The gear wheels just described are called spur gears. The tooth outline for gears may be either a cycloid or an involute. The cycloidal system is used for large cast gears. For most purposes cut gears are now used. These are made on both the involute system, and the American Standard Composite System which uses both cycloidal and involute curves.

(DP) = diametral pitch	$(DP) = \dfrac{\pi}{(CP)}$	$D_p = \dfrac{N}{(DP)}$	$N = D_p \times (DP)$
(CP) = circular pitch	$(DP) = \dfrac{N}{D_p}$	$D_p = D_0 - \dfrac{2}{(DP)}$	$N = (DP) \times D_0 - 2$
N = number of teeth	$(CP) = \dfrac{\pi}{(DP)}$	$D_0 = \dfrac{N+2}{(DP)}$	$N = \dfrac{\pi \times D_p}{(CP)}$
D_p = pitch diameter	$(CP) = \dfrac{\pi \times D_p}{N}$	$D_0 = D_p + \dfrac{2}{(DP)}$	
D_0 = outside diameter			

The American Standard includes the spur gear tooth form for the: 14$\frac{1}{2}$ Deg. Composite System; 14$\frac{1}{2}$ Deg. Full Depth Involute System; 20 Deg. Full Depth Involute System; 20 Deg. Stub Involute System. The 14$\frac{1}{2}$ Deg. and 20 Deg. refer to the pressure angle, Fig. 225. *Notation:* N = number of teeth. DP = Diametral pitch. CP = Circular pitch.

The 14$\frac{1}{2}$ Deg. Composite System tooth form has an involute curve for the middle portion and cycloidal curves for the top and bottom positions.

The 14$\frac{1}{2}$ Deg. and 20 Deg. Full Depth Involute System, and the 20 Deg. Stub Involute System tooth forms, have an involute curve.

PROPORTIONS FOR SPUR GEARS

(Condensed from American Standards)

System	14$\frac{1}{2}$ Deg. Composite 14$\frac{1}{2}$ Deg. and 20 Deg. Full Depth Involute		20 Deg. Stub Involute [5]	
	In Terms of Diametral Pitch 1 (Inches)	In Terms of Circular Pitch 1 (Inches)	In Terms of Diametral Pitch 1 (Inches)	In Terms of Circular Pitch 1 (Inches)
1. Addendum	$\frac{1}{DP}$	$0.3183 \times CP$	$\frac{0.8}{DP}$	$0.2546 \times CP$
2. Minimum Dedendum [2]	$\frac{1.157}{DP}$	$0.3683 \times CP$	$\frac{1}{DP}$	$0.3183 \times CP$
3. Working Depth	$\frac{2}{DP}$	$0.6366 \times CP$	$\frac{1.6}{DP}$	$0.5092 \times CP$
4. Minimum Total Depth [2]	$\frac{2.157}{DP}$	$0.6866 \times CP$	$\frac{1.8}{DP}$	$0.5729 \times CP$
5. Pitch Diameter	$\frac{N}{DP}$	$0.3183 \times N \times CP$	$\frac{N}{DP}$	$0.3183 \times N \times CP$
6. Outside Diameter	$\frac{N+2}{DP}$	$0.3183 \times (N+2) \times CP$	$\frac{N+1.6}{DP}$	$PD + (2\ \text{Addendums})$
7. Basic Tooth Thickness on Pitch Line	$\frac{1.5708}{DP}$	$0.5 \times CP$	$\frac{1.5708}{DP}$	$0.5 \times CP$
8. Minimum Clearance [2, 3]	$\frac{0.157}{DP}$	$0.05 \times CP$		
9. Minimum Clearance [2, 4]			$\frac{0.2}{DP}$	$0.0637 \times CP$
10. Radius of Fillet [6]				

N = Number of Teeth. DP = Diametral Pitch. CP = Circular Pitch.

[1] NOTE: The term Diametral Pitch is used up to 1 DP inclusive and the term Circular Pitch is used for 3 inches CP and over.

[2] NOTE: A suitable working tolerance should be considered in connection with all minimum recommendations.

[3] NOTE: Minimum clearance refers to the clearance between the top of the gear tooth, and the bottom of the mating gear space, and is specified as "minimum" so as to allow for necessary cutter clearance for all methods of producing gears. At the present time this value cannot be standardized.

[4] NOTE: A minimum root clearance of 0.2 inch/Diametral Pitch is recommended for new cutters and gears. There is correct tooth action, however, between gears cut to this standard system and those cut to the Nuttall system, the only dimension affected being the clearance. Where the proposed gear tooth meshes with a Nuttall gear space there is a clearance of 0.1425 inch/Diametral Pitch, and where the Nuttall tooth runs with the proposed gear space there is a clearance of 0.2146 inch/Diametral Pitch.

[5] NOTE: These proportions are identical with those of the A.G.M.A. recommended practice for Herringbone Gears.

[6] RADIUS OF FILLET: For 14$\frac{1}{2}$ deg. Composite and 14$\frac{1}{2}$ deg. Full Depth Involute = 1$\frac{1}{3}$ $\times$ Clearance; for 20 deg. Full Depth Involute = 1$\frac{1}{2}$ $\times$ Clearance.

175. Spur Gear Drawing.—It is not necessary to draw the tooth outline for cut gears. The gear specifications required for cut gears are outside diameter, diametral pitch, depth of cut, and number of teeth. A spur gear drawing with dimensions is shown in Fig. 226. Note that

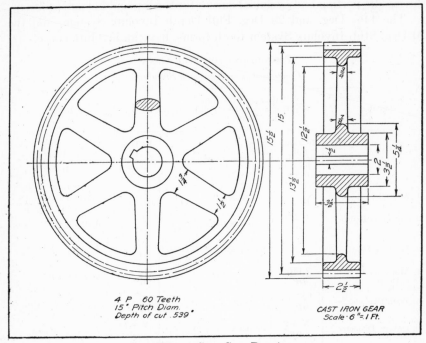

4 P   60 Teeth
15″ Pitch Diam.
Depth of cut .539″

CAST IRON GEAR
Scale · 6″= 1 Ft.

FIG. 226.   A Spur Gear Drawing.

the teeth are not shown and are not sectioned. Root diameter is represented by a dash line, the pitch diameter by a dot and dash line, and the outside diameter by a full line. Hubs, arms and rims are discussed in Chap. VII.

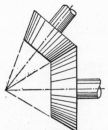

FIG. 227.   Friction Cones.

176. Bevel Gears.—Two cones in contact might be used to transmit motion from one shaft to another as in Fig. 227. To prevent slipping, teeth may be used and the cones become bevel gears. Two bevel gears

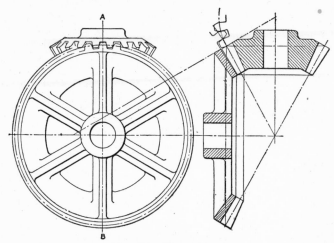

FIG. 228. Bevel Gears.

of the same size with shafts at right angles are called mitre gears. A pair of bevel gears is shown in Fig. 228. The shafts may make any angle with each other. The terms used and the parts of a bevel gear are given

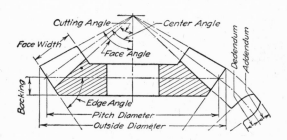

FIG. 229. Bevel Gear Terms.

in Fig. 229. Note the location of the pitch diameter and that the addendum and dedendum are measured at the large end of the gear tooth. A bevel gear drawing is shown in Fig. 230.

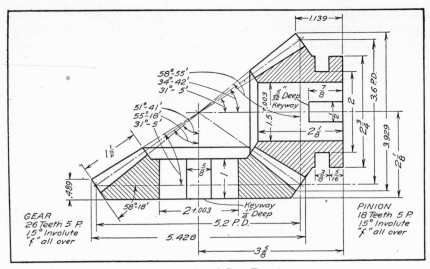

Fig. 230.   Bevel Gear Drawing.

177. Worm Gearing.—A worm and wheel are shown in Fig. 231.   A worm is a screw having a section on a plane through its axis of the same form as an involute rack tooth.   The gear which is driven by the worm

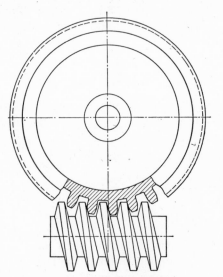

Fig. 231.   Worm and Wheel.

is called a worm wheel. The worm may have single, double, or multiple threads as explained in Chapter II for screw threads. The velocity ratio is found by dividing the number of teeth in the worm wheel by 1 for a single thread worm, by 2 for a double thread worm, etc. A worm and wheel drawing is given in Fig. 232.

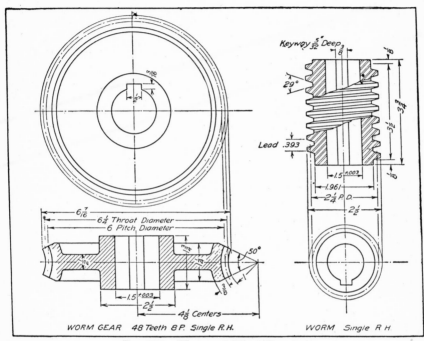

FIG. 232. Worm and Wheel Drawing.

178. Cams.—A cam is a plate having a curved outline or groove, or a cylinder having a groove, and is used to change rotary motion to re-

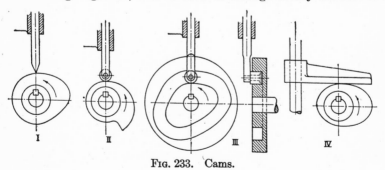

FIG. 233. Cams.

ciprocating motion. The reciprocating motion may be variable or intermittent. The part to which motion is given is called the follower. Several forms of cams are shown in Fig. 233.

179. To Draw a Plate Cam.—A cam outline is required which will raise the follower with uniform motion a distance of $1\frac{1}{2}''$ during one third of a revolution of the cam.

The follower is dropped uniformly during the next third of a revolution and remains at rest for one-third of a revolution. Refer to Fig. 234.

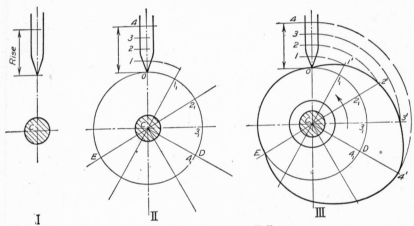

FIG. 234.   Cam with Point Follower.

Given the center of the cam, C and the rise of the follower, $O4$. With C as a center and radius CO, draw a circle. Divide this circle into three equal parts by radii CD, and CE. Then divide rise into a number of equal parts as shown at 1, 2, 3 and 4. Divide arc OD into same number of equal parts and draw radii through points thus located as at II. With C as a center and radius $C1$ draw arc cutting radius $C1_1$, produced at $1'$ as shown at III. Then $C2' = C2$; $C3' = C3$; $C4' = C4$. A smooth curve through points $1'$, $2'$, $3'$, and $4'$ will give a part of the cam outline. The curve from $4'$ to E is found by laying off the true distances on each radius as for the rise. Since the follower is to be at rest an arc from E to O with radius CO will complete the cam outline.

180. If a roller is used instead of a point on the follower the cam will be smaller. Proceed as for Fig. 234 which will give the curve followed by the center of the roll shown in Fig. 235 as a dot and dash line and called the pitch line. With a radius equal to the radius of the roll and centers on the pitch line draw arcs to which a tangent curve can be drawn to give the cam outline.

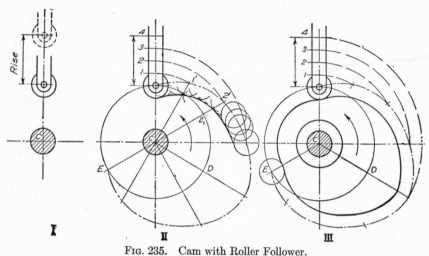

FIG. 235.   Cam with Roller Follower.

181. Kinds of Motion.—The follower may have *uniform motion* as in the cases described,—*harmonic motion, uniformly accelerated motion,* or *irregular motion.*   If the follower rises equal distances in equal intervals of time, we have uniform motion, shown in a diagram at I, Fig. 236.   When uniform motion is used, a circular arc is often used at the

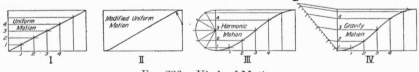

FIG. 236.   Kinds of Motion.

beginning and end to decrease the shock of sudden starting and stopping, Fig. 236 at II.

182. The diagram for harmonic motion is shown at III.   Points on the travel of the follower are located by drawing a semi-circle, dividing it into a number of equal parts and drawing lines to the line of travel as shown.   A cam with this motion can be run at a higher speed.   The unequal distances vertically on the line of travel are moved over in equal intervals of time.

183. Uniformly accelerated motion gives the easiest working cam. The follower has the same motion as a falling body.   The distance passed

over is proportional to the square of the time.   The distances on the
travel of the follower are made proportional to 1, 3, 5, 7, etc., and reverse
as shown at IV, Fig. 236.

Other kinds of motion are used to meet special conditions.

184. When the follower is not over the center of the cam, Fig. 237.
The follower is to rise with harmonic motion during one-half revolution
and fall during the second half.   Draw center line of follower down until

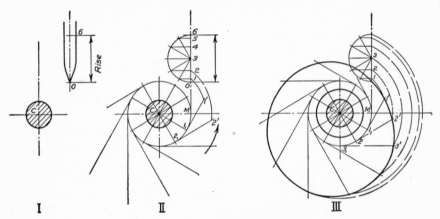

FIG. 237.   Cam with Offset Follower.

it crosses horizontal center line through cam at *M*.   With *CM* as a radius
draw a circle.   Divide rise of follower in parts to give harmonic motion.
Divide one-half of the circle just drawn into as many equal parts as there
are spaces in the rise, and draw tangents at each point as shown.   With

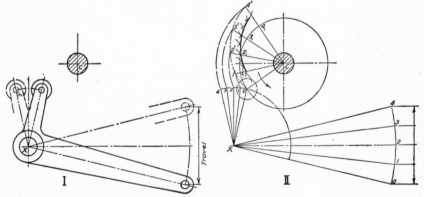

FIG. 238.   Cam with Lever Follower.

C as a center draw an arc passing through point 1 on the rise and cutting tangent from point 1_1 at $1'$. Arcs with C as a center and passing through points 2, 3, and 4 will locate other points through which a smooth curve can be passed.

185. When levers are used to transmit motion from the cam, Fig. 238, the method of solution is similar to the previous cases. Given the center of the cam shaft, center of bell crank shaft, lengths of arms and travel required at end of long arm as shown at I.

The end of the long arm is to rise uniformly during one-third revolution, drop half way down instantly, remain at rest one-third revolution and drop uniformly during the remaining third of a revolution.

Draw arcs with X as a center. Divide the travel into a number of equal parts and draw horizontal lines to locate points on the large arc. Find corresponding points on the small arc. The points on the cam outline are then located as shown in the figure.

186. The construction for a cam with flat follower is shown in Fig. 239. The follower is to rise during one-half revolution, remain at rest

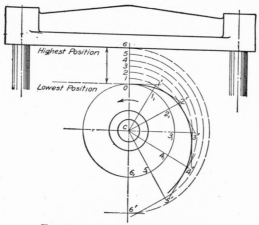

FIG. 239.   Cam with Flat Follower.

one-sixth of a revolution and fall during the remaining one-third revolution. Divide the rise into a number of equal parts. Draw circle with CO as a radius. Divide sections into same number of equal parts as rise. Draw radial lines. Lay off distances $C1$, $C2$, etc., on the radii to locate points 1, 2, etc., at points $1'$, $2'$, etc., draw perpendiculars to the radii. A smooth curve drawn tangent to these perpendiculars will be the cam outline.

187. Cylindrical Cams.—A cylindrical cam is a cylinder having a groove which gives the desired motion to a roller, Fig. 240. The pitch line for a cylindrical cam is first drawn on the development of the cam surface. Fig. 241 illustrates the solution of a cylindrical cam problem. The travel is indicated on the figure. The follower is to move one-half the distance with uniform motion during one-fourth of a revolution,

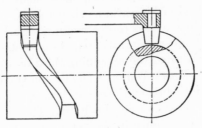

FIG. 240.   Cylindrical Cam.

remain at rest one-fourth of a revolution, rise uniformly during one-fourth revolution and drop with harmonic motion during the remaining one-fourth revolution. Divide the circle into a number of equal parts and lay them off on the stretchout line. The first three-quarters of a revolu-

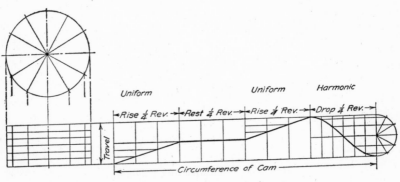

FIG. 241.   Cylindrical Cam Development.

tion are evident in the figure. The last quarter has as many equal horizontal divisions as there are unequal or harmonic divisions in the travel.

, For a complete treatment of the subject of cams consult Professor Furman's "Cams—Elementary and Advanced," Wiley, N. Y.

CHAPTER XI

PIPING DRAWINGS

188. Piping.—The frequent occurrence of piping in engineering work makes some knowledge of piping materials, sizes, and practice a necessary part of machine drawing. Pipe is used to convey liquids and gases. It is made of materials which are adapted to the various purposes for which it is used.

188A. American Standard Wrought-Iron and Wrought-Steel Pipe. —In the new standard the terms "standard," "extra strong," and "double extra strong" formerly used have been discarded and have been replaced by schedule numbers. Sizes of pipe are identified by "nominal pipe sizes." For complete information on materials, wall thicknesses, and weights, the published standard (A.S.A. B36.10) should be consulted. The table shown here for steel pipe is from the above standard. A table for wrought iron pipe and tables of weights in pounds per linear foot for welded and seamless steel pipe, and for welded wrought iron pipe, are included in the ASA report.

A pipe size may be designated by giving the nominal size and wall thickness, or the nominal pipe size and weight per foot. In general the wall thickness at any point should not be more than 12.5 per cent under the nominal wall thickness shown in the tables, unless otherwise specified.

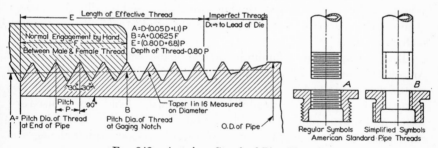

FIG. 242. American Standard Pipe Thread.

188B. Pipe threads are formed with an angle of 60° between the sides with the crest and root slightly flattened so that the depth of the thread is eight-tenths of the pitch. Tapered threads (1 to 16 measured on the diameter), Fig. 242, are desirable to make tight joints, but straight threads are used for some purposes. American Standard conventional representations are shown at **A** and **B**.

145

188C. American Standard wrought pipe, made of steel or wrought iron, is used more generally than other kinds of pipe and is suitable for many purposes such as high pressure steam, gas, water, etc. Wrought pipe is specified by its nominal inside diameter. The nominal diameter differs from the actual diameter by varying amounts. The terms "Standard" pipe, "Extra Strong" pipe, and "Double Extra Strong" pipe have been used to designate schedules of wall thicknesses until the development of the new American Standard (ASA B 36.10). Standard pipe was indicated for pressures up to 125 pounds per square inch, Extra Strong, and Double Extra Strong for higher pressures. The extra thickness was obtained by reducing the inside diameter as shown by the actual sizes of the cross sections for the three weights of $3/4$ inch pipe in Fig. 242A. Tables 33 and 34 are included for reference as these terms will be encountered on many drawings. Above twelve inches, pipe is known as O.D., or outside diameter pipe and is specified accordingly together with the desired thickness of walls. Wrought pipe may be put together by using threads, Fig. 242, or by welding, Fig. 245.

188D. Materials used for piping are selected according to the qualities required for different purposes. As already mentioned wrought iron and steel pipe are very widely used as they meet a large number of engineering requirements. Other materials used for piping include cast iron, brass, copper, aluminum, lead, lead-lined steel, earthenware, wood, and concrete. Cast-iron pipe is used for underground gas, water, and drain pipes. Sizes range from 3″ to 84″ nominal inside diameter. Outside diameters vary with the thickness of metal used for different classes of pipe from A to H or heads of 100 to 800 feet (43 to 347 lbs. per square inch).

Brass, copper, and aluminum pipe is made with the dimensions of American Standard wrought pipe for certain sizes. Tubing of these materials is specified by outside diameter. Brass is preferred for hot water, and copper where flexibility is necessary. Lead pipe is used for water and waste pipes, for acids, and for various chemical solutions. Sizes range from $1/8$″ to 12″, with varying thicknesses which change the outside diameters. Large pipes are made of riveted or welded steel plates, concrete, and wood staves. Such pipe is designed for the particular pressure and purpose for which it is to be used.

For information on various pipe materials and data on sizes, consult the manufacturer's literature, engineering handbooks and the ASA Standards.

189. Pipe Fittings.—Couplings, tees, elbows, crosses, etc., used for joining lengths of pipe and making turns and connections are called

Nominal Pipe Size	Outside Diam.	Nominal Wall Thicknesses for Schedule Numbers									
		Sched. 10	Sched. 20	Sched. 30	Sched. 40	Sched. 60	Sched. 80	Sched. 100	Sched. 120	Sched. 140	Sched. 160
$1/8$	0.405	...	...	...	0.068	...	0.095	...	...	...	...
$1/4$	0.540	...	...	...	0.088	...	0.119	...	...	...	...
$3/8$	0.675	...	...	...	0.091	...	0.126	...	...	...	...
$1/2$	0.840	...	...	...	0.109	...	0.147	...	...	...	0.187
$3/4$	1.050	...	...	...	0.113	...	0.154	...	...	...	0.218
1	1.315	...	...	...	0.133	...	0.179	...	...	...	0.250
$1 1/4$	1.660	...	...	...	0.140	...	0.191	...	...	...	0.250
$1 1/2$	1.900	...	...	...	0.145	...	0.200	...	...	...	0.281
2	2.375	...	...	...	0.154	...	0.218	...	...	...	0.343
$2 1/2$	2.875	...	...	...	0.203	...	0.276	...	...	...	0.375
3	3.5	...	...	...	0.216	...	0.300	...	...	...	0.437
$3 1/2$	4.0	...	...	...	0.226	...	0.318	...	...	...	...
4	4.5	...	...	...	0.237	...	0.337	...	0.437	...	0.531
5	5.563	...	...	...	0.258	...	0.375	...	0.500	...	0.625
6	6.625	...	...	...	0.280	...	0.432	...	0.562	...	0.718
8	8.625	...	0.250	0.277	0.322	0.406	0.500	0.593	0.718	0.812	0.906
10	10.75	...	0.250	0.307	0.365	0.500	0.593	0.718	0.843	1.000	1.125
12*	12.75	...	0.250	0.330	0.406*	0.562*	0.687	0.843	1.000	1.125	1.312
14 O.D.	14.0	0.250	0.312	0.375	0.437	0.593	0.750	0.937	1.062	1.250	1.406
16 O.D.	16.0	0.250	0.312	0.375	0.500	0.656	0.843	1.031	1.218	1.437	1.562
18 O.D.	18.0	0.250	0.312	0.437	0.562	0.718	0.937	1.156	1.343	1.562	1.750
20 O.D.	20.0	0.250	0.375	0.500	0.593	0.812	1.031	1.250	1.500	1.750	1.937
24 O.D.	24.0	0.250	0.375	0.562	0.687	0.937	1.218	1.500	1.750	2.062	2.312
30 O.D.	30.0	0.312	0.500	0.625	...	...	...	...	...	...	...

All dimensions are given in inches.

The decimal thicknesses listed for the respective pipe sizes represent their nominal or average wall dimensions. For tolerances on wall thickness, see appropriate material specification.

Thicknesses shown in bold face type in Schedules 30 and 40 are identical with thicknesses for "standard weight" pipe in former lists; those in Schedules 60 and 80 are identical with thicknesses for "extra strong" pipe in former lists.

The Schedule Numbers indicate approximate values of the expression $1000 \times P/S$. (See Introductory Notes, Section 8.)

* Owing to a necessary departure from the old "standard weight" and "extra strong" thicknesses in the 12 in. size, Schedules 40 and 60, the new thicknesses are not as yet stocked by all manufacturers and jobbers. Hence, where agreeable to the purchaser and suitable for the service conditions, the old "standard-weight" 0.375 in. wall pipe corresponding to a 1000 P/S value of 37.7 is still available and can be substituted for the 0.406 in. wall, and the old "extra-strong" 0.500 in. wall pipe corresponding to a 1000 P/S value of 55 can be substituted for the 0.562 in. wall.

Note: (Section 8 states that this formula permits an approximation of the wall thickness if service pressure (P) and value of allowable stress (S) are known.)

TABLE 33

AMERICAN STANDARD PIPE

Nominal Size		Inside Diameter		External Diameter		Nominal Thickness		Number of Threads	
Inches	Mm.	Inches	Mm.	Inches	Mm.	Inches	Mm.	Per Inch	Per 254 Mm.
$1/8$	3	.269	6.833	.405	10.287	.068	1.727	27	270
$1/4$	6	.364	9.246	.540	13.716	.088	2.235	18	180
$3/8$	10	.493	12.522	.675	17.145	.091	2.311	18	180
$1/2$	13	.622	15.799	.840	21.336	.109	2.769	14	140
$3/4$	19	.824	20.930	1.050	26.670	.113	2.870	14	140
1	25	1.049	26.645	1.315	33.401	.133	3.378	$11^1/2$	115
$1^1/4$	32	1.380	35.052	1.660	42.164	.140	3.556	$11^1/2$	115
$1^1/2$	38	1.610	40.894	1.900	48.260	.145	3.683	$11^1/2$	115
2	50	2.067	52.502	2.375	60.325	.154	3.912	$11^1/2$	115
$2^1/2$	64	2.469	62.713	2.875	73.025	.203	5.156	8	80
3	76	3.068	77.927	3.500	88.900	.216	5.486	8	80
$3^1/2$	90	3.548	90.119	4.000	101.600	.226	5.740	8	80
4	100	4.026	102.261	4.500	114.300	.237	6.020	8	80
$4^1/2$	113	4.506	114.453	5.000	127.000	.247	6.274	8	80
5	125	5.047	128.194	5.563	141.300	.258	6.553	8	80
6	150	6.065	154.051	6.625	168.275	.280	7.112	8	80
7	175	7.023	178.385	7.625	193.675	.301	7.645	8	80
8	200	8.071	205.004	8.625	219.075	.277	7.036	8	80
8	200	7.981	202.718	8.625	219.075	.322	8.179	8	80
9	225	8.941	227.102	9.625	244.475	.342	8.687	8	80
10	250	10.192	258.877	10.750	273.050	.279	7.087	8	80
10	250	10.136	257.455	10.750	273.050	.307	7.798	8	80
10	250	10.020	254.508	10.750	273.050	.365	9.271	8	80
11	275	11.000	279.400	11.750	298.450	.375	9.525	8	80
12	300	12.090	307.087	12.750	323.851	.330	8.382	8	80
12	300	12.000	304.801	12.750	323.851	.375	9.525	8	80

TABLE 34

EXTRA STRONG AND DOUBLE EXTRA STRONG PIPE

Nominal Size	External Diameter, Inches	Internal Diameter		Nominal Size	External Diameter, Inches	Internal Diameter	
		Extra Strong	Double Extra Strong			Extra Strong	Double Extra Strong
$1/8$	.405	.215	....	$1^1/2$	1.900	1.500	1.100
$1/4$	.540	.302	....	2	2.375	1.939	1.503
$3/8$	.675	.423	....	$2^1/2$	2.875	2.323	1.771
$1/2$	.840	.546	.252	3	3.500	2.900	2.300
$3/4$	1.050	.742	.434	$3^1/2$	4.00	3.364	2.728
1	1.315	.957	.599	4	4.50	3.826	3.152
$1^1/4$	1.660	1.278	.896				

STANDARD   EXTRA STRONG   DOUBLE EXTRA STRONG

FIG. 242A. Full Size Sections of $\frac{3}{4}''$ Pipe.

fittings. Small pipe is often " made up " by means of screwed fittings. Small pipe is often " made up " by means of screwed fittings, Fig. 243. Welded fittings and joints are used for all sizes, especially for permanent

Tee   Elbow   Cross   Right & Left Coupling   Lateral   Return Bend

FIG. 243. Screwed Pipe Fittings.

connections. Such fittings are made of steel of the same thickness as the pipe, Fig. 244. Types of butt welds are indicated in Fig. 245.

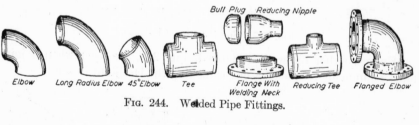

Elbow   Long Radius Elbow   45° Elbow   Tee   Bull Plug   Reducing Nipple   Flange With Welding Neck   Reducing Tee   Flanged Elbow

FIG. 244. Welded Pipe Fittings.

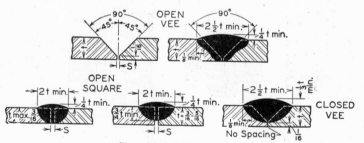

FIG. 245. Pipe Welds.

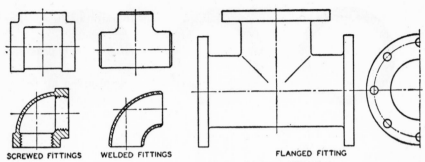

SCREWED FITTINGS   WELDED FITTINGS   FLANGED FITTING

Fɪɢ. 246.   Screwed, Welded and Flanged Fittings.

Sizes of fittings are specified by the sizes of pipe, as a 1-inch tee, or 2-inch tee, etc.   When the openings differ, the " run " is given first and then the outlet as, a 3 x 3 x 2 tee or a 2 x 1$^1/_2$ x 1 tee, Fig. 247.   Short pieces of pipe used to join fittings which are near together are called " short nipples."   When they are threaded the whole length they are called " close nipples."

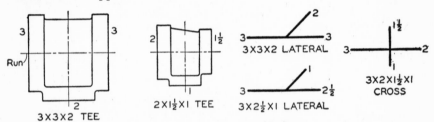

Fɪɢ. 247.   Specification of Fittings.

Unions, either screwed or flanged, Fig. 248, are used when a joint must be unmade frequently, or for making the last joint in a line.

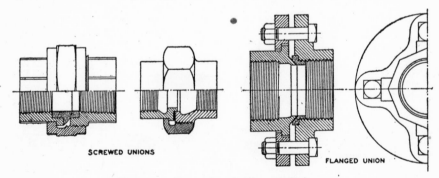

SCREWED UNIONS   FLANGED UNION

Fɪɢ. 248.   Screwed and Flanged Unions.

Fittings are generally made of cast iron, malleable iron or steel. For some purposes brass or other materials are used.

Flanged fittings are generally used for large sizes or high pressures (see Figs. 244 and 246).

Dimensions of some American Standard fittings are given in Tables 35 to 37, Figs. 249 to 251.

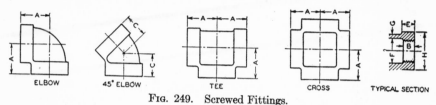

FIG. 249. Screwed Fittings.

TABLE 35 (Fig. 249)

DIMENSIONS OF AMERICAN STANDARD 125 LB. CAST IRON SCREWED FITTINGS

Nominal Pipe Size	A	C	B	E	F		G	H
			Min.	Min.	Min.	Max.	Min.	Min.
1/4	0.81	0.73	0.32	0.38	0.540	0.584	0.110	0.93
3/8	0.95	0.80	0.36	0.44	0.675	0.719	0.120	1.12
1/2	1.12	0.88	0.43	0.50	0.840	0.897	0.130	1.34
3/4	1.31	0.98	0.50	0.56	1.050	1.107	0.155	1.63
1	1.50	1.12	0.58	0.62	1.315	1.385	0.170	1.95
1 1/4	1.75	1.29	0.67	0.69	1.660	1.730	0.185	2.39
1 1/2	1.94	1.43	0.70	0.75	1.900	1.970	0.200	2.68
2	2.25	1.68	0.75	0.84	2.375	2.445	0.220	3.28
2 1/2	2.70	1.95	0.92	0.94	2.875	2.975	0.240	3.86
3	3.08	2.17	0.98	1.00	3.500	3.600	0.260	4.62
3 1/2	3.42	2.39	1.03	1.06	4.000	4.100	0.280	5.20
4	3.79	2.61	1.08	1.12	4.500	4.600	0.310	5.79
5	4.50	3.05	1.18	1.18	5.563	5.663	0.380	7.05
6	5.13	3.46	1.28	1.28	6.625	6.725	0.430	8.28
8	6.56	4.28	1.47	1.47	8.625	8.725	0.550	10.63
10	8.08	5.16	1.68	1.68	10.750	10.850	0.690	13.12
12	9.50	5.97	1.88	1.88	12.750	12.850	0.800	15.47
14 O.D.	10.40	....	2.00	2.00	14.000	14.100	0.880	16.94
16 O.D.	11.82	....	2.20	2.20	16.000	16.100	1.000	19.30

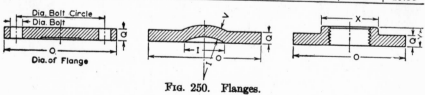

FIG. 250. Flanges.

TABLE 36 (Fig. 250)

DIMENSIONS OF AMERICAN STANDARD 125 LB. CAST IRON FLANGES

Size Inches *I*	*O*	*Q*	*V*	*X*	*Y*	Dia. Bolt Circle	No. of Bolts	Dia. Bolts
1	4 1/4	7/16	......	1 15/16	0.68	3 1/8	4	1/2
1 1/4	4 5/8	1/2	......	2 5/16	0.76	3 1/2	4	1/2
1 1/2	5	9/16	......	2 9/16	0.87	3 7/8	4	1/2
2	6	5/8	......	3 1/16	1.00	4 3/4	4	5/8
2 1/2	7	11/16	......	3 9/16	1.14	5 1/2	4	5/8
3	7 1/2	3/4	......	4 1/4	1.20	6	4	5/8
3 1/2	8 1/2	13/16	......	4 13/16	1.25	7	8	5/8
4	9	15/16	......	5 5/16	1.30	7 1/2	8	5/8
5	10	15/16	......	6 7/16	1.41	8 1/2	8	3/4
6	11	1	......	7 9/16	1.51	9 1/2	8	3/4
8	13 1/2	1 1/8	......	9 11/16	1.71	11 3/4	8	3/4
10	16	1 3/16	......	11 15/16	1.93	14 1/4	12	7/8
12	19	1 1/4	13/16	14 1/16	2.13	17	12	7/8
14 O.D.	21	1 3/8	7/8	15 3/8	2.25	18 3/4	12	1
16 O.D.	23 1/2	1 7/16	1	17 1/2	2.45	21 1/4	16	1
18 O.D.	25	1 9/16	1 1/16	19 5/8	2.65	22 3/4	16	1 1/8

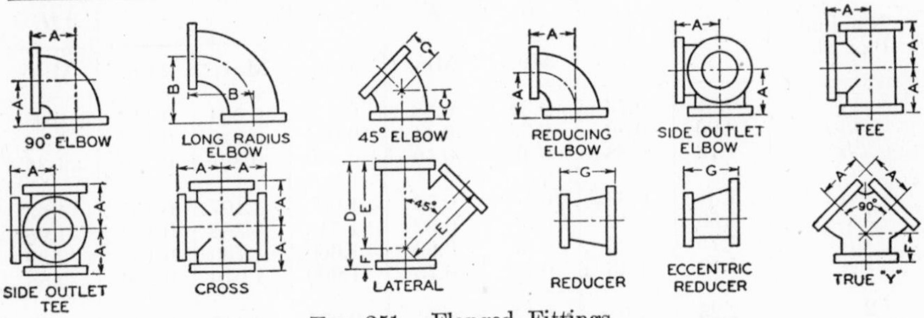

FIG. 251. Flanged Fittings.

TABLE 37 (Fig. 251) For flange dimensions see Table 36.

DIMENSIONS OF AMERICAN STANDARD 125 LB. CAST IRON FLANGED FITTINGS

Nominal Pipe Size	*A*	*B*	*C*	*D*	*E*	*F*	*G*
1	3 1/2	5	1 3/4	7 1/2	5 3/4	1 3/4	....
1 1/4	3 3/4	5 1/2	2	8	6 1/4	1 3/4	....
1 1/2	4	6	2 1/4	9	7	2	....
2	4 1/2	6 1/2	2 1/2	10 1/2	8	2 1/2	5
2 1/2	5	7	3	12	9 1/2	2 1/2	5 1/2
3	5 1/2	7 3/4	3	13	10	3	6
3 1/2	6	8 1/2	3 1/2	14 1/2	11 1/2	3	6 1/2
4	6 1/2	9	4	15	12	3	7
5	7 1/2	10 1/4	4 1/2	17	13 1/2	3 1/2	8
6	8	11 1/2	5	18	14 1/2	3 1/2	9
8	9	14	5 1/2	22	17 1/2	4 1/2	11
10	11	16 1/2	6 1/2	25 1/2	20 1/2	5	12
12	12	19	7 1/2	30	24 1/2	5 1/2	14
14 O.D.	14	21 1/2	7 1/2	33	27	6	16
16 O.D.	15	24	8	36 1/2	30	6 1/2	18
18 O.D.	16 1/2	26 1/2	8 1/2	39	32	7	19

190. Valves.—Valves are used to stop or regulate the flow in pipe. Several valves are illustrated in Figs. 252 to 255. The globe valve has a

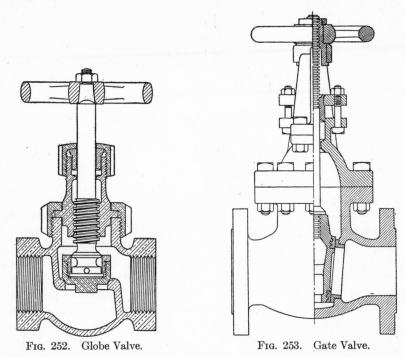

FIG. 252.   Globe Valve.   FIG. 253.   Gate Valve.

spherical body and a circular opening at right angles to the axis of the pipe.   It offers more resistance to flow than the gate valve but is desirable

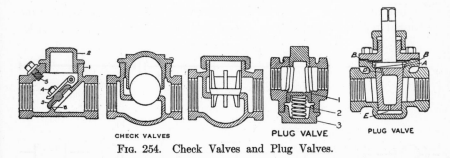

CHECK VALVES   PLUG VALVE   PLUG VALVE

FIG. 254.   Check Valves and Plug Valves.

when throttling is necessary.   The gate valve has its opening parallel to the cross section of the pipe, and offers comparatively little resistance to flow. Other common forms of valves include check valves, plug valves and butterfly valves.

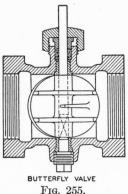

BUTTERFLY VALVE
Fig. 255.

191. Piping Drawings.—Piping drawings vary from a single freehand sketch to an elaborate scale drawing with working drawings of details.

Most of the general rules for dimensioning hold for piping drawings. Always give dimensions to the centers of pipe, valves and fittings. Wrought pipe sizes are given in a note using nominal diameters.   Flanged valves when drawn to large scale may have overall dimensions given, the distance from center to top of handwheel or valve stem when open and when closed, diameter of handwheel, etc.

Final drawings should be made after the engines, boilers and other machinery have been decided upon, as they can then be drawn completely and accurately.   At least two views should be drawn, a plan and an elevation.   A scale of $3/8''$ equals 1 foot is desirable for piping drawings as it is large enough to show the system to scale.

When drawn to a small scale, valves, fittings, etc., are shown by conventional representations as in Fig. 256.   When the scale permits, the

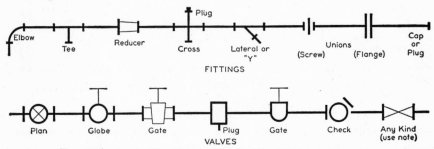

Fig. 256.   Single Line Conventions for Pipe Fittings and Valves.

representations of Fig. 257 may be used. Welded pipe and fittings may
be represented as in Fig. 258.

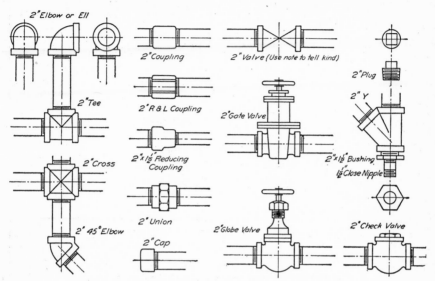

FIG. 257. Double Line Conventions for Screwed Fittings.

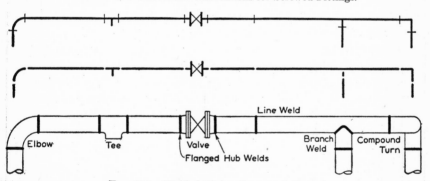

FIG. 258. Welded Piping Representations.

192. Piping Sketches.—Where only a small amount of work is to be
done, a sketch may be used. The piping, valves, fittings, etc., should be
sketched and noted. Dimensions and notes together with the date and
a title can then be added. Pictorial methods can be used to advantage
for preliminary layouts, as the directions and changes in levels can be
shown clearly. A pictorial view and sketch are shown in Figs. 259 and
260.

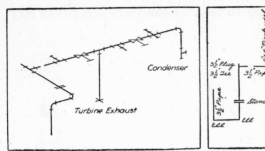

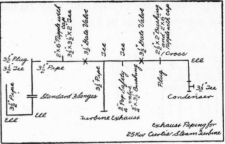

Fig. 259. Pictorial View.   Fig. 260. Developed Sketch.

193. Developed or Single Plane Drawings.—It will often be found convenient to swing the various parts of a piping layout into a single plane in order to show the various lengths and fittings in one view. Such a drawing is shown in Fig. 261 for the sketch of Fig. 260.

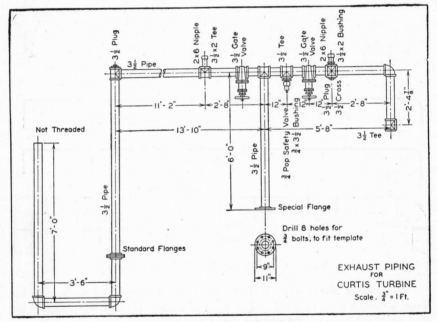

Fig. 261. Developed Drawing.

194. Welded Piping Drawings.—The use of welded joints and fittings has been mentioned in Art. 189. A drawing using such joints and fittings is shown in Fig. 262, which shows the piping for the central high

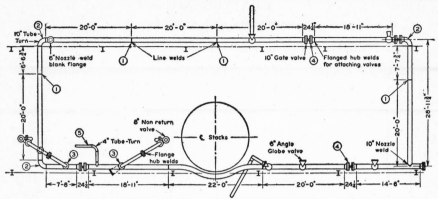

FIG. 262. Welded Piping Drawing.

pressure power station of the Bureau of Standards, Washington, D. C. Dimensions locate the various welds. A comparison of flanged and welded joints for the drawing of Fig. 262 is given in Fig. 263.

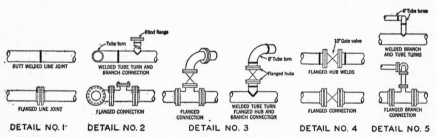

FIG. 263. Details of Welded Piping Compared with Flanged Piping.

195. American Standards.—Dimensions and sizes of pipe fittings, flanges, etc., have been developed under the procedure of the American Standards Association, 70 E. 45th St., New York City. They can be obtained at a nominal price.

CHAPTER XII

PROBLEMS AND STUDIES

196. Preliminary Instructions.—A thorough understanding of the graphic language—the language of engineering—can be had only by applying it to a large number of problems. The problems in this chapter

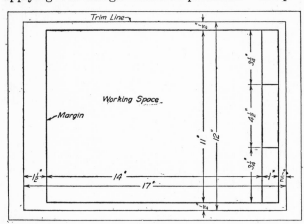

FIG. 264. Layout.

are sufficient to allow changes in the course given from year to year. The subjects as arranged follow the text in a general way and suggest the outline for a course. Since working directions are given for each problem the order of presenting them can be varied at the discretion of the instructor.

197. Most of the drawing studies can be worked in an 11' x 14" space with the layout of Fig. 264 or in a division of the working space. The American Standard sheet size B (11" x 17"), Fig. 266, may be used in place of Fig. 264 by adjusting the positioning dimensions according to the size of margin specified by the instructor. If a double size sheet is required, use American Standard sheet, size C (17" x 22"). Problems designed for 5½" x 7" spaces may be worked, one or two, on American Standard sheet, size A (8½" x 11").

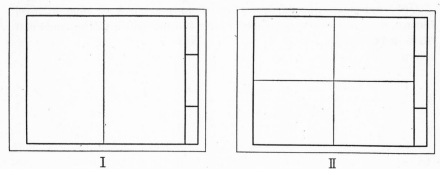

I   II

FIG. 265. Two-Part and Four-Part Layout.

156

Many of the problems given for a $5^1/_2''$ x $7''$ space can be worked to advantage in an $11''$ x $14''$ space by using a different scale or in a few cases by doubling all dimensions. A form of record strip is given in Fig. 267. A record strip or a title should be a part of every drawing.

FIG. 266. American Standard, Size B.

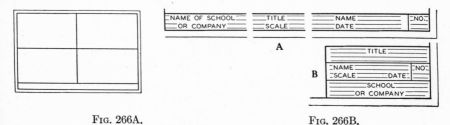

FIG. 266A.   FIG. 266B.

The record strip may be placed the long way of the sheet as in Fig. 266A which also indicates a four part division of the sheet. For some drawings the instructor may wish to use a corner block-title as suggested at **B** in Fig. 266B.

FIG. 267. Record Strip Form.

Extra working drawing problems are given in Chapter XIII beginning on page 240, from which a selection can be made to suit the requirements of a particular course.

MACHINE DRAWING

ELEMENTARY PRINCIPLES

198. The problems given in this section are intended for review purposes. It is not necessary to work all of them. Lay out the regular size sheet as shown in Fig. 264 and divide the working space into four equal spaces, $5^1/_2'' \times 7''$ each. Do not copy the dimensions given to locate views. Draw orthographic views. Do not copy the pictures which are used to present some of the problems.

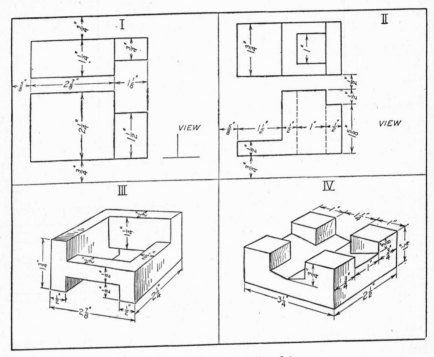

FIG. 268. Probs. 1, 2, 3 and 4.

PROB. 1, Fig. 268 Space I.—Draw three complete views of the RECTANGULAR STOP BAR.

PROB. 2, Fig. 268, Space II.—Draw three complete views of the GUIDE FOR SQUARE BAR.

PROB. 3, Fig. 268, Space III.—Draw three complete views of the POSITIONING BLOCK. (Orthographic Projection.)

PROB. 4, Fig. 268, Space IV.—Draw three complete views of the SPECIAL DIE.

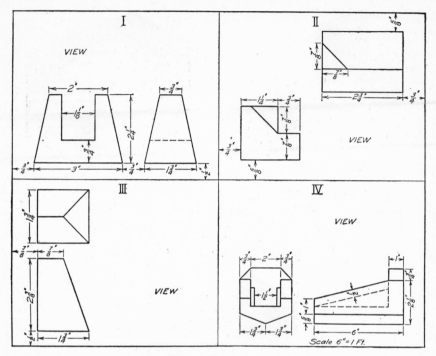

FIG. 269.   Probs. 5, 6, 7 and 8.

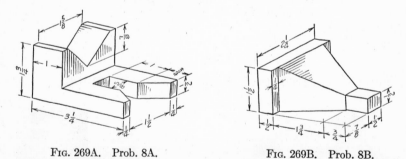

FIG. 269A.   Prob. 8A.   FIG. 269B.   Prob. 8B.

PROB. 5, Fig. 269, Space I.—Draw three complete views of the SLIDER.

PROB. 6, Fig. 269, Space II.—Draw three complete views of the BRACE BLOCK.

PROB. 7, Fig. 269, Space III.—Draw three complete views of the SPECIAL WEDGE.

PROB. 8, Fig. 269, Space IV.—Draw three complete views of the ADJUSTING SLIDE.   Scale 6″ = 1 ft.

PROB. 8A, Fig. 269A.—Draw the views of the SUPPORT.

PROB. 8B, Fig. 269B.—Draw the views of the WEDGE.

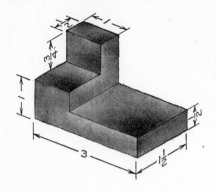

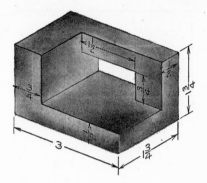

FIG. 269C.   Prob. 8C.   FIG. 269D.   Prob. 8D.

PROB. 8C, Fig. 269C.—Draw three complete views of the STEP LUG.
PROB. 8D, Fig. 269D.—Draw three complete views of the HOOK.

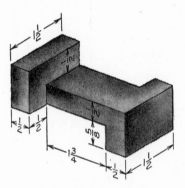

FIG. 269E.   Prob. 8E.

PROB. 8E, Fig. 269E.—Draw three complete views of the GUIDE.

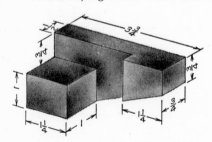

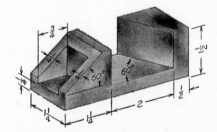

FIG. 269F.   Prob. 8F.   FIG. 269G.   Prob. 8G.

PROB. 8F, Fig. 269F.—Draw three complete views of the CHECK BLOCK.
PROB. 8G, Fig. 269G.—Draw three complete views of the STOP ANGLE.

PROB. 9, Fig. 270, Space I.—Draw three complete views of the LUG.

PROB. 10, Fig. 270, Space II.—Draw three complete views of the ROD CLAMP.

PROB. 11, Fig. 270, Space III.—Draw three complete views of the CHAMFERED LOCK WASHER.

PROB. 12, Fig. 270, Space IV. Draw three complete views of the LOCKING CATCH.

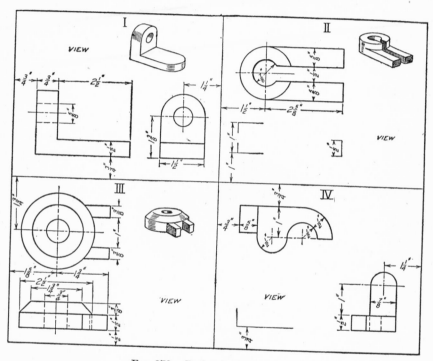

FIG. 270. Probs. 9, 10, 11 and 12.

PROB. 12A, Fig. 270A.—This picture shows a CENTER GUIDE. Lay out a full size sheet with minimum working space of 9″ x 14″. Make a three-view working drawing. Plan the arrangement and spacing of the views by making a freehand sketch which should be submitted to the instructor for approval.

PROB. 12B, Fig. 270B.—This picture shows a HUNG SUPPORT. Lay out a full size sheet with minimum working space of 9″ x 14″. Make a three-view working drawing. Plan the arrangement and spacing of the views by making a freehand sketch which should be submitted to the instructor for approval.

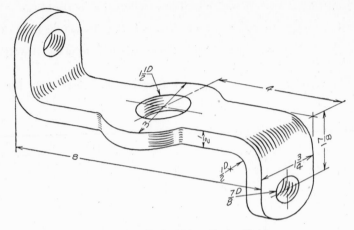

Fig. 270A.   Prob. 12A.   Center Guide.

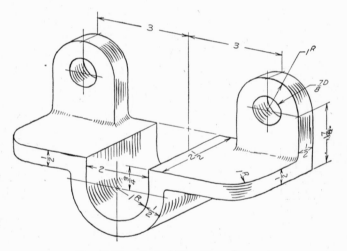

Fig. 270B.   Prob. 12B.   Hung Support.

PROB. 13, Fig. 271.—The picture shows a SLIDING BRACE. Lay out a sheet with 11″ x 14″ working space (Fig. 264). Make a three view working drawing. Plan the arrangement and spacing of views by making a freehand sketch which should be submitted to the instructor.

PROB. 14, Fig. 272.—The picture shows a SADDLE PIVOT. Lay out a sheet with 11″ x 14″ working space. Make a three view working drawing.

PROB. 15, Fig. 273.—The illustration shows the *top, front* and *left end* views of a BRACKET. Make a three view drawing showing the *front, bottom* and *right end* views.

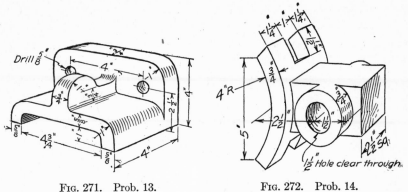

FIG. 271.   Prob. 13.   FIG. 272.   Prob. 14.

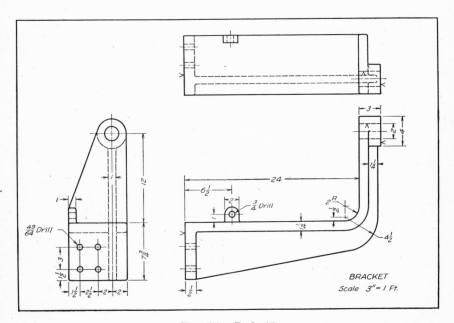

FIG. 273.   Prob. 15.

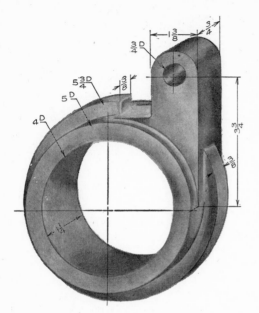

PROB. 15A, Fig. 273A.—
Draw the views necessary to describe the LOCK RING shown in
the picture.

PROB. 15B, Fig. 273B.—The
illustration shows the *front, bottom,*
and *right-end* views of the BEAR-
ING. Draw the *front, top,* and
left-end views.

FIG. 273A.   Prob. 15A.   Lock Ring.

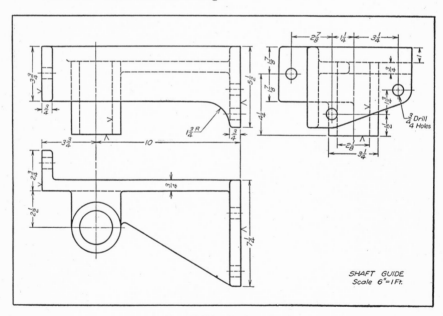

FIG. 273B.   Prob. 15B.

199. Auxiliary Views.—Center or reference lines are shown on the layouts for the following problems. Draw auxiliary view of cut face only or of whole object as required by the instructor. Refer to Art. 19 and note which case covers each problem.

PROB. 16, Fig. 274, Space I.—Draw views given and auxiliary view.

PROB. 17, Fig. 274, Space II.—Draw views given and auxiliary view.

PROB. 18, Fig. 274, Space III.—Draw views given and auxiliary view.

PROB. 19, Fig. 274, Space IV.—Draw views given and auxiliary view.

PROB. 20, Fig. 275.—Draw the two views shown and an auxiliary view of the FOOT PEDAL. Front view is to be complete. Top and auxiliary views will be partial views. Do not put the location dimensions on your drawing. (11″ x 14″ space.)

PROB. 21, Fig. 276.—Draw the view shown and as much as may be necessary of the other two views indicated, for the ANGLE JOINT (11″ x 14″ space). Inclined base is ³/₄″ thick and 7″ long as indicated. Its width is 3¹/₂″ and the corners are square.

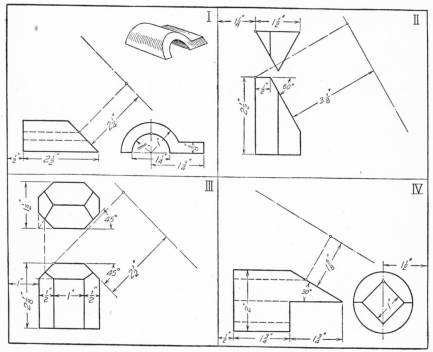

FIG. 274.   Probs. 16, 17, 18 and 19.

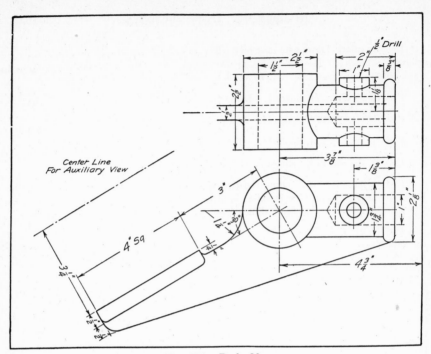

FIG. 275. Prob. 20.

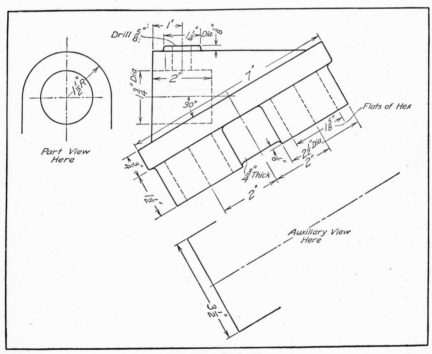

FIG. 276. Prob. 21.

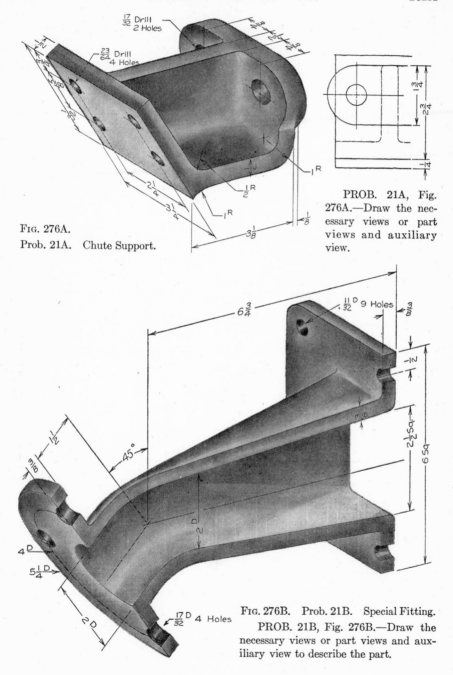

FIG. 276A.
Prob. 21A.   Chute Support.

PROB. 21A, Fig. 276A.—Draw the necessary views or part views and auxiliary view.

FIG. 276B.   Prob. 21B.   Special Fitting.
PROB. 21B, Fig. 276B.—Draw the necessary views or part views and auxiliary view to describe the part.

200. Sectional Views.—The following problems are for the study of sectional views. Do not copy the views as given but make the required sectional views directly on your drawing. Indicate the cut surface by section lining.

PROB. 22, Fig. 277, Space I.—Draw two views of the BUSHING. Left hand view in section.

PROB. 23, Fig. 277, Space II.—Draw two views of the SPECIAL COLLAR. Left hand view in section.

PROB. 24, Fig. 277, Space III.—Draw two views of the GLAND. Left hand view in section.

PROB. 25, Fig. 277, Space IV.—Draw two views of the SHIFTING COLLAR. Left hand view in section.

PROBS. 25A to 25F, Figs. 277A to 277F.—Draw two views, one view to be a section.

PROB. 26, Fig. 278, Space I.—Draw two views of the PISTON with right hand view in section.

PROB. 27, Fig. 278, Space II.—Draw two views of the PISTON FOLLOWER with left hand view in section.

PROB. 28, Fig. 278, Space III.—Draw two views of the ECCENTRIC with the left hand view in section.

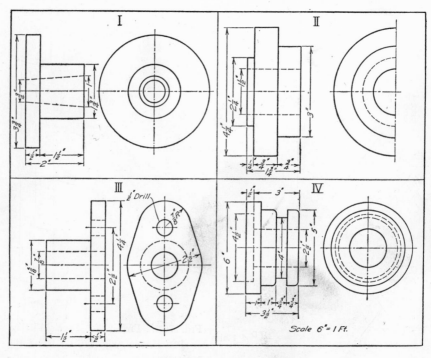

FIG. 277.   Probs. 22, 23, 24 and 25.

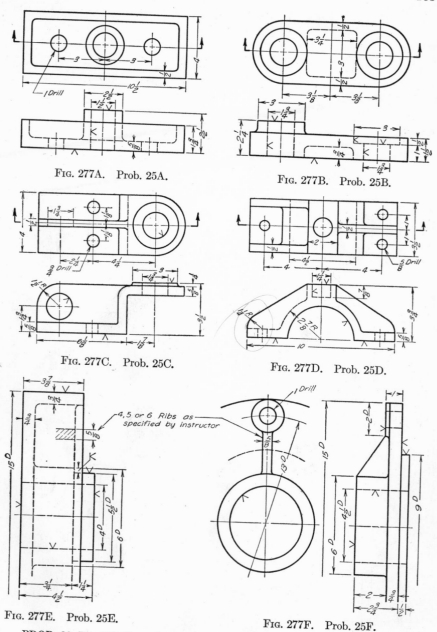

FIG. 277A.   Prob. 25A.

FIG. 277B.   Prob. 25B.

FIG. 277C.   Prob. 25C.

FIG. 277D.   Prob. 25D.

FIG. 277E.   Prob. 25E.

FIG. 277F.   Prob. 25F.

PROB. 29, Fig. 278, Space IV.—Draw two views of the PULLEY, with the right hand view in section.

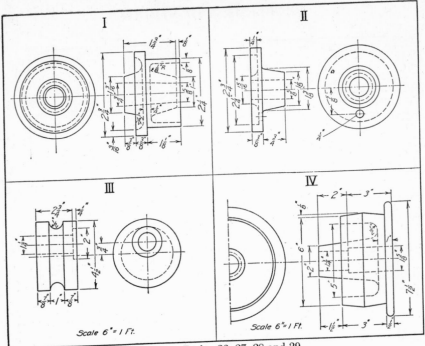

F<small>IG</small>. 278.   Probs. 26, 27, 28 and 29.

SCREWS AND BOLTS

201. The Helix.—A cylindrical helix is a curve generated by a point on the surface of a cylinder, moving equal distances lengthwise of the cylinder while it is moving equal distances around the cylinder.

In Fig. 279 the diameter and pitch of the helix are indicated. Divide the circle of the top view into any convenient number of equal parts, and draw vertical lines through each point. Divide the pitch distance into the same number of equal parts and draw horizontal lines through each point. The intersection of a horizontal line from a division of the pitch distance with a vertical line from the corresponding division

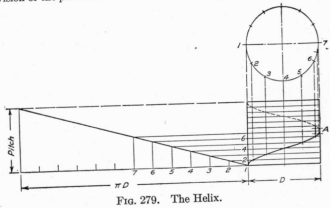

F<small>IG</small>. 279.   The Helix.

of the circle will locate a point on the projection of the helix. Proceed in this way for each of the points. It is desirable to locate extra points by taking half divisions where the curve changes direction as at A.

202. Screws and Bolts.—The following problems are representative. The student should solve them with as little help as possible after studying the text. The proportions and appearances of the screw threads and bolts occur so frequently that they should be familiar without looking them up every time they occur on a drawing.

PROB. 30, Fig. 280.—Draw $1^1/_2$ turns of a right hand helix. Pitch 2″. Diameter 2″. (Space $5^1/_2$″ x 7″.)

PROB. 31, Fig. 280.—Draw 3 turns of a left hand helix. Pitch 1″. Diameter $1^3/_4$″. (Space $5^1/_2$″ x 7″.)

PROB. 32, Fig. 280.—Draw a square thread screw. Pitch $^3/_4$″. Major dia. 2″. (Space $5^1/_2$″ x 7″.)

PROB. 33, Fig. 281.—Draw profiles of V, Am. Std., British Standard and square thread. Eight threads per inch. Use scale of eight times full size. (Space $5^1/_2$″ x 7″.)

PROB. 34, Fig. 281.—Draw profiles of Am. Std., Dardelet, Acme and Harvey Grip threads. Ten threads per inch. Use scale of ten times full size. (Space $5^1/_2$″ x 7″.)

PROB. 35, Fig. 282.—Draw three different conventional representations of screw threads on one end of rods $^3/_4$″ dia., and $3^1/_2$″ long. Thread length $1^1/_2$″. Use center lines A, B, and C. (Space $5^1/_2$″ x 7″.)

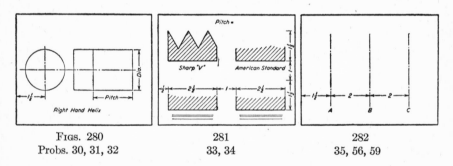

FIGS. 280	281	282
Probs. 30, 31, 32	33, 34	35, 56, 59

PROB. 36, Fig. 283.—Draw threaded rods as follows. Use different conventional representations on each rod. On line A, rod $5^1/_2$″ long, $^7/_8$″ dia., thread length $1^1/_2$″ on both ends. On line B, rod $4^3/_4$″ long, $^1/_2$″ dia., thread length 1″ on both ends. On line C, rod $5^1/_2$″ long, $^5/_8$″ dia., thread length $1^1/_4$″ on both ends. (Space $5^1/_2$″ x 7″.)

PROB. 37, Fig. 284.—Draw top and full front views of threaded holes. Use three different conventional representations. Dia., $^1/_2$″, $^5/_8$″, $^3/_4$″ or $^7/_8$″ as directed by instructor. (Space $5^1/_2$″ x 7″.)

PROB. 38, Fig. 284.—Draw top and sectional front views of threaded holes. Use three different conventional representations. Dia., $^1/_2$″, $^5/_8$″, $^3/_4$″ or $^7/_8$″ as directed by instructor. (Space $5^1/_2$″ x 7″.)

PROBS. 39 to 46.—($5^1/_2$″ x 7″ space.) Draw American Standard Bolts and Nuts as specified. Either rough or finished as directed by instructor. Problems call for 2″ dia. bolt but diameters of $1^1/_2$″, $1^3/_4$″, $2^1/_4$″, or $2^1/_2$″ may be assigned to increase the number of problems. In representing bolt heads show a part of the unthreaded bolt as indicated in Fig. 285.

PROB. 39, Fig. 285.—Draw one view of hex bolt head across flats for 2″ dia. bolt.
PROB. 40, Fig. 285.—Draw one view of hex bolt head across corners for 2″ dia. bolt.

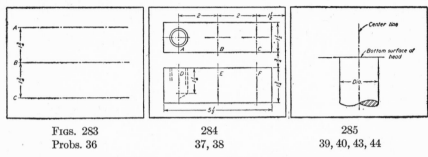

FIGS. 283　　　　　284　　　　　285
Probs. 36　　　　37, 38　　　39, 40, 43, 44

PROB. 41, Fig. 286.—Draw one view of hex nut across flats for 2″ dia. bolt.
PROB. 42, Fig. 286.—Draw one view of hex nut across corners for 2″ dia. bolt.
PROB. 43, Fig. 285.—Draw one view of square bolt head across flats for 2″ dia. bolt.
PROB. 44, Fig. 285.—Draw one view of square bolt head across corners for 2″ dia. bolt.
PROB. 45, Fig. 286.—Draw one view of square nut across flats for 2″ dia. bolt.
PROB. 46, Fig. 286.—Draw one view of square nut across corners for 2″ dia. bolt.
PROB. 47, Fig. 287.—Draw two views of a $^7/_8$″ bolt, 4″ long. Hex head. Length of thread $1^3/_4$″.
PROB. 48, Fig. 287.—Draw two views of a $^7/_8$″ bolt, 4″ long. Square head. Length of thread $1^3/_4$″.
PROB. 49, Fig. 288.—On axis AB draw a $^3/_4$″ through bolt. Hex head across corners and hex nut across flats. On axis CD draw a $1^1/_8$″ bolt, hex head across flats and hex nut across corners. Give specification dimensions.

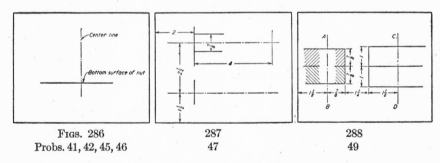

FIGS. 286　　　　　287　　　　　288
Probs. 41, 42, 45, 46　　47　　　　　49

PROB. 50, Fig. 289.—Make a drawing of the bolts, studs, etc., as shown in the figure. (11″ x 14″ space.)
PROB. 51, Fig. 290.—On axis AB draw a $^7/_8$″ bolt, square head across corners and square nut across flats. On axis CD draw a $^7/_8$″ cap screw, hex head across flats. On axis EF draw a $^7/_8$″ cap screw, hex head across corners. ($5^1/_2$″ x 7″ space.)

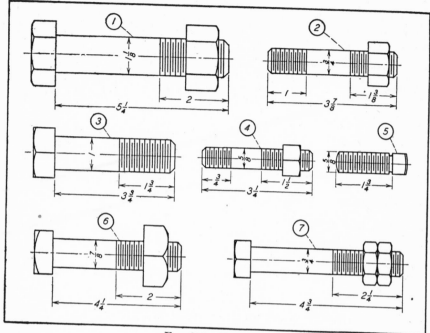

Fig. 289.   Prob. 50.

PROB. 52, Fig. 291.—Draw gland and stuffing box.   On axis AB draw a $\frac{1}{2}''$ stud and nut.   Show nut across flats.   To find length of stud, allow it to enter one and one-fourth times diameter at A.   Allow about two threads to project beyond flange of gland at B.   Am. Std. coarse threads, class 2.   Show specification dimensions. $(5\frac{1}{2}'' \times 7''$ space.)

PROB. 53, Fig. 292.—Draw two views of a collar and shaft.   On axis AB, draw a $\frac{5}{8}''$ set screw, square head across flats.   On axis CD draw same set screw, head across corners. $(5\frac{1}{2}'' \times 7''$ space.)

PROB. 54, Fig. 292.—Same as Prob. 53, but use one of the headless set screws shown in Fig. 50. $(5\frac{1}{2}'' \times 7''$ space.)

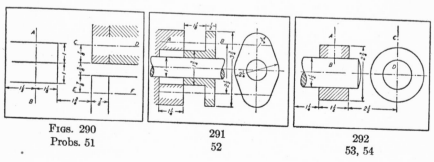

Figs. 290   291   292
Probs. 51   52   53, 54

PROB. 55.—Lay out 11″ x 14″ working space divided as in Fig. 265 at II. Draw 1³/₄″ hex nut across flats and 1³/₄″ square nut across corners. Compare them as to appearance and distance required for turning. Draw a 1³/₄″ hex nut across corners and a 1³/₄″ square nut across flats. Compare them.

PROB. 56, Fig. 282.—On center lines A, B and C draw machine screws. Dia. ³/₈″; length 2″; length of thread 1¹/₄″. Use three different forms of heads. Refer to Fig. 49. (5¹/₂″ x 7″ space.)

PROB. 57.—Draw a ⁷/₈″ track bolt with square nut. Length 4³/₄″. Refer to Fig. 55. (5¹/₂″ x 7″ space.)

PROB. 58.—Same as Prob. 57 but use recessed nut.

PROB. 59, Fig. 282.—On center line A, draw oval head wood screw, 2″ long, No. 20 dia. (use ⁵/₁₆″). On line B, draw round head wood screw, 2¹/₂″ long, No. 20 dia. (use ⁵/₁₆″). On line C, draw flat head wood screw, 3″ long, No. 24 dia. (use ³/₈″). (5¹/₂″ x 7″ space.)

DIMENSIONING

203. The study of dimensioning will occur every time a working drawing is made. The rules and systems given in Chapter III should be carefully studied, and their application observed. The location of finished surfaces and center lines must always be considered. Go slowly and give a reason for every dimension and for its location. Views are to be drawn from measurements obtained with the dividers and scale. Set your dividers on the drawing as at I, Fig. 293, and then place the points on the printed scale as at II when the reading shows the distance to be 1¹/₄″. Use 1¹/₄″ from your full size scale in laying out your drawing. Obtain other distances in the same way using the dividers and the printed scale.

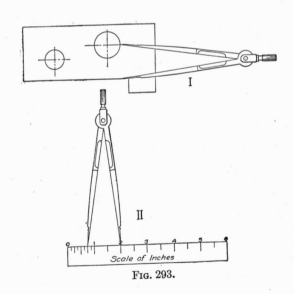

FIG. 293.

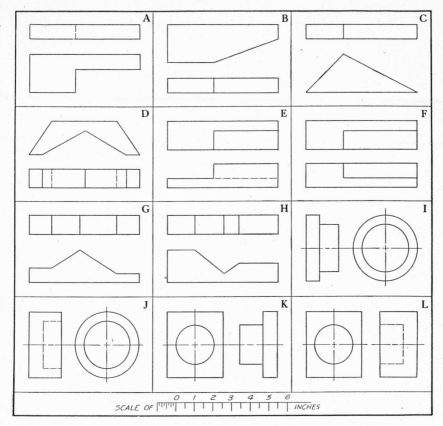

Fig. 293A.   Probs. 59A to 59L.

PROBS. 59A to 59L, Fig. 293A.—Draw the views shown.   Determine measurements by using the dividers and graphic scale as explained in connection with Fig. 293. Put on dimension lines for *size dimensions*.   Scale your drawing to nearest $^1/_8''$ and put on the dimensions.

PROB. 59A, Fig. 293A at **A**.   PROB. 59G, Fig. 293A at **G**.

PROB. 59B, Fig. 293A at **B**.   PROB. 59H, Fig. 293A at **H**.

PROB. 59C, Fig. 293A at **C**.   PROB. 59I, Fig. 293A at **I**.

PROB. 59D, Fig. 293A at **D**.   PROB. 59J, Fig. 293A at **J**.

PROB. 59E, Fig. 293A at **E**.   PROB. 59K, Fig. 293A at **K**.

PROB. 59F, Fig. 293A at **F**.   PROB. 59L, Fig. 293A at **L**.

PROB. 59**M**, Fig. 293B, Space **A**.—Draw the two views of the BLOCK BEAR-
ING, using the method described in Fig. 293.   Put on dimension lines for *location
dimensions*.   Scale your drawing to nearest $1/8''$ and put on the dimensions.

PROB. 59**N**, Fig. 293B, Space **B**.—Draw the two views of the LOCATING
BRACKET, using the method described in Fig. 293.   Put on dimension lines for
location dimensions.   Scale your drawing to nearest $1/8''$ and put on the dimensions.

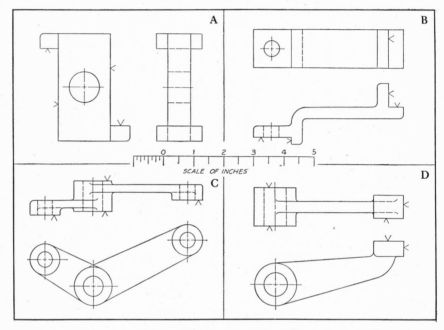

Fig. 293B.   Probs. 59M to 59P.

PROB. 59**O**, Fig. 293B, Space **C**.—Draw the two views of the CRANK, using the
method described in Fig. 293.   Put on dimension lines for *location dimensions*.   Scale
your drawing to nearest $1/8''$ and put on the dimensions.

PROB. 59**P**, Fig. 293B, Space **D**.—Draw the two views of the STOB LINK,
using the method described in Fig. 293.   Put on dimension lines for *location dimensions*.
Scale your drawing to nearest $1/8''$ and put on the dimensions.

PROB. 60, Fig. 294, Space **I**.—Draw the two views of the DISTANCE PIECE,
using the method described in Fig. 293.   Scale your drawing to nearest $1/8''$ and put
on dimension lines and dimensions.

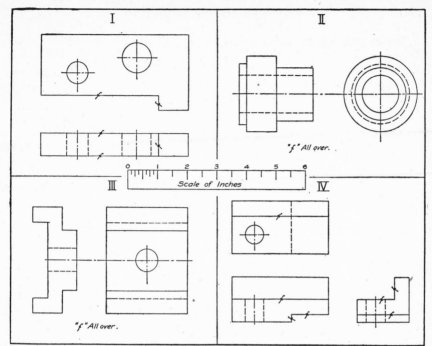

FIG. 294. Probs. 60, 61, 62 and 63.

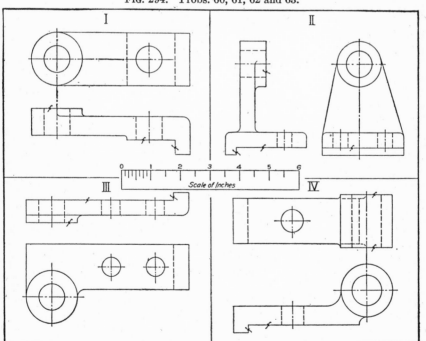

FIG. 295. Probs. 64, 65, 66 and 67.

169

PROB. 61, Fig. 294, Space II.—Draw and dimension the views of the BUSHING.

PROB. 62, Fig. 294, Space III.—Draw and dimension the views of the SLIDE.

PROB. 63, Fig. 294, Space IV.—Draw the views of the CORNER CLAMP and dimension your drawing.

PROB. 64, Fig. 295, Space I.—Draw the views of the PROJECTING BEARING and dimension your drawing.

PROB. 65, Fig. 295, Space II.—Draw and dimension the views of the SUPPORT.

PROB. 66, Fig. 295, Space III.—Draw the views of the HUNG BEARING and dimension your drawing.

PROB. 67, Fig. 295, Space IV.—Draw and dimension the views of the GUIDE.

PROB. 68, Fig. 104, Chap. IV.—Make a detail drawing of TYPE B MOTOR BEARING DETAILS. Show views as half sections instead of full sections as given.

PROB. 69, Fig. 112, Chap. IV.—Make a two view drawing, both views in full for the PULLEY. Completely dimension.

PROB. 70, Fig. 112, Chap. IV.—Make a two view drawing one view in half section. Completely dimension.

PROB. 71, Fig. 116, Chap. IV.—Make a two view drawing, both views in full for the VERTICAL GUIDE. There are 8 holes equally spaced in the flange. Completely dimension.

PROB. 72, Fig. 116, Chap. IV.—Make a two view drawing, one view in section. Completely dimension.

PROB. 73, Fig. 117, Chap. IV.—Make a three view drawing of the BOLSTER SUPPORT. Show views in full, section, or half section as directed by the instructor.

PROBS. 74 and 75, Figs. 296 and 297.—Draw the views of the objects shown. Refer to Art. 203 for method of procedure. Put on all dimensions.

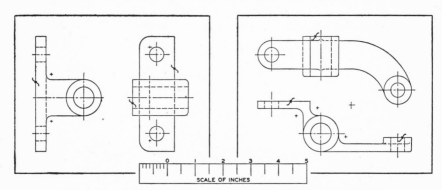

FIG. 296.   Prob. 74.   FIG. 297.   Prob. 75.

PROBS. 76 to 95, Figs. 323 to 342.—Sketch proper views and indicate positions for all dimensions. Use letter S for size dimensions and L for location dimensions. Use numbers as subscripts to indicate the order in which the dimensions are put on the views.

204. The following problems are planned for an $11'' \times 14''$ working space. Plan the arrangement, spacing, and choice of views, by making a freehand sketch which should be submitted to the instructor. The treatment of the views should have very careful attention and frequent reference should be made to the text of Chap. IV for comparison with the illustrations there given.

PROB. 96, Fig. 298.—The picture shows a FORKED LEVER.   Make a detail working drawing.

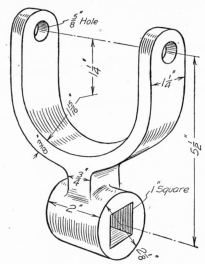

FIG. 298.   Prob. 96.

PROB. 97, Fig. 299.—Make a detail working drawing of the ANGLE BRACE BEARING.

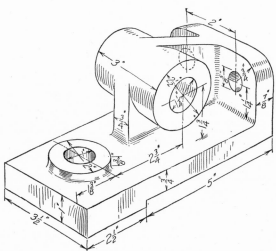

FIG. 299.   Prob. 97.

PROB. 98, Fig. 300.—Make a working drawing of the STIRRUP.

PROBS. 99 to 104, Figs. 301 to 306.—Make complete working drawings of each of the objects shown.   (11″ x 14″ working space.)

PROB. 105, Fig. 307.—Make a working drawing of the ADJUSTABLE GUIDE. Note the method of laying out the top view.   Do not copy the picture.

PROB. 106, Fig. 308.—The front, top, and right end views of a COLUMN GUIDE are shown.   Draw the front *bottom* and right end view as a section.

PROB. 107, Fig. 309.—Make a three view working drawing of the CLAMP PIECE. Do not use the top and front views which are given but show the piece in such a position that the views will not contain so many dotted lines.

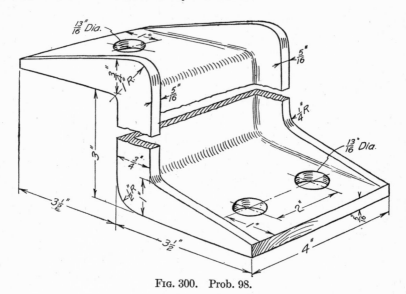

FIG. 300.   Prob. 98.

FIG. 301.   Prob. 99.   Arc Hinge.   FIG. 302.   Prob. 100.   Latch Pivot.

PROB. 108, Fig. 310.—Draw the top view and a section of the SUPPORT.

PROB. 109, Fig. 311.—Make a working drawing of the HEAD PLATE. Show the right hand view as a section.

PROB. 110, Fig. 312.—Make a three view assembly drawing of the STEP BEARING. Show the front view as a half section. Scale 6″ = 1 ft.

PROB. 111, Fig. 312.—Make a separate detail drawing of each part of the STEP BEARING. 11″ x 14″ working space. Scale 6″ = 1 ft.

PROB. 112, Fig. 313.—Make an assembly working drawing of the FOUNDATION BOLT PLATE. Show the front view as a section. The top and right side views can be represented as shown. Look up dimensions of 2″ pipe.

PROB. 113, Fig. 314.—Make a working drawing of the VALVE. Show the right hand view with proper treatment as a section.

PROB. 114, Fig. 315.—Make a working drawing of the ADJUSTING LEVER.

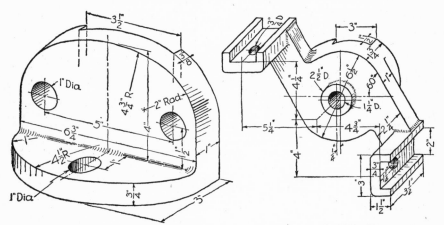

FIG. 303.   Prob. 101.   Angle Guide.   FIG. 304.   Prob. 102.   Locator.

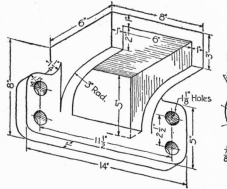

FIG. 305.   Prob. 103.   Open Bracket.

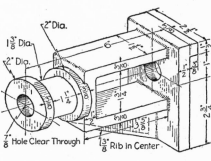

FIG. 306.   Prob. 104.   Tail Piece.

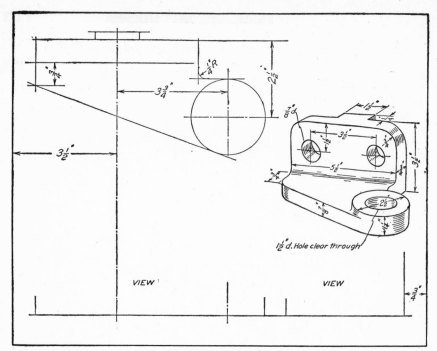

VIEW   VIEW

$1\frac{1}{2}''$ d. Hole clear through

Fig. 307.   Prob. 105.

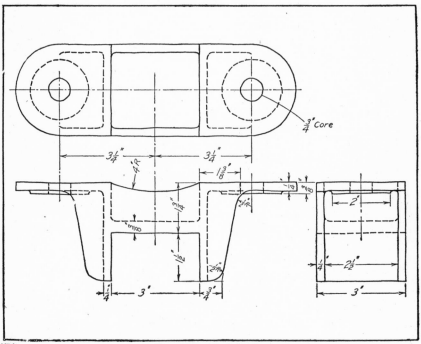

$\frac{3}{4}''$ Core

Fig. 308.   Prob. 106.

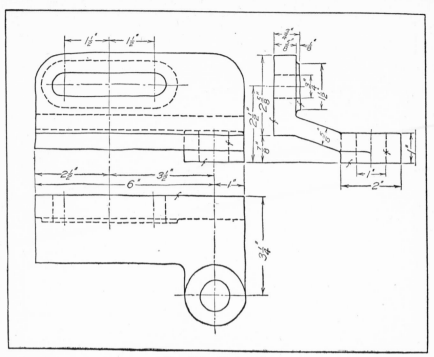

FIG. 309. Prob. 107.

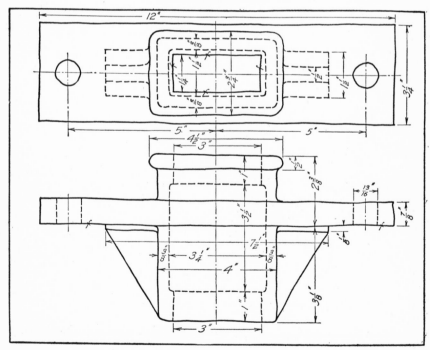

FIG. 310. Prob. 108.

175

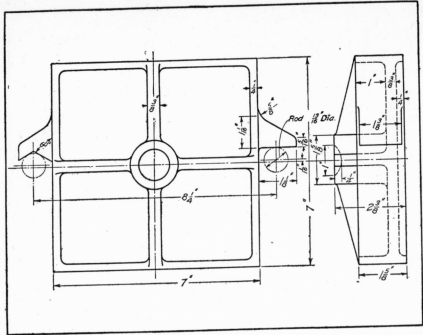

FIG. 311.   Prob. 109.

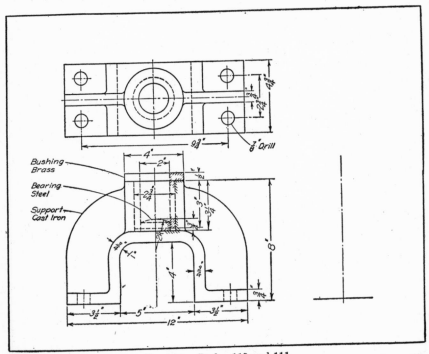

FIG. 312.   Probs. 110 and 111.

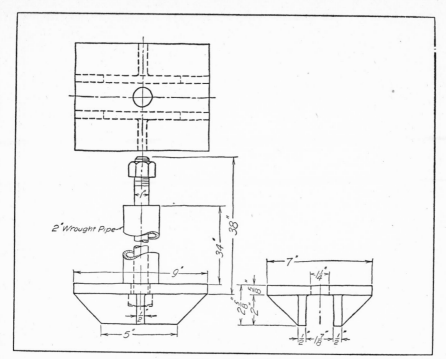

FIG. 313. Prob. 112.

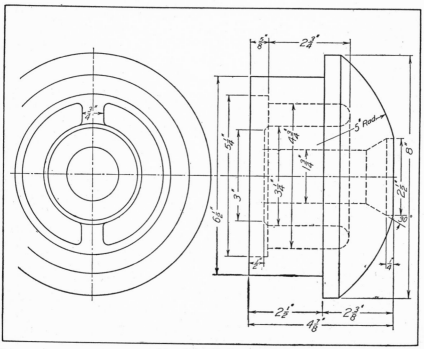

FIG. 314. Prob. 113.

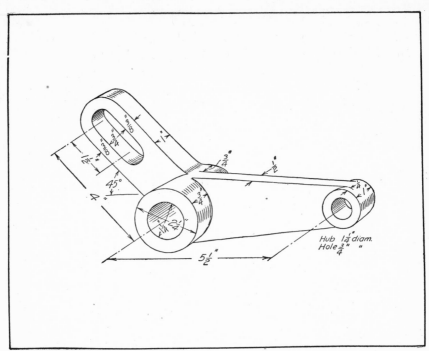

Fig. 315.   Prob. 114.

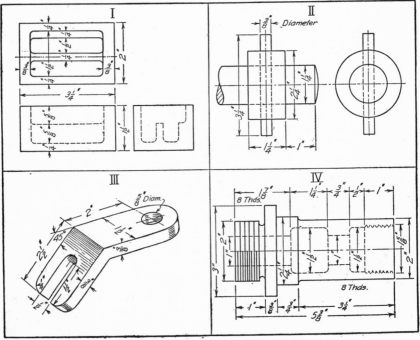

178   Fig. 316.   Probs. 115, 116, 117, and 118.

PROB. 115, Fig. 316, Space I.—Draw front view as section with proper treatment.
PROB. 116, Fig. 316, Space II.—Draw section on plane through axis.
PROB. 117, Fig. 316, Space III.—Represent the bent iron by proper views.
PROB. 118, Fig. 316, Space IV.—Draw a section on plane through axis.
PROB. 119, Fig. 317.—Make a working drawing of the LEVER.

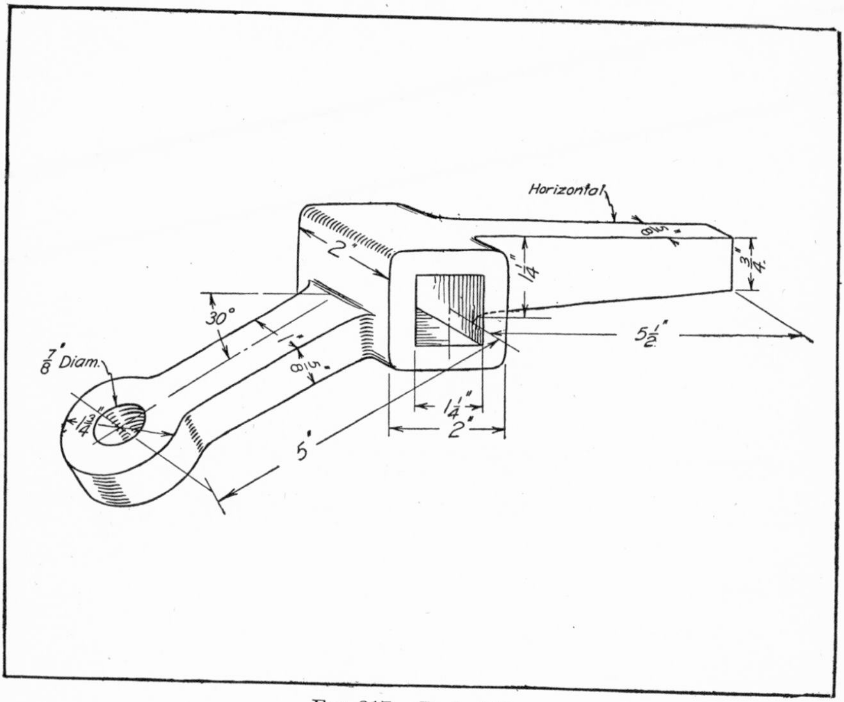

FIG. 317.   Prob. 119.

PROB. 120, Fig. 318.—Draw two full views of the TRUNNION.
PROB. 121, Fig. 318.—Draw two views of the TRUNNION, one a section through the axis.
PROB. 122, Fig. 319.—Make working drawing of the T-SLOT LEVER. Completely dimension. Consider true distances and treatment of views. Submit a preliminary freehand sketch to your instructor.
PROB. 123, Fig. 320.—Draw two exterior views of LUG COLLAR.
PROB. 124, Fig. 320.—Make a working drawing of the LUG COLLAR. Show right hand view with proper treatment as a section.
PROB. 125, Fig. 321.—Make a working drawing of the SPREADER in full or section. There are four arms, equally spaced.

MACHINE SKETCHING

205. Sketching practice must be carefully done to be of value for engineering purposes. Constant reference should be made to Chap. V.

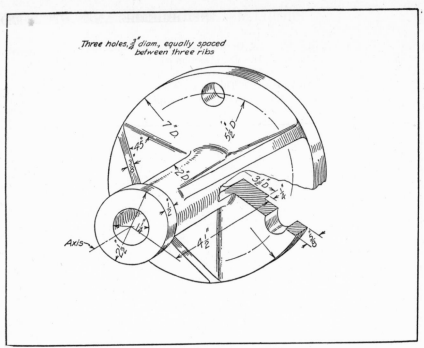

Three holes, $\frac{3}{4}$" diam., equally spaced
between three ribs

Axis

FIG. 318.   Probs. 120 and 121.

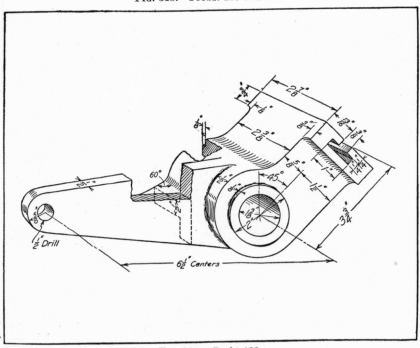

$\frac{1}{2}$" Drill

$6\frac{1}{2}$" Centers

60°

45°

FIG. 319.   Prob. 122.

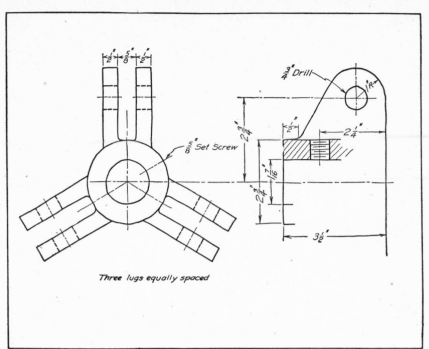

Fig. 320.   Probs. 123 and 124.

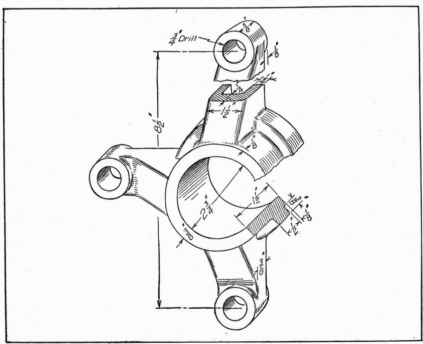

Fig. 321.   Prob. 125.

PROBS. 126, 127, 128, Fig. 322.—Sketch the exercises shown. Two exercises from each figure may be sketched in a $5^1/_2''$ x $7''$ space or four exercises may be sketched on $8^1/_2''$ x $11''$ paper.

PROBS. 129 to 148, Figs. 323 to 342.—Make freehand sketches (orthographic views) of the objects shown. Use $8^1/_2''$ x $11''$ paper or regular layout of Figs. 264 and 265 as directed by instructor. Consider choice of views, treatment of views, size of views, etc.

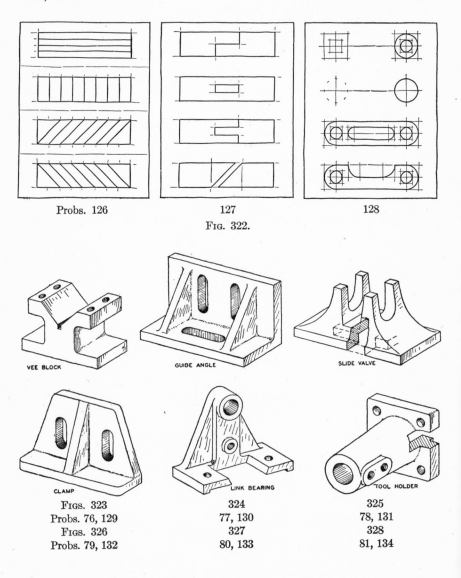

Probs. 126   127   128

Fig. 322.

VEE BLOCK   GUIDE ANGLE   SLIDE VALVE

CLAMP   LINK BEARING   TOOL HOLDER

Figs. 323   324   325
Probs. 76, 129   77, 130   78, 131
Figs. 326   327   328
Probs. 79, 132   80, 133   81, 134

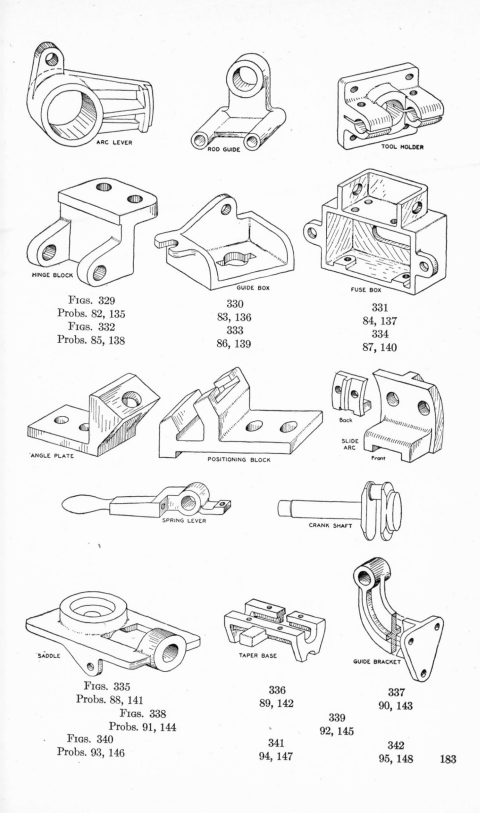

ARC LEVER

ROD GUIDE

TOOL HOLDER

HINGE BLOCK

GUIDE BOX

FUSE BOX

FIGS. 329
Probs. 82, 135
FIGS. 332
Probs. 85, 138

330
83, 136
333
86, 139

331
84, 137
334
87, 140

ANGLE PLATE

POSITIONING BLOCK

Back

SLIDE
ARC

Front

SPRING LEVER

CRANK SHAFT

SADDLE

TAPER BASE

GUIDE BRACKET

FIGS. 335
Probs. 88, 141
FIGS. 338
Probs. 91, 144
FIGS. 340
Probs. 93, 146

336
89, 142

339
92, 145

337
90, 143

341
94, 147

342
95, 148   183

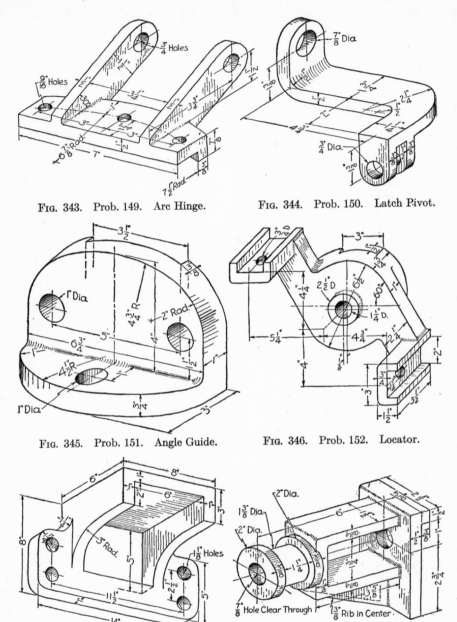

FIG. 343. Prob. 149. Arc Hinge.

FIG. 344. Prob. 150. Latch Pivot.

FIG. 345. Prob. 151. Angle Guide.

FIG. 346. Prob. 152. Locator.

FIG. 347. Prob. 153. Open Bracket.

FIG. 348. Prob. 154. Tail Piece.

PROBS. 149 to 154, Figs. 343 to 348.—Make freehand sketches (orthographic views).

PROBS. 155 to 182.—Make freehand pictorial sketches of the objects shown. Use the most suitable form of representation.

PROB........	155	156	157	158	159	160	161
Fig..........	7	11	12	13	112	114	115
PROB........	162	163	164	165	166	167	168
Fig...........	116	117	122	129	130	134	136
PROB........	169	170	. 171	172	173	174	175
Fig..........	85	86	160	165	189	192	209
PROB........	176	177	178	179	180	181	182
Fig..........	273	309	391	392	397	401	404

206. Graphical Data.—Under certain conditions graphical methods may be used to determine dimensions of machines or parts. Problems 183 to 185 may be solved by this method. The equations for the straight lines or curves are sometimes worked out

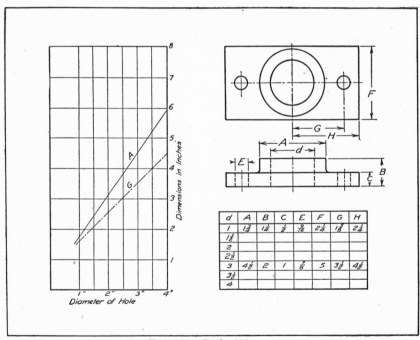

Fig. 349.   Prob. 183.

giving formulas for use in calculation. Refer to Art. 124 before working **Problems 183 to 185.**

PROB. 183, Fig. 349.—The dimensions for two sizes of the VERTICAL GUIDE are given in the table shown on Fig. 349. With these values draw a chart with a line for each dimension, as shown for A and G. Scale your chart and fill in the table with dimensions for each size. Indicate the dimensions by letters, on the views of a convenient size as shown. Derive a formula for one or more dimensions as directed by your instructor.

PROB. 184, Fig. 350.—Make a graphical chart, drawing, and table of dimensions similar to Fig. 349 for the SUPPORT shown in Fig. 350, for values of R of $1''$, $2''$, $3''$,

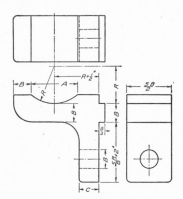

FIG. 350. Prob. 184.

$4''$ and $5''$. Obtain sufficient values to plot graphical chart from equations which follow:

$$A = \sqrt{12R - R^2 - 7}, \qquad B = \frac{R}{4} + \frac{3''}{4}, \qquad C = \frac{3}{4}B.$$

PROB. 185, Fig. 351.—Make a graphical chart, drawing and table of dimensions for the BRACKET. Values of "d" are $2''$, $4''$, $6''$, $8''$, $10''$ and $12''$. Obtain sufficient values to plot chart from the equations which follow and from your drawing.

When $d = 2''$, $A = 4''$; $d = 6''$; $A = 15^1/_2''$; $d = 9''$, $A = 19^3/_4''$; $d = 12''$, $A = 22''$.
Develop formula for values of A in terms of d and identify curve.

When $d = 4''$, $B = 9^1/_2''$; $d = 12''$, $B = 27''$.
Develop straight line formula for values of B in terms of d.

$$C = \frac{120 - (12 - d)^2}{4} \text{ (Identify curve)}.$$

$$E = C + \frac{B}{2}; \qquad F = \frac{1}{8}d + {}^1/_2''; \qquad G = 1^1/_2 F.$$

The equation for the cissoid is

$$x^2 = \frac{y^3}{2R - y}.$$

For point 2, $x = E - G$ and $y = A - F$.

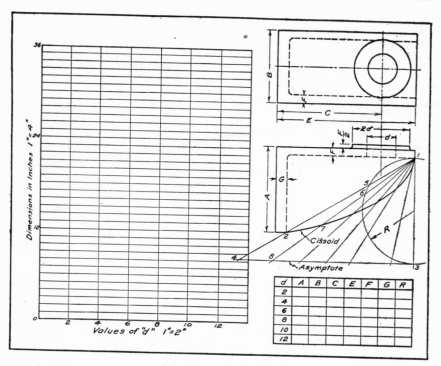

FIG. 351. Prob. 185.

Calculate value of R and draw semi-circle and asymptote.

To locate points on your drawing of cissoid, draw lines from point 1 by marking off distances from asymptote equal to chords as: $4 - 2 = 1 - 5$, $8 - 7 = 1 - 6$, etc. ($11'' \times 14''$ space.)

MACHINE DETAILS

207. The contents of Chap. VI should be studied carefully while working the following problems. If reference books on Machine Design are available they should be consulted.

PROB. 186, Fig. 352.—Make a working drawing of the STEAM PISTON. Show one view as a half section.

PROB. 187.—Make a complete two view working drawing for a steam engine piston. Material is cast iron. Diameter of cylinder is $8''$. Hollow part of piston is divided into four sections by ribs. Piston rings $1/2''$ wide and $1/4''$ thick. Obtain dimensions d, A, B, and C from diagram of Fig. 353. It will be necessary to provide a hole from each section of the piston to allow for support of cores. These holes can be tapped and closed with pipe plugs. There should be two shallow tapped holes in the head end of the piston into which rods can be screwed to remove the piston from the cylinder. Show method of fastening rod and piston ($11'' \times 14''$ working space). Refer to Chapter VI.

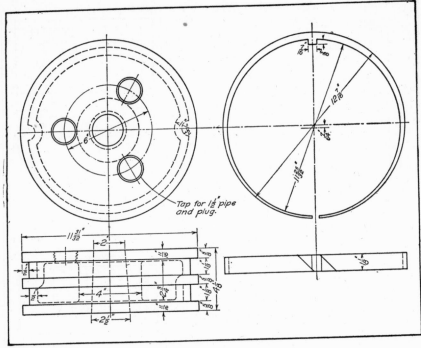

FIG. 352.　Prob. 186.

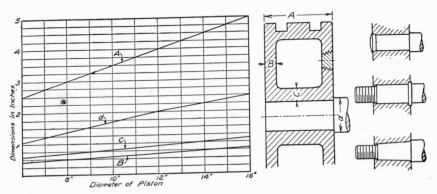

FIG. 353.　Piston Dimensions.

PROB. 188.—Make a complete two view working drawing of a steam piston as described for Prob. 187 but diameter of cylinder $= 14''$ and piston rings $5/8''$ wide and $1/2''$ thick. Divide hollow part of piston into six equal sections. Refer to Chapter VI.

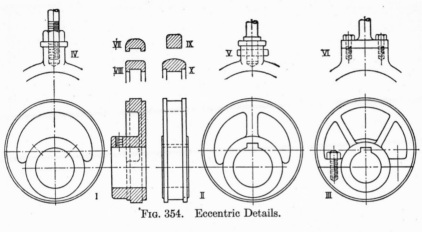

'Fig. 354. Eccentric Details.

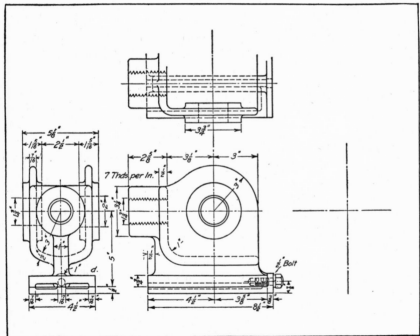

Fig. 355. Probs. 190 and 191.

PROB. 189.—Make a working drawing for an eccentric sheave and straps for the diameter of shaft specified by the instructor. Dimensions not given in table are to be worked out on your drawing. Suggestions for design are given in Fig. 354. Make a sketch and submit for criticism before starting your drawing.

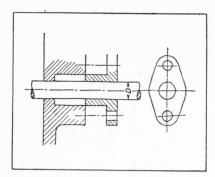

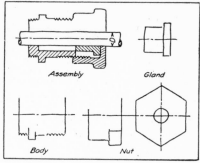

Fig. 356. Prob. 192.   Fig. 357. Prob. 193.

DIMENSIONS IN INCHES

Diameter of Shaft	$2^1/_2$	$2^3/_4$	3	8
Throw of Eccentric	$^7/_8$	1	$1^1/_8$	$2^1/_4$
Width of Eccentric	$1^1/_2$	$1^5/_8$	$1^3/_4$	$3^1/_2$
Diameter of Eccentric Rod	$^3/_4$	$^7/_8$	1	2
Diameter of Bolts	$^1/_2$	$^9/_{16}$	$^5/_8$	1 to $1^1/_8$

PROB. 190, Fig. 355.—Draw three views of the CROSSHEAD SHOE.

PROB. 191, Fig. 355.—Make a complete working drawing of the CROSSHEAD only. Show complete top, right end, and left end views in section.

PROB. 192, Fig. 356.—Make a drawing for a gland stuffing box—either plain or brass lined. Give complete dimensions for gland, box, and studs. Diameter of rod as specified by instructor. Study Art. 132.

PROB. 193, Fig. 357.—Make assembly and detail drawings for a screw type STUFFING BOX. Diameter of rod as specified by instructor. Variations in the

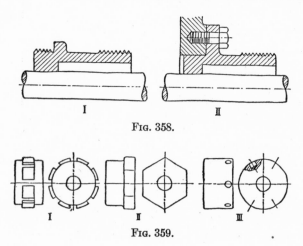

I   II

Fig. 358.

I   II   III

Fig. 359.

design of the body and gland nut are given in Figs. 358 and 359. See Art. 132.
$N = 20 - 16D + 4D^2$ = number of threads per inch for values of D from $\frac{5}{8}''$ to $2''$.
D = diam. of rod.

PROB. 194, Fig. 360.—Make detail working drawings for the parts of the IDLER PULLEY and FRAME. Select proper scale and treatment of views.

PROB. 195, Fig. 360.—Make an assembly drawing of the IDLER PULLEY and FRAME. Show front view in section. Show frame only, in right-hand view.

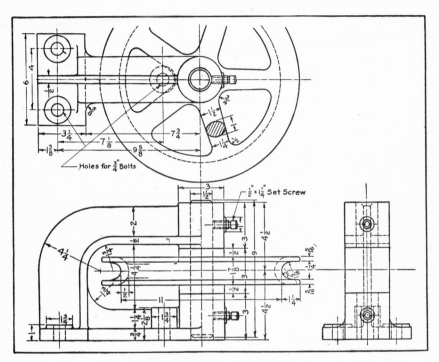

FIG. 360. Probs. 194 and 195.

BEARINGS AND PULLEYS

208. The following problems are based upon Chap. VII. Only the elements are considered and the question of design is left for books on Machine Design. The catalogs of transmission machinery manufacturers can be studied to advantage.

PROB. 196, Fig. 188, Chap. VII.—Make a working drawing of a solid BABBITTED BEARING. Size as specified by instructor.

PROB. 197, Fig. 189, Chap. VII.—Make a working drawing for size specified by instructor.

PROB. 198, Fig. 190, Chap. VII.—Make an outline drawing for size specified by instructor.

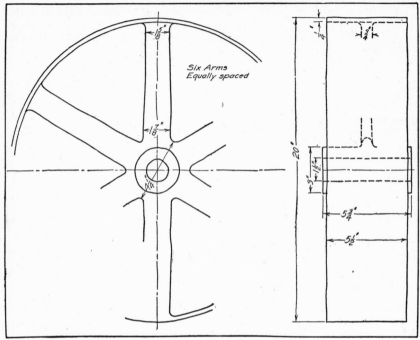

Six Arms
Equally spaced

FIG. 361.   Prob. 202.   C. I. Pulley.

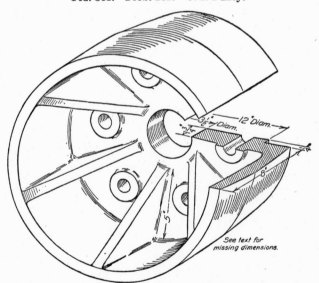

FIG. 362.   Prob. 203.   Special Pulley.

PROB. 199, Fig. 363.—Make working drawing of FLANGED PULLEY. (11″ x 14″ working space.)

PROB. 200 Fig. 364.—Make working drawing of FLYWHEEL. (11″ x 14″ working space.)

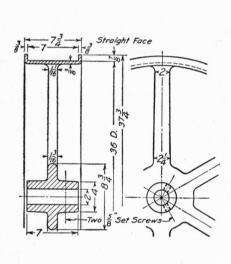

FIG. 363. Prob. 199.   FIG. 364. Prob. 200.

PROB. 201, Fig. 192, Chap. VII.—Make a drawing of POST BOX for size specified by instructor.

PROB. 202, Fig. 361.—Make a working drawing of the cast iron PULLEY. Show right hand view in section.

PROB. 203, Fig. 362.—Make a two view working drawing of the SPECIAL PULLEY. Diameter of pulley is 16″. There are six ribs $3/4$″ thick and six holes 1″ diameter equally spaced on a 9″ bolt circle. The bosses are $2^1/8$″ diameter and $1/4$″ out from surface. Flange $1/2$″ thick. Crown $3/16$″. Other dimensions on figure.

SHAFTING AND COUPLINGS

209. The drawings for shafting layouts must be carefully checked. Complete details of standard bearings, pulleys, etc., are not necessary but sufficient information should be given for purposes of ordering and erection.

PROB. 204, Fig. 365.—Make a complete shafting drawing as shown.

PROB. 205, Fig. 366.—Make a complete shafting drawing with all dimensions, similar to Fig. 365, for the shaft shown in Fig. 366. The smaller pulley is 16″ diameter and the larger pulley 24″ diameter. Get other dimensions from the tables given in Chap. VII. For flat box, see Figs. 188 and 189. For drop shaft hanger, see Fig. 190.

PROB. 206, Fig. 206, Chap. VIII.—Make a drawing for a SOLID SLEEVE COUPLING for size specified by instructor.

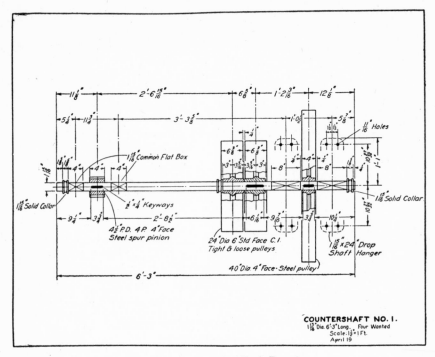

COUNTERSHAFT NO. 1.
1¹⁵⁄₁₆" Dia. 6'-3" Long.   Four Wanted
Scale: 1½"=1 Ft.
April 19

FIG. 365.   Prob. 204.   Shaft Drawing.

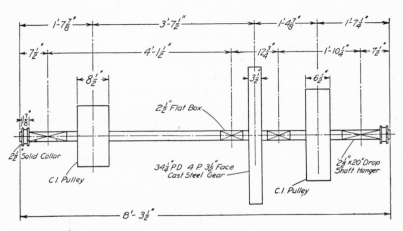

FIG. 366.   Prob. 205.   Shaft Drawing.

PROB. 207, Fig. 207, Chap. VIII.—Make a drawing for a CLAMP COUPLING for size specified by instructor.

PROB. 208, Fig. 208, Chap. VIII.—Make a drawing for a FLANGE COUPLING for size specified by instructor.

JIGS AND FIXTURES

210. The following problems emphasize points to be considered in shop drafting.

PROB. 209, Fig. 368.—Make a working drawing for the MAIN CASTING of a jig for the LINK of Fig. 367. The letters A, B, C, etc., are for reference when making

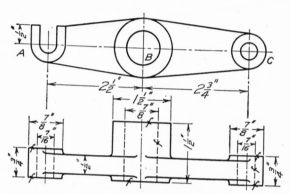

FIG. 367. Detail of Link.

an assembly. Dimensions not given are to be worked out by the student. Refer to Fig. 370.

PROB. 210, Fig. 369.—Draw the JIG DETAILS. Refer to Figs. 367, 368 and to Chap. IX. Use standard bushings as dimensioned in Table 29, Chap. IX.

PROB. 211, Figs. 367, 368, and 369.—Make an assembled jig drawing showing the piece to be drilled in its position in the jig. The drawing should be similar to Fig. 211. Letters A, B, C on Fig. 367 are also given on Fig. 368 to indicate position of the LINK. The LOCATING PIN is put in place at A and the HAND SCREW screws through the tapped hole E and holds the link against the locating pin. The SCREW BUSHING and ⁷/₈″ SLIP BUSHING go in place at B. The screw bushing presses against the link. The LINER BUSHING and ⁷/₁₆″ SLIP BUSHING are used at C. The V-BLOCK is held against the end of the link marked C by the SCREW and HANDWHEEL. The screw stem passes through the PLATE. The plate is held at D by countersunk screws.

PROB. 212, Figs. 212 and 213, Chap. IX.—Make a working drawing for the details of the FIXTURE. Show each part separately. Obtain dimensions by use of dividers and the scale shown on the figure, by method described in Art. 203.

PROB. 213, Figs. 212 and 213, Chap. IX.—Make a drawing of the complete fixture with the *work* in place as in the figure. Obtain dimensions as described in Art. 203.

PROB. 214, Figs. 210 and 211, Chap. IX.—Make a drawing of the JIG as shown in the figure. Obtain dimensions by using dividers and the scale shown on the figure by method described in Art. 203. The sketches of Fig. 370 will help in reading Fig. 211.

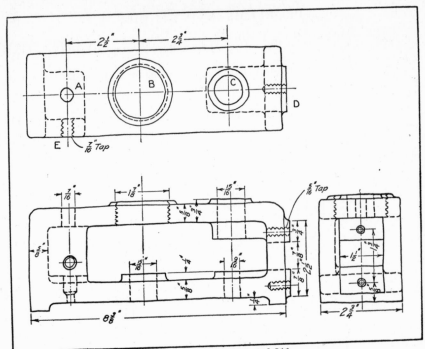

FIG. 368.   Probs. 209 and 211.

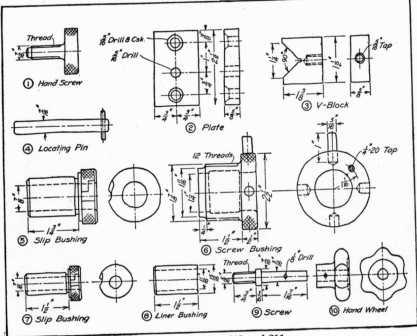

FIG. 369.   Probs. 210 and 211.

PROB. 215, Figs. 210 and 211, Chap. IX.—Make a working drawing showing each of the details of the jig separately. Obtain dimensions as described in Art. 203. The sketches of Fig. 370 will help in reading Fig. 211.

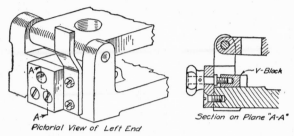

Pictorial View of Left End

Section on Plane "A-A"

V-Block

FIG. 370.   Probs. 214 and 215.

GEARS AND CAMS

211. The following problems are suggestive and can be easily multiplied by modifying the conditions stated.   For a complete study of the drafting of gears, see Anthony's Essentials of Gearing, D. C. Heath Co., Boston.

PROB. 215-A, Fig. 226, Chap. X.—Make a SPUR GEAR drawing as shown in Fig. 226.

PROB. 216, Fig. 371.—Make a SPUR GEAR drawing similar to Fig. 226 for conditions which follow.   Four sections are shown in Fig. 372 where a plain gear is shown at I, plain with hub at II, webbed at III and with arms at IV.   Various combinations can, of course, be made.

Details or dimensions not specified are to be worked out by the student on his drawing.   Letters refer to Fig. 371.   Solve problem using values given in the following table for gear specified by instructor.   Choose scale so that gear can be drawn in 11″ x 14″ space.

PROB.	Pitch	Number of Teeth	A	B	C	d
216	8	68	$2^1/_8$	$1^3/_8$	$1^1/_8$	$1^1/_{16}$
217	7	62	$2^1/_4$	$1^1/_2$	$1^1/_4$	$1^1/_8$
218	6	58	$2^1/_2$	2	$1^1/_2$	$1^1/_4$
219	5	43	3	$2^1/_4$	$1^3/_4$	$1^1/_2$
220	4	66	$3^1/_4$	$2^1/_2$	2	$1^5/_8$
221	$3^1/_2$	64	4	3	$2^1/_2$	2
222	3	28	$3^1/_2$	3	$2^1/_2$	$1^3/_4$
223	$2^3/_4$	44	4	$3^1/_4$	$2^3/_4$	2
224	$2^1/_4$	70	$5^1/_4$	$3^3/_4$	$3^1/_4$	$2^1/_4$
225	2	30	$5^1/_2$	$4^1/_2$	4	$2^1/_2$

PROB. 226, Fig. 230, Chap. X.—Make a BEVEL GEAR drawing as shown in Fig. 230 (11″ x 14″ space).

PROB. 227, Fig. 373.—Make a drawing for the MITRE GEAR.   Give complete dimensions, angles, etc.

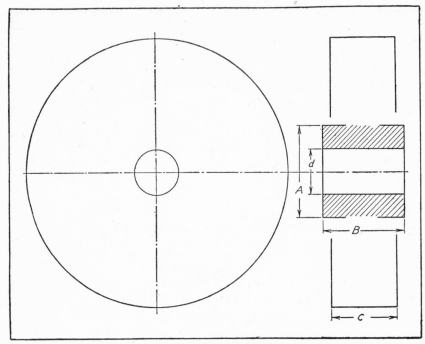

FIG. 371.   Probs. 216 to 225.

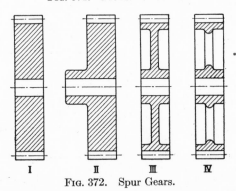

I   II   III   IV

FIG. 372.   Spur Gears.

PROB. 228.—Make a drawing for a MITRE GEAR similar to the previous problem but for 6 pitch and 54 teeth.   Use same size shaft and hub.

PROB. 229, Fig. 374.—Make a drawing for the WORM and WHEEL.

PROB. 230, Fig. 375.—Design a PLATE CAM with point contact (as in Fig. 234) to raise follower during one half revolution with uniform motion and allow it to drop during remaining half revolution with uniform motion.

$$x = 9'', \qquad y = 5'', \qquad AB = \text{rise} = 1^3/_4'', \qquad \text{Distance } OA = 2^3/_4''.$$

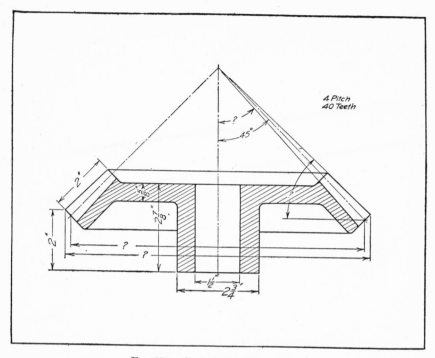

FIG. 373.   Prob. 227.   Mitre Gears.

PROB. 231, Fig. 375.—PLATE CAM with point contact to raise follower during one third revolution, drop during one third revolution at rest during one third revolution.   Uniform motion up and down.

$$x = 9'', \qquad y = 5'', \qquad AB = 2'', \qquad OA = 2^1/_2''.$$

PROB. 232, Fig. 375.—PLATE CAM with point contact.   Motion as follows: Up 1 inch during $^1/_4$ rev. with gravity motion.   At rest during $^1/_8$ rev.   Up 1 inch during $^1/_4$ rev. with gravity motion.   Down 2 inches during $^1/_4$ rev. with uniform motion. At rest during $^1/_8$ rev.

$$x = 9'', \qquad y = 5'', \qquad AB = 2'', \qquad OA = 2^1/_2''.$$

PROB. 233, Fig. 375.—PLATE CAM with point contact.   Motion as follows: Up $1^1/_2$ inches during $^1/_3$ rev. with harmonic motion at rest during $^1/_6$ rev.   Drop $1^1/_2$ inches during $^1/_3$ rev. with harmonic motion.   At rest during $^1/_6$ rev.

$$x = 9'', \qquad y = 5'', \qquad AB = 1^1/_2'', \qquad OA = 3^1/_4''.$$

PROB. 234, Fig. 375.—PLATE CAM with roller $^3/_4$ inches diameter.   Same motion as for Prob. 230. $x = 9''$, $\qquad y = 5''$, $\qquad AB = 1^3/_4''$, $\qquad OA = 2^3/_4''$.

PROB. 235, Fig. 375.—PLATE CAM with roller $^3/_4$ inches diameter.   Same motion as for Prob. 231. $x = 9''$, $\qquad y = 5''$, $\qquad AB = 2''$, $\qquad OA = 2^1/_2''$.

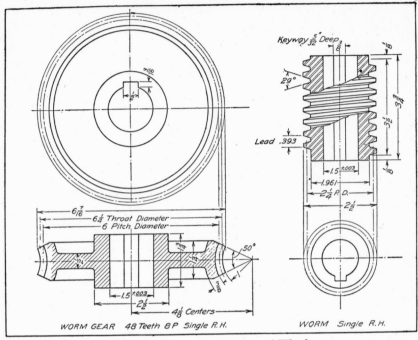

FIG. 374.   Prob. 229.   Worm and Wheel.

PROB. 236, Fig. 375.—PLATE CAM with roller $^3/_4$ inches diameter. Same motion as for Prob. 233. $x = 9''$, $y = 5''$, $AB = 1^1/_2''$, $OA = 3^1/_4''$.

PROB. 237, Fig. 376.—Design a PLATE CAM with *point* or *roller* contact as directed by instructor. Motion as follows: Up $1^3/_4$ inches during $^1/_2$ rev. with uniform motion. Down $1^3/_4$ inches during $^1/_2$ rev. with uniform motion. Shaft revolves left hand. $x = 9''$, $y = 5''$, $AB = 1^3/_4''$, $CA = 2^1/_2''$, $OC = 1^1/_4''$.

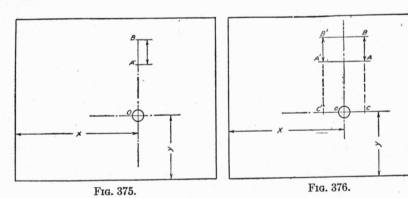

FIG. 375.   FIG. 376.

PROB. 238, Fig. 376.—Same as Prob. 237 except,

$$x = 9'', \qquad y = 5'', \qquad A'B' = 1^{1}/_{2}'', \qquad C'A' = 3'', \qquad OC' = 1''.$$

PROB. 239, Fig. 376.—PLATE CAM with either point or roller contact. Motion as follows: Up during $^{1}/_{3}$ rev. with gravity motion. Down during $^{1}/_{3}$ rev. with gravity motion. Rest during $^{1}/_{3}$ rev. $x = 9''$, $y = 5''$, $AB = 1^{3}/_{4}''$, $CA = 2^{1}/_{2}''$, $OC = 1^{3}/_{8}''$.

PROB. 240, Fig. 376.—PLATE CAM. Same as Prob. 237, harmonic motion.

PROB. 241, Fig. 375.—PLATE CAM with flat follower (as in Fig. 239). Motion and distances as in Prob. 236 except $x = 7''$.

PROB. 242, Fig. 375.—PLATE CAM with flat follower. Motion and distances as follows: Up during $^{1}/_{3}$ rev. with harmonic motion. At rest $^{1}/_{6}$ rev. Down during $^{1}/_{3}$ rev. with gravity motion. At rest $^{1}/_{6}$ rev. Dimensions as for Prob. 234.

PROB. 243, Fig. 377.—Design a PLATE CAM similar to Fig. 238. Show cam outline complete. Motion as follows: Up from A to B during $^{1}/_{2}$ rev. with gravity motion. Drop from B to A during $^{1}/_{4}$ rev. with gravity motion. At rest during $^{1}/_{4}$ rev.

$$W = 5'', \qquad x = 2^{1}/_{2}'', \qquad y = 3^{1}/_{2}'', \qquad AB = 3'', \qquad R_{1} = 10'', \qquad R_{2} = 3^{1}/_{2}''.$$

PROB. 244, Fig. 377.—Same as Prob. 243, but for uniform motion.

PROB. 245, Fig. 378.—Draw the development of the pitch line for a CYLINDRICAL CAM (as in Fig. 241) for the following motion.

Parallel to axis $2^{1}/_{2}$ inches during $^{1}/_{3}$ rev. with harmonic motion. At rest $^{1}/_{6}$ rev. Return parallel to axis $2^{1}/_{2}$ inches during $^{1}/_{4}$ rev. with harmonic motion. At rest $^{1}/_{4}$ rev. Diameter = $3''$. Travel = $2^{1}/_{2}''$.

PROB. 246, Fig. 378.—Same as Prob. 245 but for gravity motion and show groove for $^{3}/_{4}''$ diameter roll.

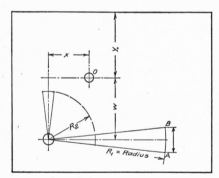
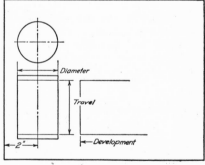

FIG. 377.   FIG. 378.

PIPING DRAWINGS

212. A piping drawing is started by laying out the center lines and locating the valves, fittings, etc., which can be shown more or less conventionally depending upon the scale. A complete treatment of the subject is given in "A Handbook on Piping," published by D. Van Nostrand Co., N. Y. Study Chap. XI.

PROB. 247, Fig. 379.—From sketch, make a piping drawing to scale.

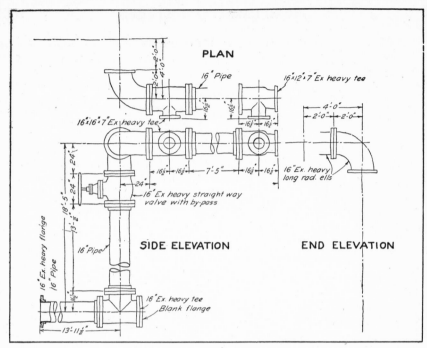

FIG. 379.   Prob. 247.   Piping Layout.

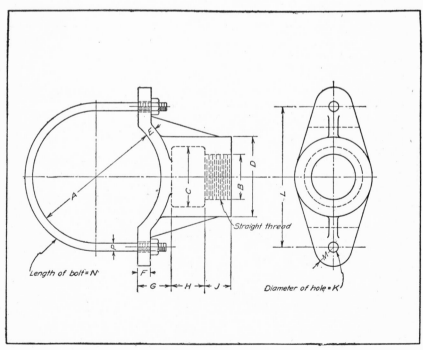

FIG. 380.   Probs. 248, 249 and 250.   Pipe Support.

Fig. 380.—Make a drawing for a PIPE SUPPORT. These supports are made in sizes from 4″ to 72″ by the Pittsburgh Piping & Equipment Company. (11″ x 14″ working space.)

DIMENSIONS FOR PIPE SUPPORTS

Size	A	B	C	D	E	F	G	H	J	K	L	M	N	P
								Pipe						
PROB. 248..	8	$8^3/_4$	3	4	$5^1/_4$	$^3/_4$	$^7/_8$	$2^1/_4$	$2^1/_4$	$1^3/_4$	$^5/_8$	$9^1/_4$	$1^1/_4$	24	$^1/_2$
PROB. 249..	24	$24^1/_4$	5	6	$7^5/_8$	$1^1/_4$	$1^3/_8$	6	$3^3/_4$	$2^1/_2$	1	$25^1/_8$	$1^3/_4$	$59^1/_2$	$^7/_8$
PROB. 250..	50	$50^1/_4$	8	9	11	$1^1/_2$	2	12	$5^1/_2$	$3^1/_2$	$1^3/_8$	$51^1/_2$	$2^1/_4$	118	$1^1/_4$

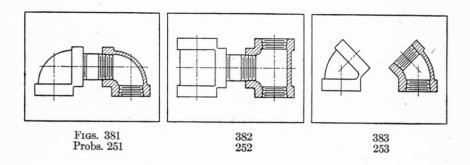

FIGS. 381   382   383
Probs. 251   252   253

PROB. 251, Fig. 381.—Make a drawing for $^1/_2$″, $^3/_4$″ or 1″, ELBOWS. See Table 35 for dimensions. ($5^1/_2$″ x 7″ space.)

PROB. 252, Fig. 382.—Make a drawing for $^1/_2$″, $^3/_4$″ or 1″, TEES. See Table 35 for dimensions. ($5^1/_2$″ x 7″ space.)

PROB. 253, Fig. 383.—Make a drawing for $^1/_2$″, $^3/_4$″ or 1″, 45° ELBOWS. See Table 35 for dimensions. ($5^1/_2$″ x 7″ space.)

Problems on pipe welds, screwed or flanged fittings, flanges, etc., may be assigned by reference to Figs. 245, 249, 250 and 251 and the tables which relate to these figures.

Practice in conventional representation of pipe and fittings may be had by drawing the illustrations of Figs. 256 to 258. Use 11″ x 14″ space and letter all notes as shown on the illustrations.

Fig. 384.—Make a drawing for an iron body EXPANSION JOINT for 125 lbs. working pressure. The dimensions given in the table are from the Pittsburgh Piping & Equipment Co. (11″ x 14″ working space).

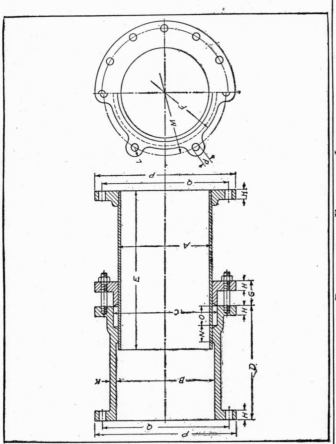

FIG. 384. Probs. 254, 255 and 256.

DIMENSIONS OF EXPANSION JOINTS

	Size	A	B	C	D	E	F	G	H	K	L	M	N	O	P	Q	No. Studs	Size Hole
PROB. 254	10	$10\frac{1}{2}$	$11\frac{1}{8}$	$11\frac{7}{8}$	13	$19\frac{1}{4}$	$13\frac{1}{4}$	3	$1\frac{3}{16}$	$\frac{3}{4}$	$1\frac{1}{4}$	$14\frac{1}{4}$	2	$2\frac{1}{2}$	16	$14\frac{1}{4}$	6 $\frac{3}{4}$	$\frac{13}{16}$
PROB. 255	12	$12\frac{5}{8}$	$13\frac{1}{4}$	14	15	21	$14\frac{5}{8}$	$3\frac{1}{4}$	$1\frac{1}{4}$	$1\frac{3}{16}$	$1\frac{1}{4}$	$16\frac{1}{2}$	$2\frac{1}{8}$	$2\frac{5}{8}$	19	17	6 $\frac{3}{4}$	$\frac{13}{16}$
PROB. 256	14	$13\frac{7}{8}$	$14\frac{1}{2}$	$15\frac{3}{8}$	$16\frac{1}{4}$	$23\frac{1}{2}$	$16\frac{7}{8}$	$3\frac{3}{8}$	$1\frac{3}{8}$	$\frac{7}{8}$	$1\frac{3}{8}$	18	$2\frac{1}{4}$	$2\frac{3}{4}$	21	$18\frac{3}{4}$	6 $\frac{7}{8}$	$\frac{15}{16}$

213. The problems relating to Figures 385 to 403 comprise a set of drawings for a 5″ x 6″ vertical steam engine. They may be worked as separate problems or as a class problem. Each problem is stated by itself so they may be used in any way desired by the instructor. In some cases one figure refers to another for dimensions or information. This will require the student to check his drawing. A sectional assembly of the engine is shown in Fig. 385. A 5″ × 6″ engine means that the diameter of the cylinder is 5″ and the stroke of the piston is 6″.

PROB. 257, Fig. 387.—From the sketch make a complete working drawing of the STEAM CHEST COVER. Give proper dimensions and indicate finished surfaces. Examine Figs. 385 and 400 to see where cover is used.

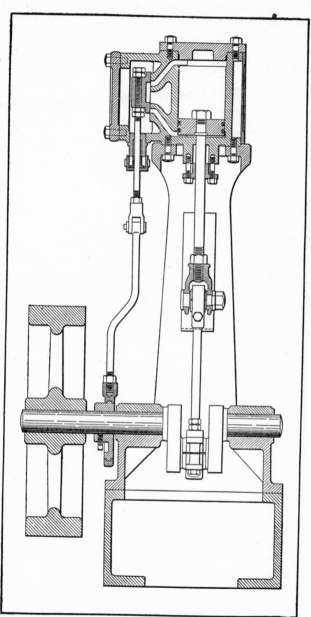

FIG. 385.   Sectional Assembly.

PROB. 258, Fig. 388.—From the sketch make a complete working drawing of the CYLINDER HEAD. Show one view in section. Examine Figs. 385 and 400 to see where head is used.

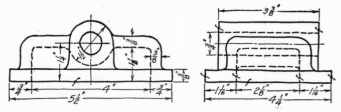

Fig. 386.　Prob. 262.　Slide Valve.

PROB. 259, Fig. 389.—From the sketch make a complete working drawing for the PISTON. Supply complete dimensions.

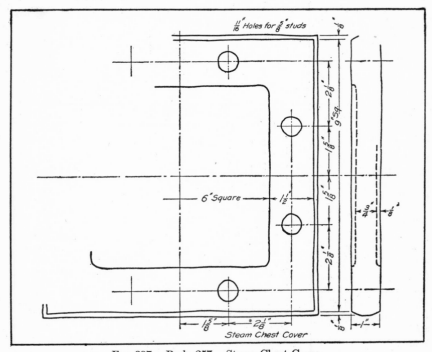

Fig. 387.　Prob. 257.　Steam Chest Cover.

PROB. 260, Fig. 390.—Make a complete working drawing of the FLY WHEEL. Show one view in section.

PROB. 261, Fig. 391.—Make a complete working drawing of the BASE. Show front and side views as half sections.

PROB. 262, Fig. 386.—Make a working drawing of the SLIDE VALVE. Show one view in section.

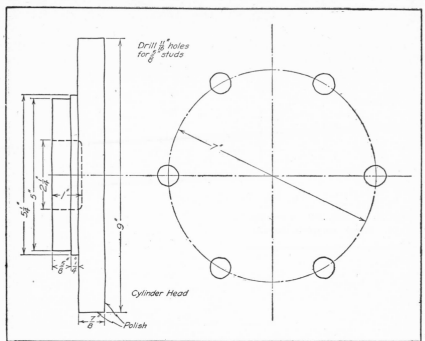

Drill $\frac{11}{16}$" holes
for $\frac{5}{8}$" studs

Cylinder Head

Polish

FIG. 388.   Prob. 258.   Cylinder Head.

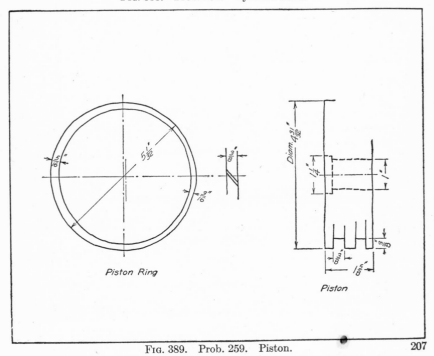

Piston Ring

Piston

FIG. 389.   Prob. 259.   Piston.

207

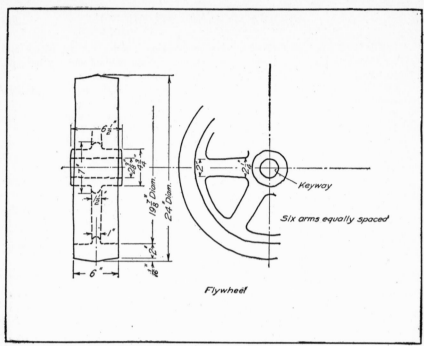

Keyway

Six arms equally spaced

Flywheel

Fig. 390. Prob. 260. Flywheel.

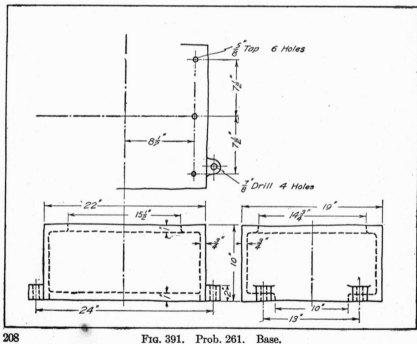

$\frac{5}{8}''$ Tap 6 Holes

$\frac{7}{8}''$ Drill 4 Holes

Fig. 391. Prob. 261. Base.

PROB. 263, Fig. 392.—Make a complete working drawing for the BEARING CAP. Show front and side views as half sections. Note babbitt and $1/4''$ oil pipe. Compare radii at A, B, and C with text and illustrations in Art. 133.

PROB. 264, Fig. 393.—Make a detail working drawing for the valve rod STUFF-ING BOX and piston rod GLAND.

PROB. 265, Fig. 394.—From the given sketch make an assembly drawing of the ECCENTRIC, with or without dimensions as directed by the instructor.

PROB. 266, Fig. 394.—From the given sketch make detail drawings of the eccentric sheave, eccentric straps, bolts and shim. Give all dimensions. Use two $11'' \times 14''$ sheets or one large sheet, Fig. 266.

PROB. 267, Fig. 395.—From the given sketch make a detail drawing of the valve and eccentric rods.

PROB. 268, Fig. 396.—From the sketch make a complete detail drawing of the CRANK SHAFT, PISTON ROD, etc. Distance between center lines for crank shaft is one-half of the stroke, or $6/2'' = 3''$.

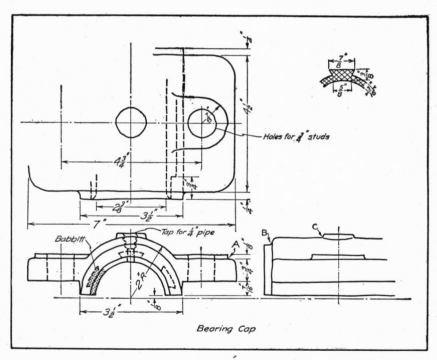

Fig. 392.   Prob. 263.   Bearing Cap

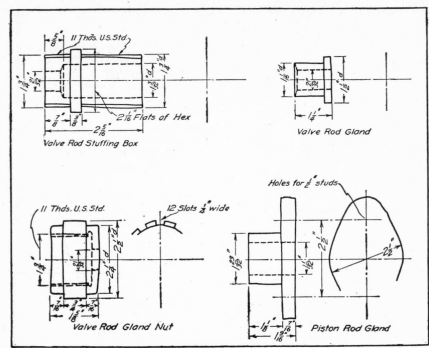

FIG. 393.   Prob. 264.   Stuffing Box Details.

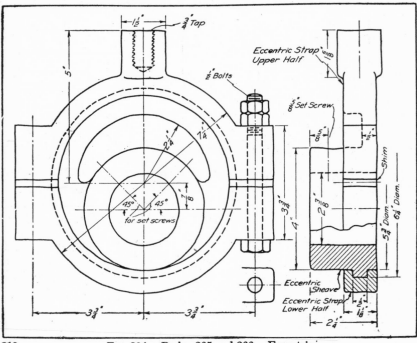

FIG. 394.   Probs. 265 and 266.   Eccentric.

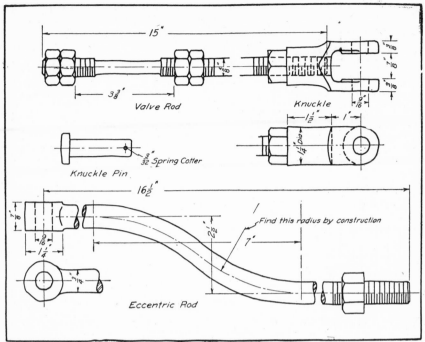

FIG. 395.　Prob. 267.　Eccentric Rod, etc.

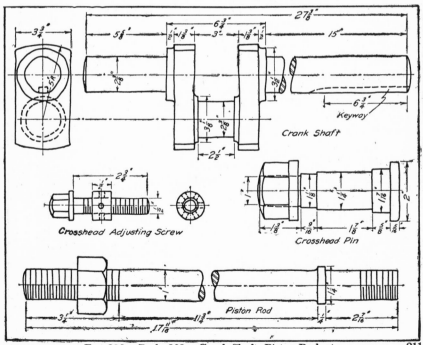

FIG. 396.　Prob. 268.　Crank Shaft, Piston Rod, etc.

x

211

PROB. 269, Fig. 397.—Make a complete working drawing of the CONNECTING ROD.

PROB. 270, Fig. 398.—Make a working drawing of the CONNECTING ROD DETAILS. Draw views as given, complete top view of wedge and draw top view of bronze box. Give complete dimensions. Obtain the bolt dimensions by reference to the places where they are used. Figs. 397 and 399.

PROB. 271, Fig. 399.—Make working drawing of the CRANK END BOXES for the connecting rod. Show the end views *with all full lines*, but *without all dotted lines*. Select dotted lines in all views carefully, omitting such as tend to confuse. Show front view in half section. Determine a few points in curve of intersection shown at *A* in top view.

PROB. 272, Figs. 397, 398, and 399.—Make a two view assembly drawing of the complete connecting rod, either with full views or part sections. Give such dimensions as would be necessary for machining or assembling. Use a large size sheet (Fig. 266) for this problem.

PROB. 273, Fig. 400.—Make a working drawing of the STEAM CYLINDER showing the front view in section. Use regular sheet.

PROB. 274, Fig. 400.—Make a working drawing of the STEAM CYLINDER with following views. Front view as section on plane *A–A*; end view in full; complete top view in full; section on plane *B–B*. Use large sheet (Fig. 266).

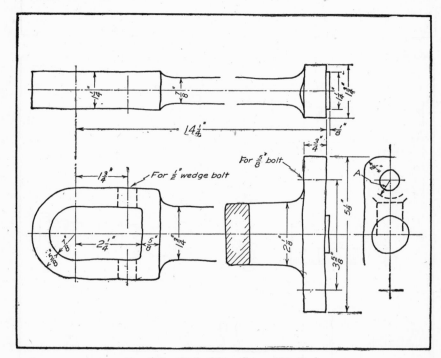

FIG. 397.   Prob. 269.   Connecting Rod.

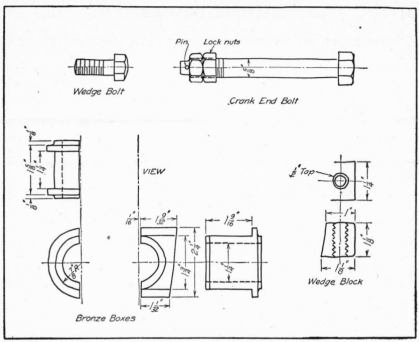

FIG. 398.   Prob. 270.   Connecting Rod Details.

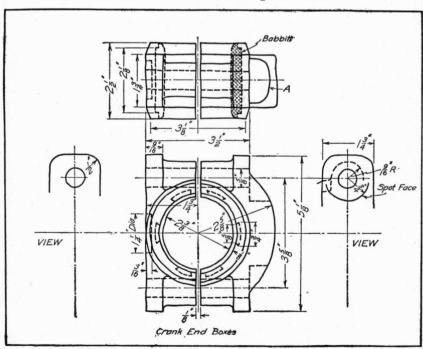

FIG. 399.   Probs. 271 and 272.   Crank End Boxes.

213

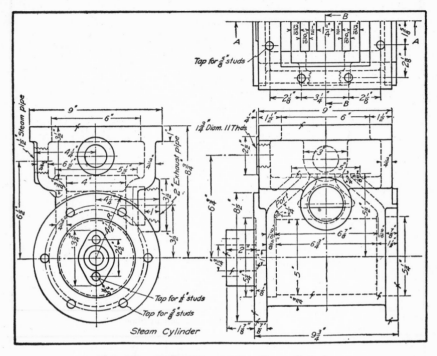

FIG. 400. Probs. 273 and 274. Steam Cylinder.

PROB. 275, Fig. 401.—Make a working drawing of the CROSSHEAD SHOE. Show front view in section.

PROB. 276, Fig. 402.—Make a working drawing of the CROSSHEAD BODY. Show views given and two end views. Use judgment as to dotted lines on end views.

PROB. 277, Figs. 401 and 402.—Make an assembly drawing of the Crosshead and Shoe. Adjusting screw will be found on Fig. 396.

PROB. 278, Fig. 403.—Make a working drawing of the FRAME. Work out curves at A very carefully to give good appearance. Curves at C and D are to be found by projection and should be analyzed carefully. Show all views as half sections. Detail for Bearing Cap is given on Fig. 392.

PROB. 279.—Make a sectional assembly of the 5″ x 6″ Engine as shown in Fig. 385.

PROB. 280.—Make a sectional assembly of the 5″ x 6″ Engine taken through the vertical axis but at right angles to section shown in Fig. 385.

PROB. 281.—Make an exterior assembly of the 5″ x 6″ Engine, which will show the crosshead, connecting rod, etc.

PROB. 282.—Make an exterior assembly of the 5″ x 6″ Engine, which does not show the crosshead, connecting rod, etc.

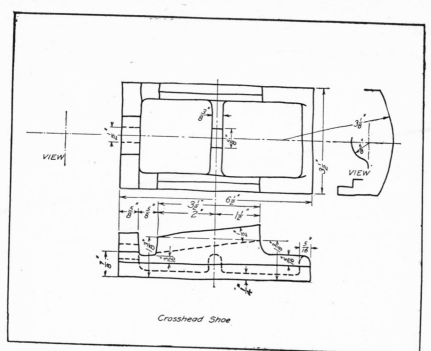

Crosshead Shoe

Fig. 401. Prob. 275. Crosshead Shoe.

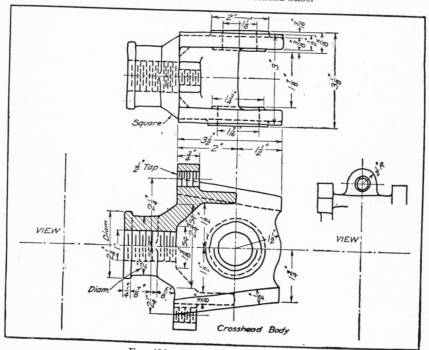

Crosshead Body

Fig. 402. Prob. 276. Crosshead.

215

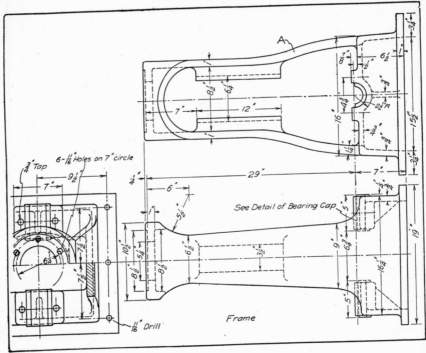

FIG. 403. Prob. 278. Frame.

ASSEMBLY AND DETAIL DRAWINGS

214. The drawings of a STEP BEARING, STEAM KETTLE, and PLUNGER PUMP are intended for reading problems as well as to give practice in applying the principles of drafting. When assembling or detailing, check each piece with the parts with which it is used.

PROB. 283, Fig. 404.—Make detail working drawings for the parts of the STEP BEARING. Scale 6″ = 1 foot. Use two regular sheets or one large sheet.

Consider the treatment of views, number of views, etc. Do not copy the dimensions but finish the views and then locate dimensions without using the book. Note that the bolt has a special head ¹/₂″ thick and 1¹/₂″ square. On the right hand view one dimension line is shown incomplete to indicate that it is taken "about" the center. This is done because the hollow space is not shown on both sides of the center line.

PROB. 284, Fig. 405.—Make detail working drawings of the STEAM KETTLE parts.

PROB. 285, Fig. 405.—Make an assembly working drawing of the STEAM JACKETED KETTLE. Draw sectional elevation or half section. Such dimensions as are not given are to be supplied by the student. The required bolts are to be drawn and specified. The bosses for the pipe may be about twice the outside diameter of the pipe.

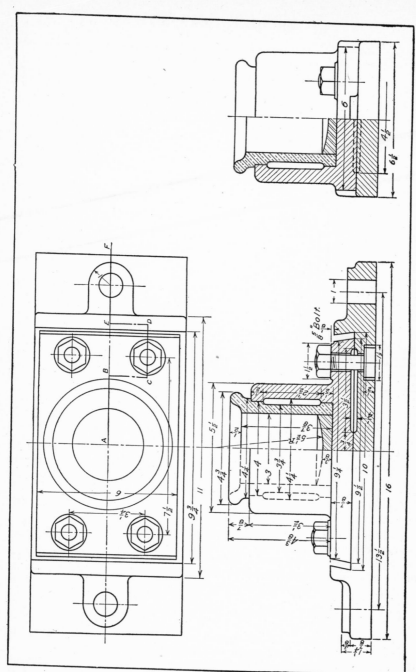

FIG. 404. Prob. 283. Step Bearing.

217

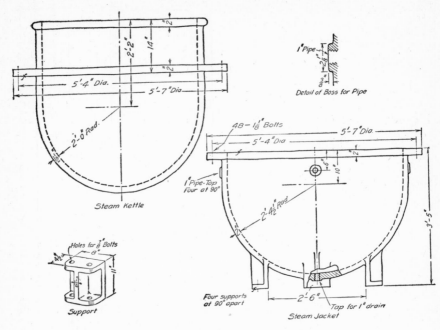

FIG. 405. Probs. 284 and 285.

Completely dimension the drawing. The jacket is supported upon four supports, shown pictorially. The flange of the kettle rests upon the flange of the jacket and is bolted to it. Use large sheet. (Fig. 266.)

PROB. 286. Fig. 406.—Make a detail working drawing of the PUMP BODY.

PROB. 287, Fig. 406.—Make a working drawing showing each detail separately for the $1^1/_8''$ plunger pump, for all parts except the pump body. Use large sheet.

PROB. 288, Fig. 406.—Make an exterior assembly drawing of the $1^1/_8''$ plunger pump. Give general dimensions only.

STEAM TURBINE BEARING

215. The steam turbine bearing shown in Figs. 407, 408, and 409 is for a Type 6, B. F. Sturtevant Steam Turbine. The bearings are split to permit easy adjustment. The two halves are held together with cap screws. The spherical seating makes the bearing self-aligning. The rapidly revolving oiling ring takes oil from the oil pocket and deposits it on the shaft where it is distributed by the oil grooves in the bearings.

An idea of the assembly may be had by reference to Fig. 103. The adjusting screw (Part No. 2, Fig. 407) is used to screw through the bearing casing cover, causing the spherical seat (Part No. 4, Fig. 407) to grip the linings (Part No. 7, Fig. 409). The lock nut (Part No. 3, Fig. 407) is used to hold the adjusting screw in position.

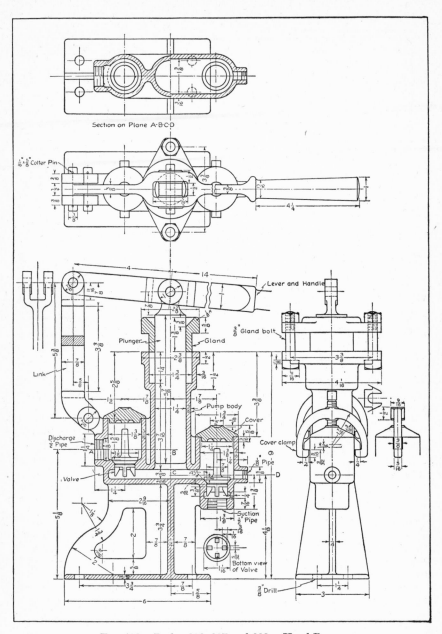

FIG. 406. Probs. 286, 287 and 288. Hand Pump.

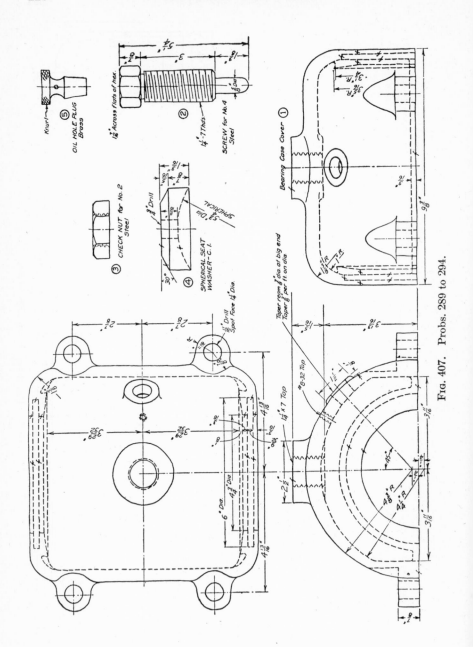

FIG. 407. Probs. 289 to 294.

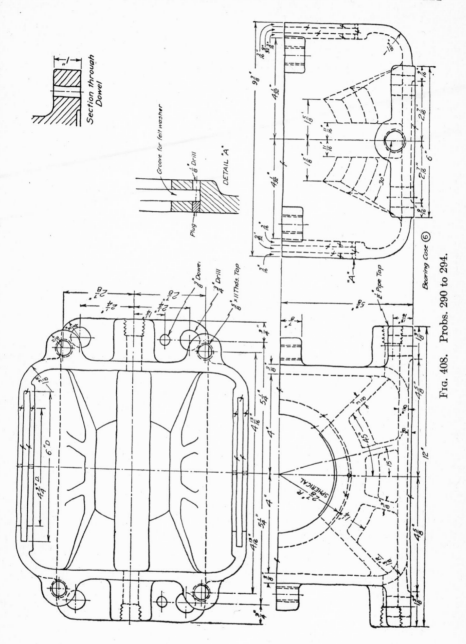

Fig. 408. Probs. 290 to 294.

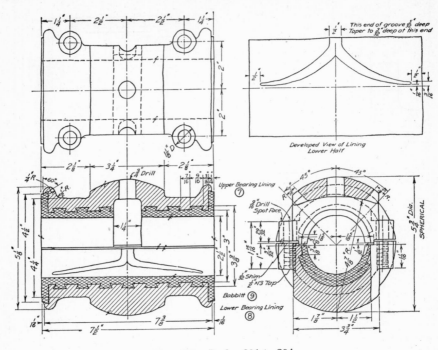

FIG. 409.   Probs. 291 to 294.

The list of parts is as follows:

1. Bearing Case Cover, Fig. 407.
2. Adjusting Screw, Fig. 407.
3. Check Nut, Fig. 407.
4. Spherical Seat, Fig. 407.
5. Oil Hole Plug, Fig. 407.
   Safety Chain for Plug, not shown.
   No. 8—32 Machine Screw $1/2''$ long
   to hold chain, not shown.
6. Bearing Case, Fig. 408.

$1/2''$ Pipe Plugs, not shown.
Felt Washers, not shown.
$3/8''$ Dowel Pins, $2''$ long, not shown.
$5/8''$ Studs, $2^7/_{16}''$ long, not shown.
7. Upper Bearing Lining, Fig. 409.
8. Lower Bearing Lining, Fig. 409.
9. Phoenix Metal, Fig. 409.
$1/2''$—13 Cap Screws, not shown.
Oil Ring $5^1/_2''$ inside diameter, $6^1/_4''$
outside diameter.

PROB. 289, Fig. 407.—Make a detail drawing of the BEARING CASE COVER.
Show the front and side views as half sections.

PROB. 290, Fig. 408.—Make a detail drawing of the BEARING CASE. Show
the front and side views as half sections.

PROB. 291, Fig. 409.—Make a detail drawing of the BEARING LINING. Will
go full size on large size sheet, Fig. 266. Draw front view as a half section.

PROB. 292, Figs. 407, 408, and 409.—Make an exterior assembly drawing of the
complete bearing. Show two or three views as specified by instructor.

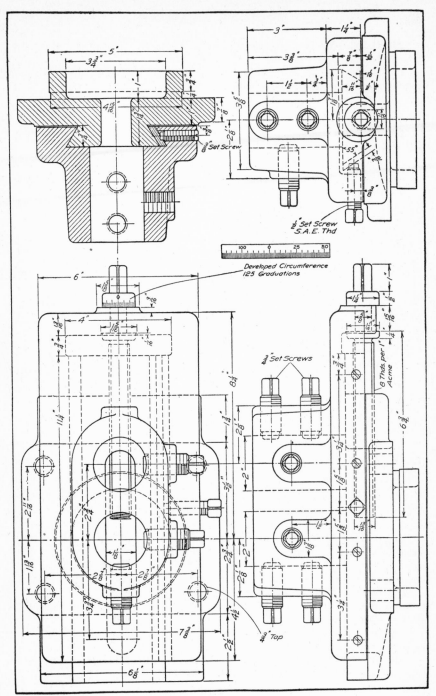

Fig. 410. Prob. 295.

PROB. 293.—Make an assembly drawing of the complete bearing showing a section through the axis. One view only.

PROB. 294.—Make an assembly drawing of the complete bearing, showing a section at right angles to the axis. One view only.

SLIDE TOOL HOLDER

216. The slide tool holder shown in Fig. 410 is from a drawing supplied by the Foster Machine Company, Elkhart, Ind., and is described by them as follows:

"Designed for boring, recessing, back facing, and like operations, this tool combines a high degree of rigidity with adaptability. The cutters can be carried in either of two holes. Wear on the slide of the tool can be taken up by means of a gib. The tool adjusting screw carries a graduated dial which feature aids materially in setting the tool. The slide tool is used on Foster turret lathes."

PROB. 295.—Make detail working drawings of each part of the vertical slide tool. Consider choice of views, treatment of views, scale, etc., very carefully. If drawn full size larger sheets than specified in Fig. 266 will be required.

POWER PUNCHING PRESS

217. The "Stiles" Punching Press, No. 2—B shown in Fig. 411 is built by the E. W. Bliss Company, Brooklyn, N. Y., who furnished drawings from which the following figures were made. This type of press is made in three sizes, either as flywheel or geared presses. Larger sheets than specified in Fig. 266 will be required. About $18'' \times 24''$ working space for a minimum if drawn to a scale of $3'' = 1$ ft.

218. The "Stiles" clutch is illustrated in partial assembly in Fig. 416. Views are shown in direction of arrows "A" and "B" from the plane indicated. The clutch collar is keyed to the shaft.

The dog holds the wheel pin in place. When the treadle is depressed one cam on the clutch fork releases the wheel pin allowing it to engage a recess in the clutch collar and revolve the shaft. When the treadle is released the wheel pin is pushed back into the wheel by a wedge cam on the clutch fork and is held by the dog. Three wheel pins are used on the flywheel of this press. Flywheel rim section $2^3/_4'' \times 4^1/_4''$, arms $1^1/_4'' \times 2^1/_2''$.

PROB. 296, Fig. 412.—Make a working drawing of the FRAME. Show top view in full and necessary sections. Do not simply copy the sketch but consider treatment of views.

PROB. 297.—Make detail drawings of the separate parts as directed by your instructor. It will be necessary to study the complete machine in order to check the parts. Use small or large standard sheets, Fig. 264 or Fig. 266. Several sheets will be required. Plan the arrangement of parts and treatment of views.

PROB. 298.—Make an assembly drawing of the complete press. Show all parts in their working positions. Section such parts as are necessary to show the construction clearly. Choose scale and plan views for instructor's criticism. Work carefully to check details. Drawing must be accurate. Do not dimension. Study clutch as given on details and in Fig. 416.

PROB. 299.—Make an exterior or full view assembly drawing of the press. Do not show hidden surfaces. Give set-up and space dimensions only.

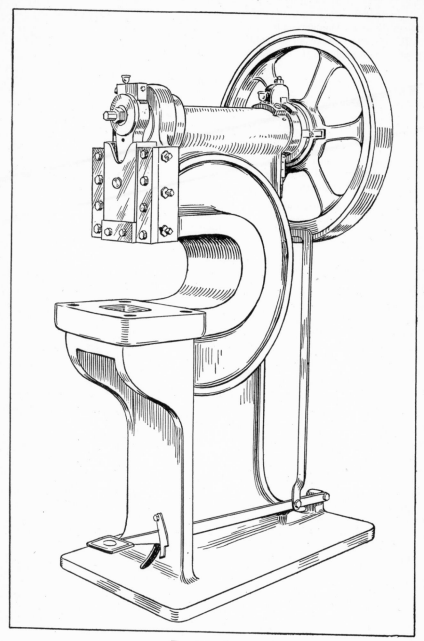

FIG. 411. Press.

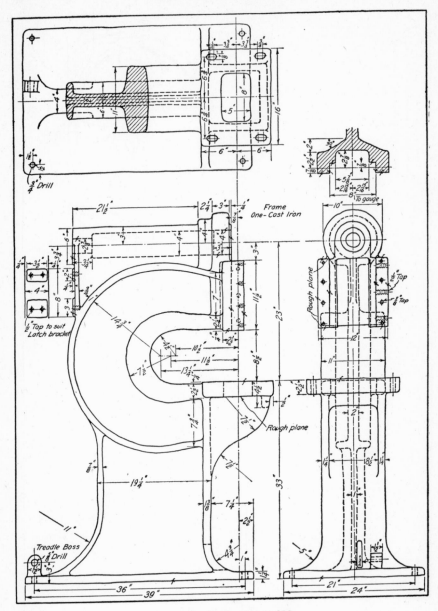

Fɪɢ. 412.　Probs. 296 to 299.

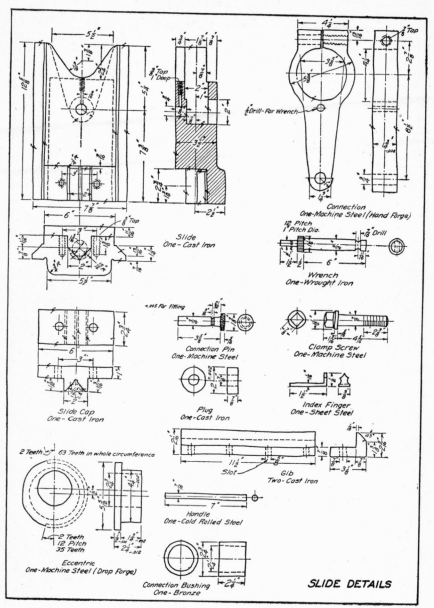

FIG. 413.   Probs. 297, 298 and 299.

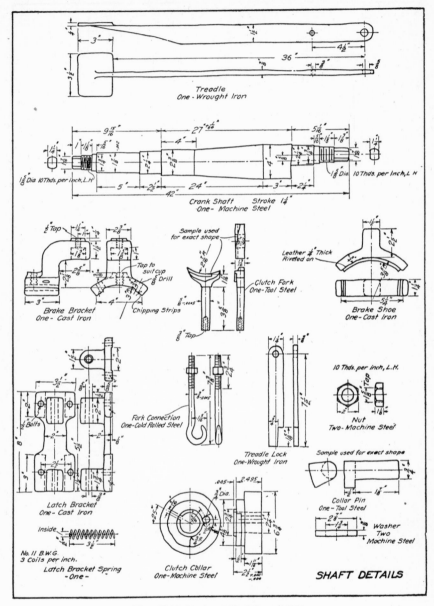

FIG. 414.   Probs. 297, 298 and 299.

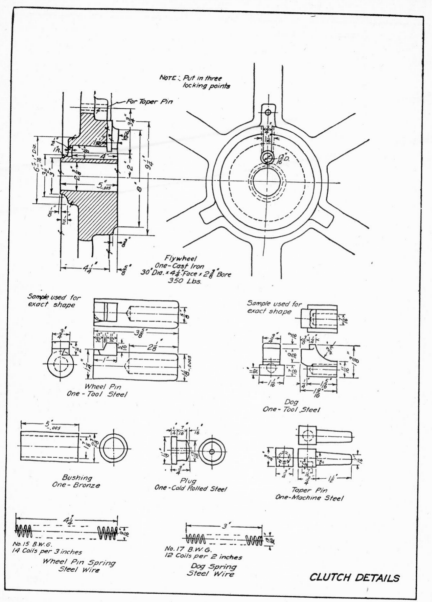

FIG. 415.   Probs. 297, 298 and 299.

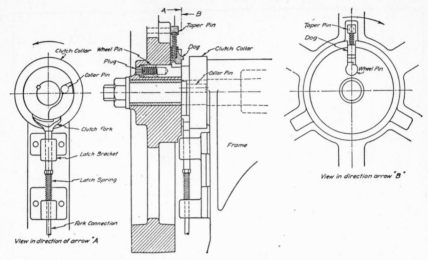

FIG. 416.   Clutch Assembly.

AMMONIA PUMP END

219. A pump for ammonia must be constructed entirely of iron or steel.   The operation of the water end of an ordinary reciprocating pump should be understood before starting this problem.   Fig. 417 shows an ammonia pump cylinder and Fig. 418 some suggested details.   If possible it would be well for the student to refer to "Pumping Machinery" by A. M. Greene.   Choose scales for details carefully, either full size or half size depending upon the piece.   Cylinder diameter $3^1/_2''$.   Stroke 12".

PROB. 300.—Fig. 417.—Make a detail working drawing of the ammonia PUMP CYLINDER.   Show top view in full, front view as a full section on planes indicated, a cross section, and a full end view.   Large sheet, Fig. 266.

PROB. 301, Fig. 418.—Make a working drawing of the AIR CHAMBER.   (11" x 14" space.)

PROB. 302, Fig. 418.—Make a working drawing of the valves, valve seats, and plugs.   The sketches are suggestive.   Wing valves are shown but ball valves may be used with advice of the instructor.   A partial assembly showing the valves in place may be necessary in order to determine dimensions.   It should be possible to remove the suction valve without taking out the discharge valve seat.   The lift of a valve to give full opening is one fourth the diameter but the practical lift is about one half this amount.   Use 11" x 14" space.

PROB. 303, Fig. 418.—Make a working drawing of the PISTON.   (11" x 14" space.)   Sketch is suggestive only.

PROB. 304, Fig. 418.—Make a working drawing of the outside CYLINDER HEAD.   Consider method of making joint (11" x 14" space).

PROB. 305, Fig. 419.—Make a working drawing of the inside CYLINDER HEAD and double stuffing box.   Note the opening from between the two packing spaces which connects with the suction chamber of the pump cylinder.   The three tie rods hold the

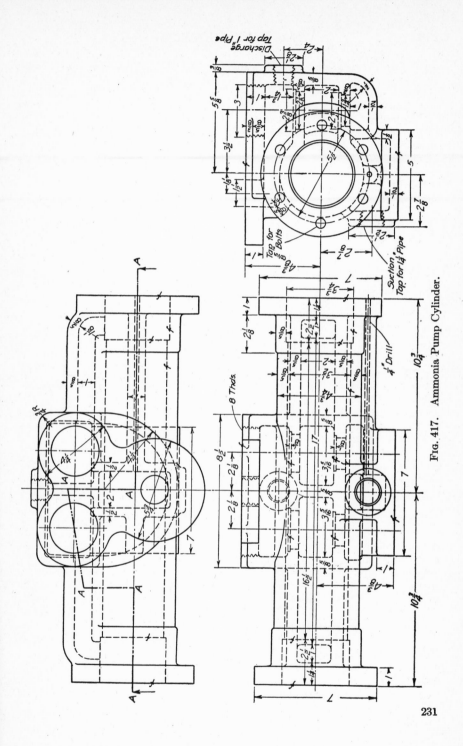

FIG. 417. Ammonia Pump Cylinder.

231

pump cylinder and steam cylinder in alignment.   The steam cylinder is not part of our
problem.   (11″ x 14″ space.)

   PROB. 306, Fig. 418.—Make a working drawing of the FOOT or support.   (11″
x 14″ space.)

   PROB. 307, Figs. 417, 418, and 419.—Make an assembly drawing of the ammonia
pump end.   Show two sectional views with all parts in working positions.   Use cutting
planes which are shown on the pump cylinder drawing.   This will require a special
size large sheet.

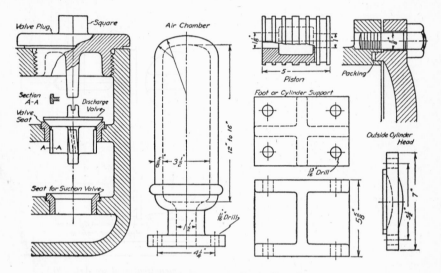

FIG. 418.   Ammonia Pump Details.

   PROB. 308, Figs. 417, 418, and 419.—Make an exterior assembly drawing of the
ammonia pump end.

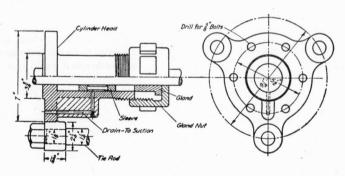

FIG. 419.   Inside Cylinder Head.

PISTON AND ROD FOR LOCOMOTIVE

220. The 25″ piston and rod shown in Fig. 420 is from a drawing supplied by The Baldwin Locomotive Works, Philadelphia, Pa. The piston head is forced on the rod with 70 tons pressure. Piston head is made of cast steel, piston is made of cast iron, lock nut is made of "dead soft" steel, piston rod and nut are made of O. H. (Open hearth) steel. There are 24 rivets, to be hot driven. Packing rings are to be furnished by The Locomotive Finished Material Co., and are not to be drawn in detail. Before starting these problems consider choice of views, treatment of views, scale, etc.

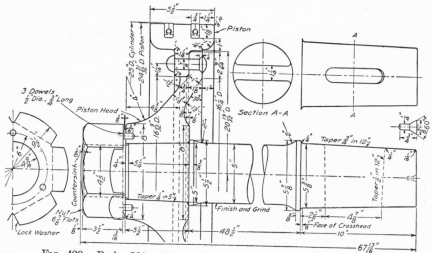

FIG. 420. Probs. 309 to 312. (*For sectional view treatment see Art. 220.*)

The representation of Fig. 420 is designed to give the information necessary for solving the problems when used in connection with notes included in this paragraph and is not to be considered as a drawing. Section lines are left out to facilitate reading the dimensions. Size of sheet and number of sheets will depend upon choice of scale, etc.

PROB. 309.—Make a detail drawing of the 25″ PISTON. Show the PISTON HEAD and the PISTON separately.

PROB. 310.—Make a detail drawing of the PISTON ROD. Include a separate detail drawing for the LOCK WASHER. The lock washer to be cut and edges turned up after the nut is drawn tight on the rod. Show lock washer as it would appear before edges are turned up.

PROB. 311.—Make a complete one view assembly drawing of the piston, rod, etc. Show as a section but without dimensions.

PROB. 312.—Make a complete assembly drawing of the piston, rod, etc. Show end view in full and side view as a half section and half full view.

LOCOMOTIVE SMOKE STACK

221. The smoke stack of Fig. 421 is from a drawing supplied by the Baldwin Locomotive Works, Philadelphia, Pa. Before starting problems, consider choice of

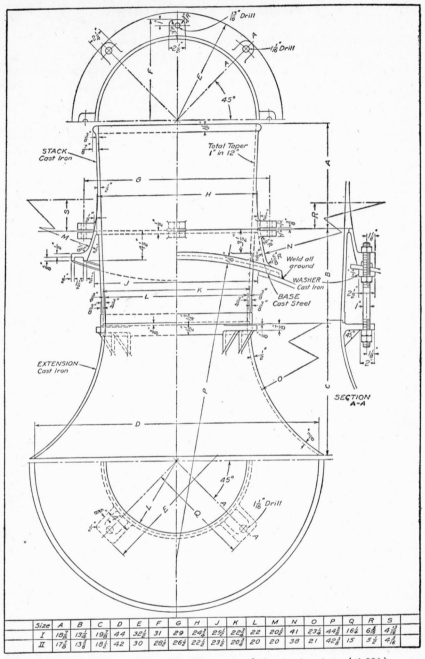

Size	A	B	C	D	E	F	G	H	J	K	L	M	N	O	P	Q	R	S
I	$18\frac{3}{8}$	$13\frac{1}{4}$	$19\frac{7}{8}$	44	$32\frac{1}{2}$	31	29	$24\frac{3}{4}$	$25\frac{1}{2}$	$22\frac{3}{4}$	22	$20\frac{1}{2}$	41	$23\frac{3}{4}$	$44\frac{3}{8}$	$16\frac{1}{4}$	$6\frac{1}{8}$	$4\frac{13}{16}$
II	$17\frac{7}{8}$	$13\frac{5}{8}$	$18\frac{1}{2}$	42	30	$28\frac{1}{2}$	$26\frac{1}{2}$	$22\frac{1}{2}$	$23\frac{1}{2}$	$20\frac{3}{4}$	20	20	38	21	$42\frac{3}{8}$	15	$5\frac{1}{2}$	$4\frac{3}{8}$

234   FIG. 421.   Probs. 313 to 319.   (*For sectional view treatment see Art 221.*)

views, treatment of views, scale, etc. Note the half sectional elevation, "right section" at the top, detail section *A–A*, and the use of a bottom view. Section lines are not necessary for reading the drawing and are not shown. This is in accord with the principle of simplification of drawings. Note also that the half section has been revolved from a plane at right angles to the half elevation. This drawing is to be used for two sizes, I and II. The dimensions which differ are given in tabular form at the bottom of the drawing. Size of sheet and number of sheets will depend upon choice of scale, etc.

PROBS. 313 to 318.—Make complete detail working drawings.

PROB......	313	314	315	316	317	318
Part.......	STACK	BASE	EXTENSION	STACK	BASE	EXTENSION
Size........	I	I	I	II	II	II

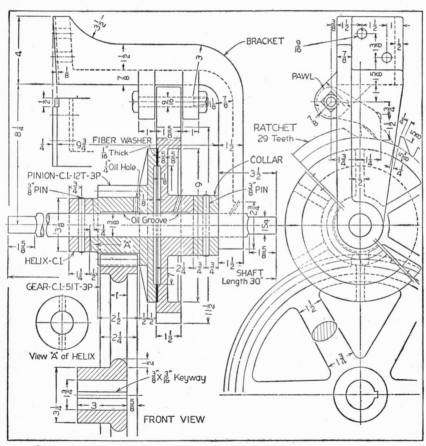

FIG. 422.   Probs. 320 to 326.

PROB. 319.—Make a one-view assembly drawing of the complete stack. Show right half in section and left half in elevation. Do not dimension. Use size I or size II as directed by instructor.

SAFETY FRICTION LOAD BRAKE

222. The friction load brake shown in Figs. 422 and 423 is from a drawing supplied by The Canton Foundry and Machine Co., Canton, Ohio. It is used on their improved portable cranes. Size of sheet and number of sheets will depend upon choice of scale, etc.

PROB. 320.—Make detail drawing of the GEAR.

PROB. 321.—Make detail drawings of the SHAFT, BOLT and PIN.

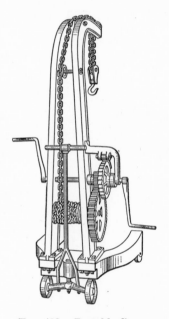

FIG. 423.   Portable Crane.

PROB. 322.—Make detail drawing of the BRACKET.

PROB. 323.—Make detail drawing of the HELIX, PINION, RATCHET, PAWL and FIBER WASHER.

PROB. 324.—Make an assembly drawing of the complete LOAD BRAKE. Show elevations of front and side views. Do not dimension.

PROB. 325.—Same as Prob. 324 but show front view in section.

PROB. 326.—Make a one view assembly drawing of the LOAD BRAKE but without the gear, bracket or pawl. Show view in elevation or section as directed by instructor.

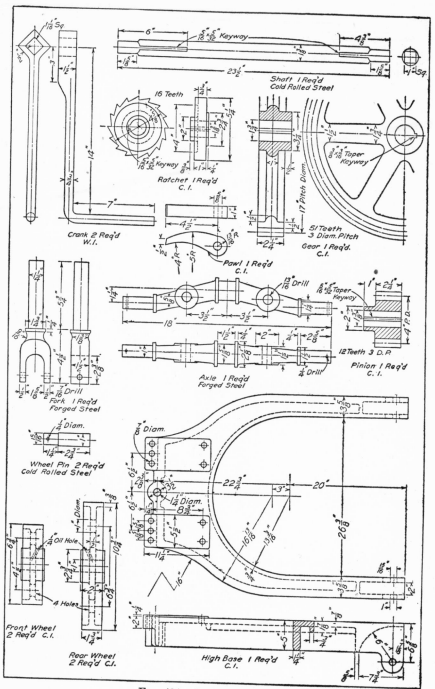

FIG. 424.   Probs. 327 to 333.

237

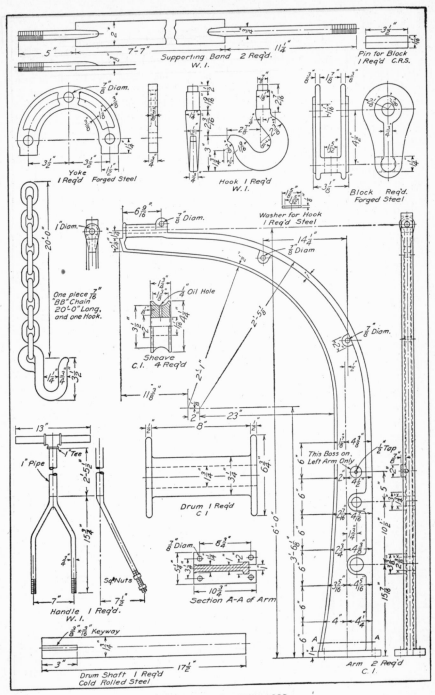

FIG. 425. Probs. 327 to 333.

PORTABLE CRANE

223. The portable crane shown in Figs. 424 and 425 is from drawings supplied by The Canton Foundry and Machine Company, Canton, Ohio. Fig. 423 shows such a crane but fitted with a safety friction load brake. Keys, pins, bolts, etc., not shown in the illustrations are to be supplied as part of the solution of the problems. Pins for the sheaves are to be made of cold rolled steel threaded on ends for nuts and designed to suit the conditions. Size of sheet and number of sheets will depend upon choice of scale, etc.

PROB. 327.—Make a three view detail drawing of the HIGH BASE (Fig. 424). Consider choice and treatment of views.

PROB. 328.—Make a detail drawing of the ARM (Fig. 425).

PROB. 329.—Make an assembly drawing of the PORTABLE CRANE. Show side view and front or back view.

PROB. 330.—Make an assembly drawing of the PORTABLE CRANE. Show top and side views.

PROB. 331.—Make an assembly drawing of the gear, pinion, ratchet, pawl, shaft and crank for the PORTABLE CRANE.

PROB. 332.—Make a sectional view on a vertical plane between the two arms. Show the chain, hook sheaves, drum, etc., in position.

PROB. 333.—Make an assembly drawing of the PORTABLE CRANE shown in Figs. 424 and 425 but fitted with the FRICTION LOAD BRAKE of Fig. 422.

CHAPTER XIII

SUPPLEMENTARY PROBLEMS

224. This chapter includes a collection of problems which may be used to supplement the problems in Chap. XII or in place of some of the working drawing problems. They are planned as a source from which the instructor can make a selection to meet the needs of his particular course.

Choice of views, scale, and other matters are part of the problem in most cases. The problem statements are to be considered as suggestions, as many of the problems lend themselves to a variety of teaching purposes.

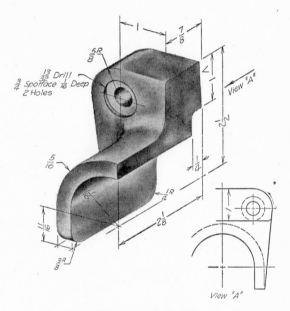

FIG. 426. Prob. 334.

PROB. 334, Fig. 426.—Make a working drawing of the cast iron GUARD. The picture shows one-half of the piece as though it had been cut in two in order to show the shape of the section. The only machined surfaces are the spotfaced holes and the surface from the back which is marked by a V.

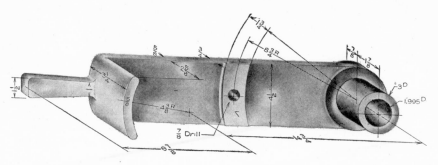

FIG. 427. Prob. 335.

PROB. 335, Fig. 427.—Make a working drawing of the cast iron EXTENSION ARM. The contact-arc surface through which the 7/8″ hole is drilled, the inside and outside of the hub, and the three vertical plane surfaces (front, end of finish exterior hub, and back surface) are machined.

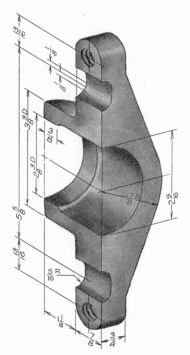

PROB. 336, Fig. 428.—Make a working drawing of the SPLIT GLAND. The right-hand half is shown. Show right- and left-hand parts assembled. Right-hand half has two holes threaded 7/16″-14NC-2. Left-hand half has two holes 15/32″ DRILL. Halves are held together by two 7/16″ x 1 1/4″ fillister-head machine screws. Contact surfaces and inside of gland are machined. Spotface for machine screw head.

FIG. 428. Prob. 336.

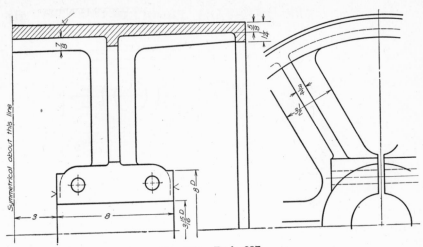

FIG. 429. Prob. 337.

PROB. 337, Fig. 429.—Make detail drawing of the double hub pulley. (The Medart Co., St. Louis, Mo.) Material is cast iron. Crown $^3/_{16}''$ in 12''. Provide four $^7/_8''$ bolts for each hub, square head, hex nut. Diameter of pulley is 28'' and face is 32''. Dimensions not shown are to be determined by the student as the drawing is worked up. Provide a keyway $^{13}/_{16}''$ wide x $^{13}/_{32}''$ deep, and two square head set-screws to hold key in each hub. Give complete dimensions. Select a proper scale.

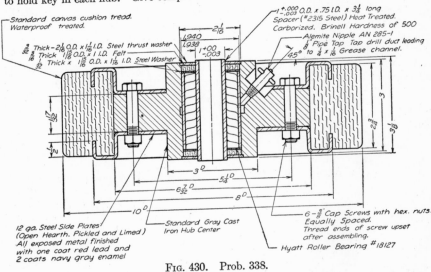

FIG. 430. Prob. 338.

PROB. 338, Fig. 430.—Make detail drawings of the following parts of the Divine Brothers 10'' x 3'' CANVAS CUSHION WHEEL. Consult a catalog of Hyatt roller bearings and select a suitable bearing. An assembly showing the sectional view and a side view, without dimensions, may be desirable in addition to the details.

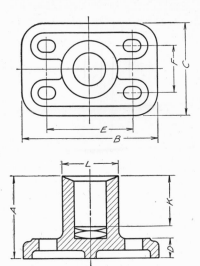

FIG. 431.

FIG. 432.   Probs. 339 to 346.

PROBS. 339 to 346, Figs. 431, 432.—Make a working drawing of one of the RIGID STEP BOXES as assigned by the instructor. The principal dimensions given are from the W. A. Jones Foundry & Machine Company tables. Dimensions not given are to be worked out as the views are drawn. The boxes are made of cast iron accurately bored to size and furnished with two hardened steel discs to take the thrust of the shaft. The top is beveled inside to keep the oil next to the shaft.

DIMENSIONS IN INCHES

Prob.	Size of Shaft	A	B	C	D	E	F	K	L	Bolts		Approx. Weight Each, Lbs.
										No.	Size	
339	$1^3/_{16}$ & $1^1/_4$	4	6	4	$^7/_8$	4	2	$2^5/_8$	$2^1/_2$	4	$^1/_2$	$6^1/_2$
340	$1^7/_{16}$ & $1^1/_2$	4	6	4	$^7/_8$	4	2	$2^5/_8$	$2^1/_2$	4	$^1/_2$	6
341	$1^{11}/_{16}$ & $1^3/_4$	$4^1/_2$	$7^1/_2$	5	$1^1/_8$	$5^1/_8$	$2^3/_4$	$2^7/_8$	3	4	$^1/_2$	$9^1/_2$
342	$1^{15}/_{16}$ & 2	$4^1/_2$	$7^1/_2$	5	$1^1/_8$	$5^1/_8$	$2^3/_4$	$2^7/_8$	3	4	$^1/_2$	$8^1/_2$
343	$2^3/_{16}$	5	9	6	$1^3/_8$	$6^3/_8$	$3^1/_2$	3	$3^3/_4$	4	$^5/_8$	18
344	$2^7/_{16}$	5	9	6	$1^3/_8$	$6^3/_8$	$3^1/_2$	3	$3^3/_4$	4	$^5/_8$	18
345	$2^{11}/_{16}$	$5^1/_2$	$10^1/_2$	7	$1^5/_8$	$7^5/_8$	$4^1/_4$	$3^1/_8$	$4^3/_4$	4	$^5/_8$	32
346	$2^{15}/_{16}$	$5^1/_2$	$10^1/_2$	7	$1^5/_8$	$7^5/_8$	$4^1/_4$	$3^1/_8$	$4^3/_4$	4	$^5/_8$	30

FIG. 433.

PROBS. 347 to 358, Figs. 433, 434.—Make a working drawing of one of the ADJUSTABLE STEP BOXES as assigned by the instructor. The principal dimensions given are from the W. A. Jones Foundry & Machine Company tables. Dimensions not given are to be worked out as the views are drawn. The boxes are made of cast iron. Lubrication is furnished by a packed grease well around the bushing which is adjustable in all directions horizontally. Steel discs are fitted into the bores to carry the weight of the shaft.

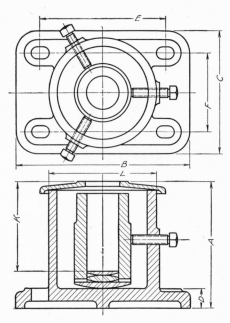

FIG. 434. Probs. 347 to 358.

DIMENSIONS IN INCHES

Prob.	Size of Shaft	A	B	C.	D	E	F	K	L	Bolts		Approx. Weight Each, Lbs.
										No.	Size	
347	$1^3/_{16}$ & $1^1/_4$	$5^5/_8$	$7^3/_4$	$5^3/_8$	$^7/_8$	$5^1/_2$	$3^1/_2$	$3^3/_4$	$4^3/_4$	4	$^1/_2$	20
348	$1^7/_{16}$ & $1^1/_2$	$5^5/_8$	$7^3/_4$	$5^3/_8$	$^7/_8$	$5^1/_2$	$3^1/_2$	$3^3/_4$	$4^3/_4$	4	$^1/_2$	20
349	$1^{11}/_{16}$ & $1^3/_4$	$6^1/_2$	$9^1/_2$	$6^1/_2$	$1^1/_8$	$6^7/_8$	$4^1/_4$	$4^1/_2$	$5^5/_8$	4	$^1/_2$	25
350	$1^{15}/_{16}$ & 2	$6^1/_2$	$9^1/_2$	$6^1/_2$	$1^1/_8$	$6^7/_8$	$4^1/_4$	$4^1/_2$	$5^5/_8$	4	$^1/_2$	25
351	$2^3/_{16}$	$7^5/_8$	$11^1/_2$	$7^5/_8$	$1^3/_8$	$8^1/_4$	$4^7/_8$	$5^1/_4$	$6^1/_2$	4	$^1/_2$	42
352	$2^7/_{16}$	$7^5/_8$	$11^1/_2$	$7^5/_8$	$1^3/_8$	$8^1/_4$	$4^7/_8$	$5^1/_4$	$6^1/_2$	4	$^1/_2$	40
353	$2^{11}/_{16}$	$8^1/_2$	$13^1/_2$	$8^3/_4$	$1^5/_8$	$9^5/_8$	$5^1/_2$	$5^7/_8$	$7^1/_2$	4	$^5/_8$	62
354	$2^{15}/_{16}$	$8^1/_2$	$13^1/_2$	$8^3/_4$	$1^5/_8$	$9^5/_8$	$5^1/_2$	$5^7/_8$	$7^1/_2$	4	$^5/_8$	60
355	$3^3/_{16}$	$9^1/_2$	$15^1/_4$	$9^3/_4$	$1^7/_8$	11	$6^1/_4$	$6^3/_8$	$8^1/_4$	4	$^3/_4$	80
356	$3^7/_{16}$	$9^1/_2$	$15^1/_4$	$9^3/_4$	$1^7/_8$	11	$6^1/_4$	$6^3/_8$	$8^1/_4$	4	$^3/_4$	96
357	$3^{11}/_{16}$	$10^1/_2$	$17^1/_4$	11	$2^1/_4$	$12^1/_2$	7	7	$9^1/_4$	4	1	116
358	$3^{15}/_{16}$	$10^1/_2$	$17^1/_4$	11	$2^1/_4$	$12^1/_2$	7	7	$9^1/_4$	4	1	130

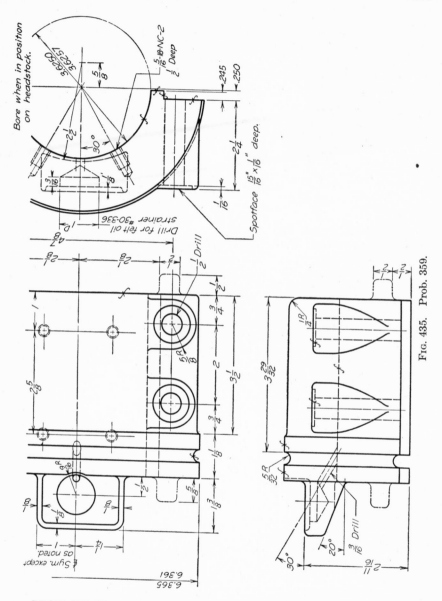

PROB. 359, Fig. 435.—Make a working drawing of the FRONT CAP. Show three exterior views and one or more sectional views. The views shown are incomplete. Note the holding parts shown by their dash and double "dot" lines. These parts are to be removed after machining.

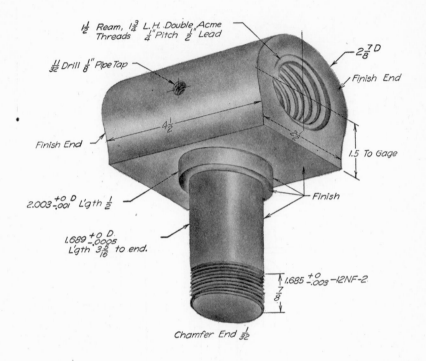

$1\frac{1}{2}$ Ream, $1\frac{3}{4}$ L.H. Double Acme
Threads $\frac{1}{4}$" Pitch $\frac{1}{2}$" Lead

$\frac{11}{32}$ Drill $\frac{1}{8}$" Pipe Tap

$2\frac{7}{8}$ D

Finish End

$4\frac{1}{2}$

Finish End

1.5 To Gage

$2.003^{+0}_{-.001}$ D L'gth $\frac{1}{2}$

Finish

$1.689^{+0}_{-.0005}$ D.
L'gth $3\frac{3}{16}$ to end.

$1.685^{+0}_{-.003}$ —12NF-2

$\frac{7}{8}$

Chamfer End $\frac{1}{32}$

FIG. 436.   Prob. 360.

PROB. 360, Fig. 436.—Make a detail drawing of the RAIL SCREW NUT for planer saddle. The G. A. Gray Co., Cincinnati, Ohio. Show necessary views, dimensions, and notes. Material is bronze. Allow $^3/_{32}$" on pattern for finish.

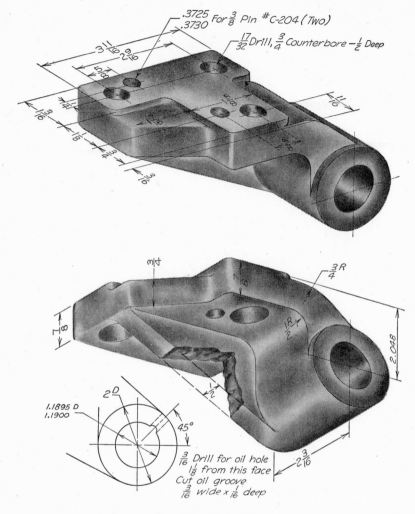

FIG. 437. Prob. 361.

PROB. 361, Fig. 437.—Make a working drawing for the FRONT BRACKET. Material is cast iron Dimensions not given on the picture are to be worked out as the views are drawn.

PROB. 362, Figs. 438, 439.—Make a detail drawing of the parts for the INNER FRICTION FLANGE for the G. A. Gray Co. (Cincinnati, O.) metal planer. Give all necessary dimensions, notes, a material list, and a suitable title. There are four parts made of SAE 1020 steel.

No. 34062, Inner Plate, made from cold rolled stock.

No. 34063, Bushing, made from $^3/_4''$ cold finished stock.

No. 34064, Stop, made from $^5/_8''$ square stock.

No. 34065, Hub, made from $4^1/_8''$ hot rolled stock.

PROB. 363, Figs. 438, 439.—Make a sub-assembly drawing as in Fig. 439 with assembling information. Note that welding and brazing are used.

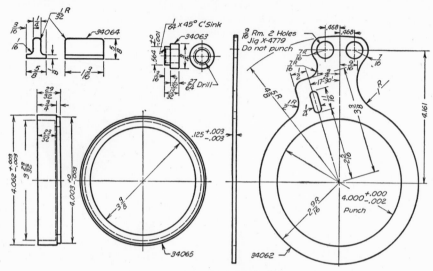

FIG. 438. Probs. 362, 363.

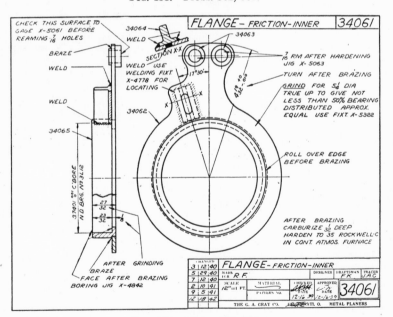

FIG. 439. Probs. 362, 363.

248

PROBS. 364 to 366, Figs. 440 to 443.—The Henna Model 4 AIR CYLINDER shown in Figs. 440, 442, and 443 is made by the Hanna Engineering Works, Chicago, Ill. Air cylinders are used for the operation of such equipment as presses, clutches, valves, furnace and oven doors, and any place where a push or pull is required, whether direct or through a lever or toggle. They are made in a variety of types and sizes, for operation by air, oil, or water. An end mounted air cylinder is shown in Fig. 441.

FIG. 441.

FIG. 440.   Probs. 364, 365, 366.

The cylinder operates the clutch on the press so that by remote control through the actuation of an air valve placed in any position in the vicinity of this press the clutch can be operated.

The Model 4 air cylinder shown has an inside diameter of $8^1/_4$ inches but is referred to as an 8 inch diameter cylinder. The length of stroke can be any distance to meet service requirements, and the overall length of the cylinder (Part 3 in Fig. 442) will be the stroke plus $3^{11}/_{16}$ inches. Thus for a stroke of 10 inches the overall length will be $13^{11}/_{16}$ inches.

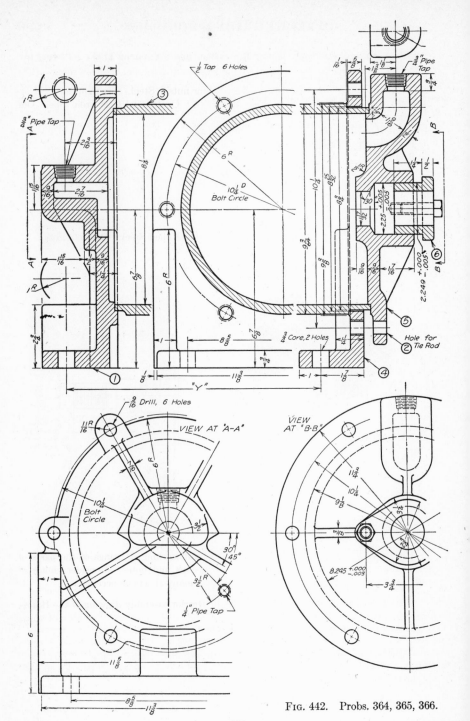

Fig. 442.   Probs. 364, 365, 366.

The parts are numbered on the illustrations and are named in the following list.

1. Back Head. Cast Iron. One required.
2. Tie Rods. $1/2$ diam. Threaded both ends for nuts. Steel. Six required.
3. Cylinder. Overall length = stroke plus $3^{11}/_{16}$. Centrifugal Cast Iron Pipe. One required.
4. Front Head Flange. Cast Iron. One required.
5. Front Head. Cast Iron. One required.
6. Rod Gland. Cast Iron. One required.
7. Piston. Semi-steel Casting. One required.
8. Piston Packing. $5/_{32}''$ Leather. Two required.
9. Follower. Cast Iron. Two required.
10. Packing Spring.
11. Hemp Packing (for piston rod gland).
12. Piston Rod. Length = stroke + $10^9/_{16}''$. Cold Rolled Steel. One required.

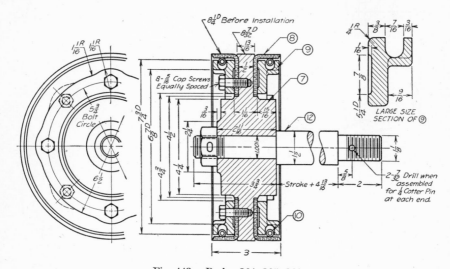

Fig. 443.   Probs. 364, 365, 366.

PROB. 364, Figs. 441, 442, 443.—Make detail working drawings of the parts of the Hanna Cylinder. Give all necessary dimensions and notes. Consider choice of scale, and choice and treatment of views. Use as many sheets as necessary.

PROB. 365, Figs. 441, 442, 443.—Make an exterior assembly drawing of the Hanna Cylinder. Give the necessary general and installation dimensions. Number of views as specified by the instructor.

PROB. 366, Figs. 441, 442, 443.—Make a longitudinal sectional assemble of the Hanna Cylinder. Give necessary general and installation dimensions. An exterior end view will be desirable in addition to the sectional view.

PROBS. 367, 368, 369, Figs. 444, 445, 446.—The Adjustable and Self-Aligning Shaft Support illustrated is one of a series manufactured by The Boston Gear Works, Inc., North Quincy, Mass. Some information for use in these problems follows: The bearing shown is for shafts of $1^1/_{16}''$, $1^1/_8''$, and $1^3/_{16}''$ diameter. The *supporting rods* are made of cold rolled steel, total height to top of rods when assembled is $10^1/_4''$. Dimensions of rods are: Diam. 1.0000; Length, 10'' .9980 $\pm$ .020''; Ends to have $^1/_{16}$ chamfer. The *pins* at the top of the supporting rods are No. 1 x $1^1/_4''$ and are to project equally on both ends. The *pins* through the base hubs are No. 1 x $1^3/_4''$. Pins at top and bottom are to be suitably placed. Size No. 1 refers to B & S Wire Gage. The *pipe plug* in the top of the bearing holder is $^1/_8''$, nominal size. The *clamp screws* for the bearing holder are $^3/_8''$ x $2^1/_4''$ Am. Std. Cap Screws with nuts to match. The *ball bearing* to be contained in the bearing holder can be a Fafnir Ball Bearing selected for one of the hole sizes of $1^1/_{16}''$, $1^1/_8''$, and $1^3/_{16}''$. This or other make should be looked up in the manufacturer's catalog.

FIG. 444.

PROB. 367, Figs. 444, 445, 446.—Make a two-view exterior assembly drawing of the BEARING SHAFT SUPPORT. Number and name the parts. Include a list of parts with the title. Pins at top of supporting rods are No. 1 x $1^1/_4''$ and are to project equally on both ends. Pins at lower ends of supporting rods, used through base hubs, are No. 1 x $1^3/_4''$. (Diam. No. of pins refers to B & S wire gage). Ball bearing is to be contained in Bearing Holder and can be a Fafnir Ball Bearing selected for holes of sizes of $1^1/_{16}''$, $1^1/_8''$, or $1^3/_{16}''$. Obtain details of ball bearings from a catalog. Clamp screws for Bearing Holder are $^3/_8''$ x $2^1/_4''$ Am. Std. Cap Screws with nuts to match. Pipe plug in top of Bearing Holder is $^1/_8''$ (nominal size). Holes for pins to be suitably placed by the student. Give all necessary installation dimensions.

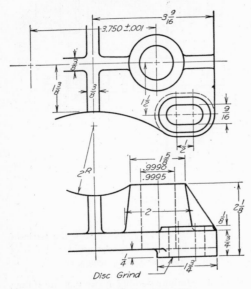

FIG. 445.   Probs. 367, 368.

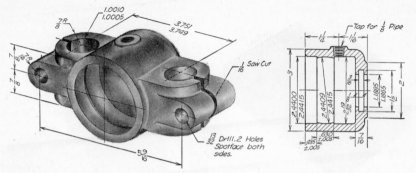

FIG. 446.   Probs. 367, 369.

PROB. 368, Fig. 445.—Make a detail working drawing for the BASE for the BEARING SHAFT SUPPORT.

PROB. 369, Fig. 446.—Make a detail working drawing for the BEARING HOLDER for the BEARING SHAFT SUPPORT.

PROB. 370.—Make detail working drawings for the supporting rods, pins, clamp screws, and pipe plug for the BEARING SHAFT SUPPORT.

PROBS. 371, 372, Figs. 447, 448.—The FLEXIBLE COUPLING illustrated is one of several types and sizes made by the Lovejoy Flexible Coupling Company, Chicago, Ill. These couplings require no lubrication and have individual free-floating load cushions between the jaws, the cushions being held in position by inside steel sleeve and removable steel collar.

FIG. 447.

PROB. 371, Figs. 447, 448.—Make detail working drawings of the parts of the heavy duty FLEXIBLE COUPLING.

PROB. 372, Figs. 447, 448.—Make a sectional assembly drawing of the FLEXIBLE COUPLING with any necessary extra or part views.   Give installation dimensions.

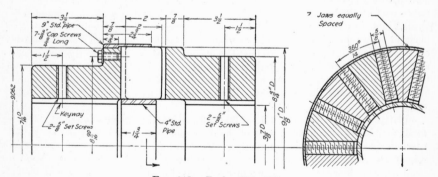

FIG. 448.   Probs. 371, 372.

253

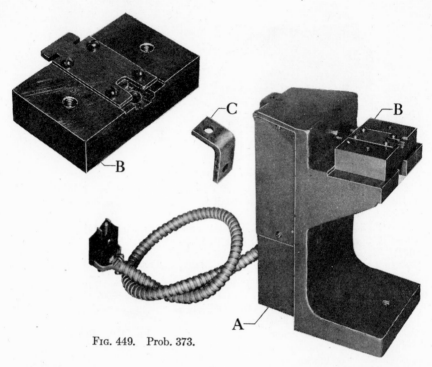

Fig. 449. Prob. 373.

PROB. 373, Figs. 449, 450, 451.—The PIECE PART CONTROL FIXTURE shown is one of the fixtures made by the R. G. Haskins Co., Chicago, for use with their tapping machines. It consists of a master base unit, **A**, and a holding fixture. A typical holding fixture is shown at **B**, a part for which it was designed is shown at **C**. The Haskins tapping machine functions under control of an automatic air valve which regulates and controls the tapping cycle. The tapping cycle is started by the insertion of the part into the fixture. The master base unit contains a micro switch which is actuated by a piece part coming in contact with the pin shown projecting through the upper part of the base casting. Another micro switch and two solenoid valves are located in the tapping machine. A low voltage circuit is used (24 volts). The combination of two micro switches and two solenoid valves functions to provide automatic electrical control of the tapping cycle. The operator inserts a part into the fixture and the tap head moves downward, starting the cycle. As soon as the tap engages the piece the operator releases the part which is then held in position by the tap. As soon as the tapping is completed the head moves upward and the part is ejected automatically from the fixture.

PROB. 373, Figs. 449, 450, 451.—Make a detail working drawing of the MASTER BASE for piece part control. Most of the dimensions are given but others are to be determined as the views are worked up on the drawing. Material is cast iron. The pad, **D**, shown in the cut-away view has three holes tapped for No. 6 x 1″, 32NC-2 round head machine screws as shown in the layout, to hold the micro switch inside of the master base. A thin sheet metal plate covering the side of the opening to the interior is to be held on by two No. 10 x ³/₈″, 32NC-2 round head machine screws. Finished surfaces are indicated by a V with an arrow pointing to the surface.

254

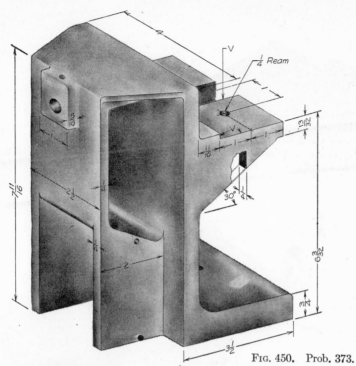

FIG. 450. Prob. 373.

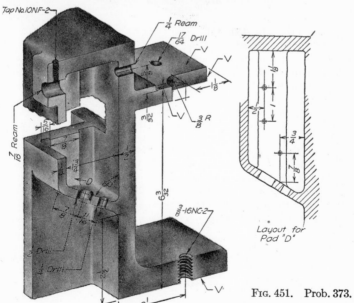

Layout for
Pad "D"

FIG. 451. Prob. 373.

255

PROBS. 374, 375, 376, Figs. 452 to 456.—The Type "LH" Handpower CRANE TROLLEY for low head room is made by the Whiting Corporation, Chicago, Ill., builders of all kinds of cranes. This trolley is of 5 to 10 tons capacity. It is designed for two hoisting speeds, one for heavy loads, and a faster one for light loads. Hyatt roller bearings are used.

An assembly diagram is shown in Fig. 453 to indicate the relation of the various parts. It is to be used to study Figs. 455 and 456. The position of the brake assembly is indicated toward the right-hand end, and a partial section of the brake is shown in Fig. 454. This mechanical brake is of the disc and ratchet type. The friction surfaces are indicated by the heavy lines.

FIG. 452.   Crane Trolley.

PROB. 374, Figs. 455, 456.—Make a complete detail drawing for each part of the CRANE TROLLEY.

PROB. 375, Figs. 452 to 456.—Make an outline assembly drawing for the CRANE TROLLEY. Give general dimensions.

PROB. 376, Figs. 452 to 456.—Make an assembly drawing for the CRANE TROLLEY to show its operation. Use sections, hidden lines, part views, or other treatments necessary to serve the purpose of the drawing.

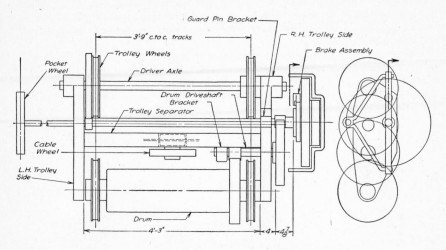

FIG. 453.   Assembly Diagram.   Probs. 374, 375, 376.

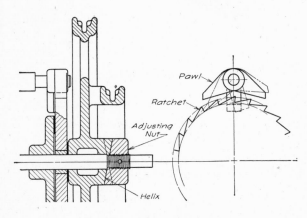

FIG. 454.   Mechanical Brake.

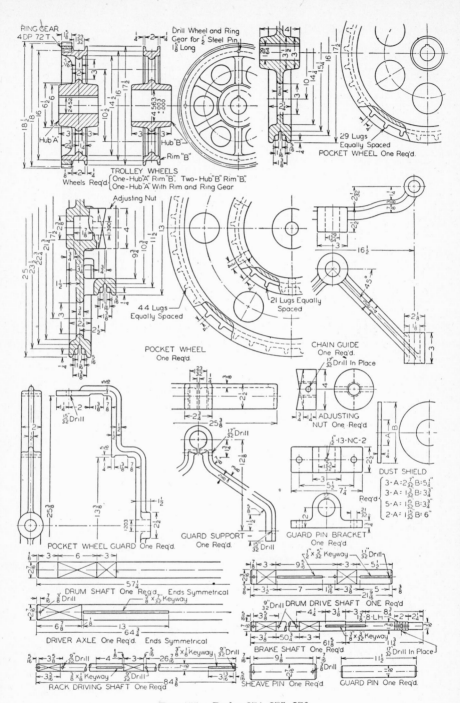

FIG. 455.   Probs. 374, 375, 376.

258

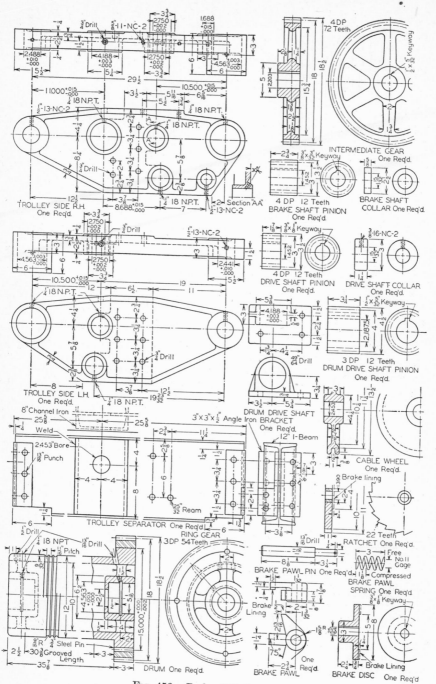

FIG. 456. Probs. 374, 375, 376.

259

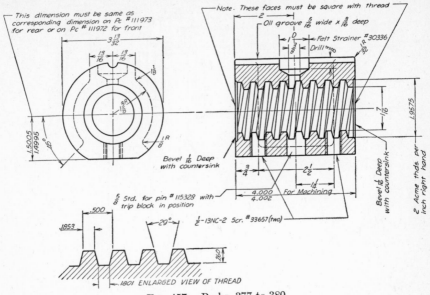

Fig. 457. Probs. 377 to 380.

PROBS. 377 to 380, Figs. 210B, 457, 458.—The MILLING FIXTURE shown is from The Lodge & Shipley Machine Tool Co., Cincinnati, Ohio. Study Fig. 210B which shows the "work" (FEED SCREW NUT) before and after the operation, and in the fixture. The feed screw nut is shown in Fig. 457 and the fixture in Fig. 458. The parts are numbered on Fig. 458 and are named in the following list. All parts are of steel except the cast iron base.

(1) Fixture Base. C.I.   (4) Bushing. St.   (7) ³/₄ Washer.
(2) Arbor. St.   (5) Bushing. St.   (8) ³/₄ Hex Nut.
(3) Bushing. St.   (6) Liner. St.

The lettered dimensions on Fig. 458 are as follows:

$A = 2^3/_8$ for Part (1)

$A = \left.\begin{matrix} 2.3765 \\ 2.3760 \end{matrix}\right\}$ for Part (3)

$B = 2$ for Part (3)

$B = \left.\begin{matrix} 1.9997 \\ 1.9995 \end{matrix}\right\}$ for Part (4)

$C = \left.\begin{matrix} 1.4980 \\ 1.4975 \end{matrix}\right\}$ for Part (4)

$C = \left.\begin{matrix} 1.4997 \\ 1.4995 \end{matrix}\right\}$ for Part (2)

$D = 2$ for Part (1)

$D = \left.\begin{matrix} 2.0015 \\ 2.0010 \end{matrix}\right\}$ for Part (6)

$E = 1^1/_2$ for Part (6)

$E = \left.\begin{matrix} 1.4997 \\ 1.4995 \end{matrix}\right\}$ for Part (5)

$F = 1$ for Part (5)

$F = \left.\begin{matrix} .9997 \\ .9995 \end{matrix}\right\}$ for Part (2)

PROB. 377, Fig. 457.—Make a drawing of the FEED SCREW NUT.
PROB. 378, Fig. 458.—Make a drawing of the cast iron FIXTURE BASE.
PROB. 379, Figs. 457, 458.—Make an assembly drawing of the MILLING FIXTURE with the FEED SCREW NUT in place. Use "dash and double-dot" thin lines for the feed screw nut.
PROB. 380, Fig. 458.—Make detail drawings of Parts (2), (3), (4), (5), and (6). Refer to Chap. IX.

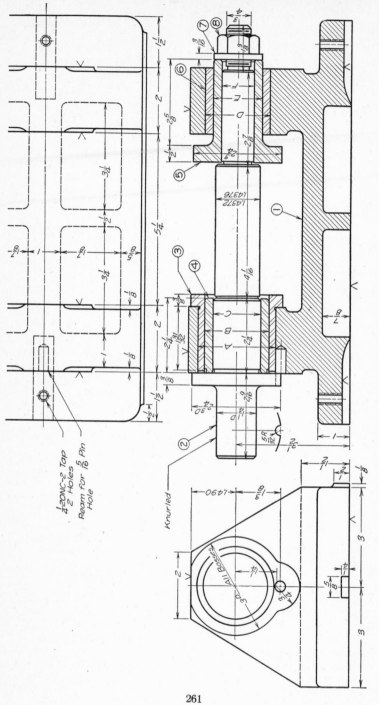

½-20NC-2 Tap
2 Holes

Ream for 5/16 Pin
Hole

Knurled

FIG. 458.   Probs. 377 to 380.

261

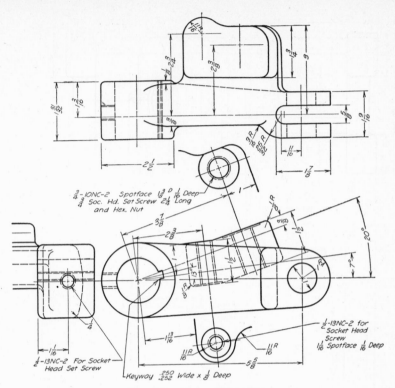

FIG. 459.   Probs. 381 to 384.

PROBS. 381 to 384, Figs. 210A, 459, 460.—The DRILL JIG for the SHIFTER LEVER is from The Lodge & Shipley Machine Tool Co., Cincinnati, Ohio. Study Fig. 210A which shows the lever before and after drilling and in the jig. The shifter lever is shown in Fig. 459 and the jig in Fig. 460. The parts are numbered on Fig. 460 and named in the following list. All parts are of steel except the cast iron jig body.

(1) Jig Body. C.I.
(2) Locating Stud. St.
(3) Slip Bushing for $^{21}/_{32}$ drill. St.
(4) Liner. St.

(5) Liner. St.
(6) Slip Bushing for $^{13}/_{32}$ drill. St.
(7) U Washer. St.
(8) Stud.

The lettered dimensions on Fig. 460 are as follows:

$A = 1^{1}/_{2}$ for Part (1)
$A = \left.\begin{array}{l} 1.5015 \\ 1.5010 \end{array}\right\}$ for Part (2)
$B = \left.\begin{array}{l} 1.4997 \\ 1.4995 \end{array}\right\}$ for Part (3)
$B = 1^{1}/_{2}$ for Part (4)

$C = \left.\begin{array}{l} 1.8765 \\ 1.8760 \end{array}\right\}$ for Part (4)
$C = 1^{7}/_{8}$ for Part (1)
$D = \left.\begin{array}{l} 1.1247 \\ 1.1245 \end{array}\right\}$ for Part (6)
$D = 1^{1}/_{8}$ for Part (5)

$E = \left.\begin{array}{l} 1.5015 \\ 1.5010 \end{array}\right\}$ for Part (5)
$E = 1^{1}/_{2}$ for Part (1)
$F = \left.\begin{array}{l} .6265 \\ .6260 \end{array}\right\}$ for Part (8)
$F = 1^{5}/_{8}$ for Part (1)

PROB. 381, Fig. 459.—Make a drawing of the cast iron SHIFTER LEVER.
PROB. 382, Fig. 460.—Make a drawing of the cast iron JIG BODY.
PROB. 383, Figs. 460, 461.—Make an assembly drawing of the JIG with the SHIFTER LEVER in place. Use "dash and double-dot" thin lines for the shifter lever.
PROB. 384, Fig. 461.—Make detail drawings for Parts (2), (3), (4), (5), (6), and (7). Refer to Chap. IX.

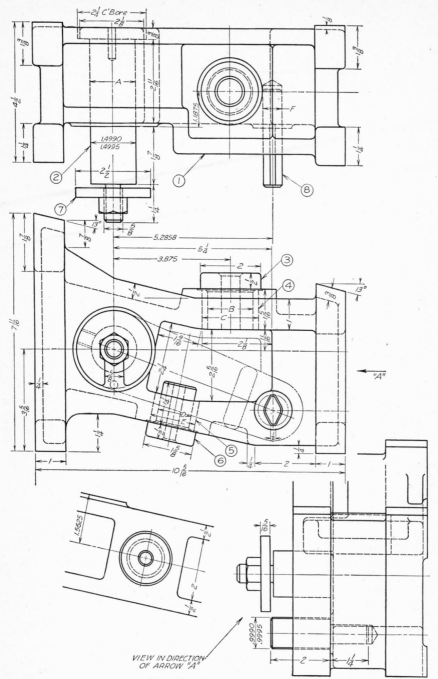

FIG. 460.   Probs. 381 to 384.

263

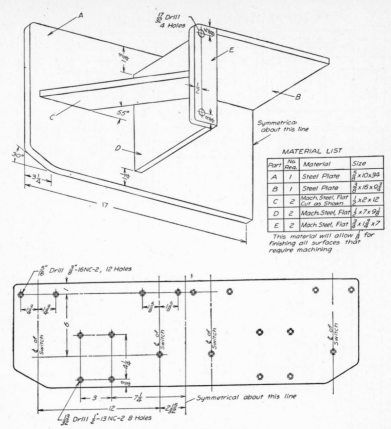

MATERIAL LIST

Part	No. Req.	Material	Size
A	1	Steel Plate	$\frac{5}{8} \times 10 \times 34$
B	1	Steel Plate	$\frac{3}{8} \times 16 \times 9\frac{3}{4}$
C	2	Mach. Steel, Flat Cut as Shown	$\frac{1}{2} \times 2 \times 12$
D	2	Mach. Steel, Flat	$\frac{1}{2} \times 7 \times 9\frac{1}{8}$
E	2	Mach. Steel, Flat	$\frac{3}{4} \times 1\frac{3}{8} \times 7$

This material will allow $\frac{1}{8}$ for finishing all surfaces that require machining

Fig. 461.   Prob. 385.

PROB. 385, Fig. 461.—Make a three-view drawing of the MASTER SWITCH BRACKET for use on a 37VEE "HYPRO" MILLING MACHINE (The Cincinnati Planer Co.). The picture shows one-half of the bracket as viewed from below. Draw a top, front, and side view. Include a material list and all necessary dimensions and notes. The bracket is to be made by welding. All welds to be approximately $\frac{1}{4}''$. Welds are not indicated on the picture. The surfaces to be machined are the back of part A, the front of part E, and the front edge of part B. The drilling layout is for part A. Radii for the rounded corners can be drawn to suit appearances. Distance from front to back when assembled is $10\frac{1}{4}''$. Part D is $7''$ high and part C is attached at mid-height.

PROB. 386, Fig. 462.—Make a detail working drawing of the BEARING BRACKET for a $6\frac{1}{2}''$ quill milling head for a milling machine made by the Cincinnati Planer Co. The top, front, and side views are shown. Draw the rear, bottom, and right-side views and a right sectional view taken on a plane through the center. Include all necessary dimensions and notes. Material is cast iron. One required. Add note: "Unless otherwise specified break all sharp corners. Fractional dimensions within plus or minus $\frac{1}{64}''$."

264

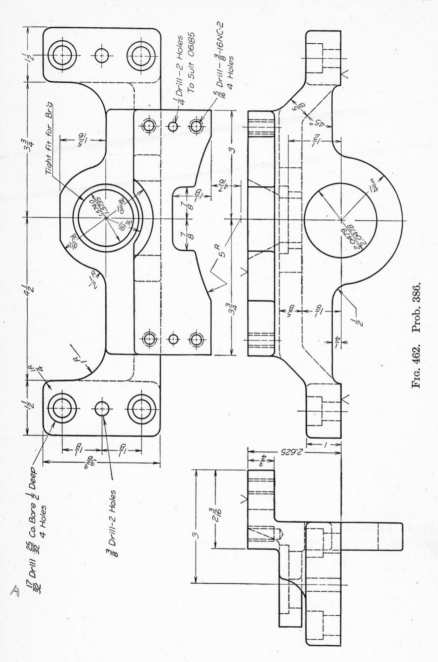

Fig. 462. Prob. 386.

APPENDIX

An important part of a course in Machine Drawing is learning the sources of information and of tabular data. The machine draftsman or engineer should become familiar with the many engineering handbooks which are now available as well as company standards, Government standards, and the published standards of the American Standards Association. All of such material is subject to revision and the latest information should always be sought.

Some frequently used data are included in this Appendix but consultation with the available sources is a necessary part of the preparation for machine drawing and design.

Keys are used to prevent relative motion between shafts and pulleys, gears, or crank arms, to hold parts in place and to serve many other purposes in machine construction. Saddle keys and flat keys are used for light service. Common proportions of square and rectangular sunk keys are $W = \dfrac{D}{4}$, $H = \dfrac{D}{6}$ to $\dfrac{D}{4}$, with the top either straight or tapered (standard taper is $1/8''$ in $12''$). A round key for light service, either straight or tapered, is often used at the end of a shaft. Standard steel taper pins may be used as round keys for light service. Nordberg round

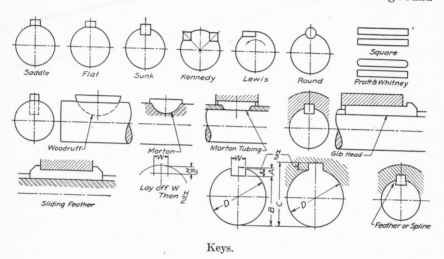

Keys.

keys may be used for large shafts. The Lewis key, if used singly, is for rotation in one direction only, two Lewis keys may be used for heavy loads and for rotation in either direction. Kennedy double keys,[1] used for large forces and alternate direction of rotation, as in rolling mills, are placed so that the diagonals intersect at the center O. The Woodruff key is a portion of a circular disc and is self adjusting for taper of keyseat or shaft. Morton keys have shoulders which facilitate assembly of shaft and tube. A feather key or spline is a key which permits sliding parallel to the axis of a shaft. It may be fastened to the shaft or to the sliding member. Feather keys are not tapered. The Pratt and Whitney round-end key is fitted into a special milled keyway.

[1] For data, refer to Machinery's Handbook.

Gib Head Taper Stock Keys (American Standard) Square and Flat

Diameters of Shafts	Square Type					Flat Type				
	Key		Gib Head			Key		Gib Head		
	Maximum Width	Height at Large End	Height	Length	Height Edge of Chamfer	Maximum Width	Height at Large End	Height	Length	Height Edge of Chamfer
(Inclusive)	W	H	C	D	E	W	H	C	D	E
$1/2 - 9/16$	$1/8$	$1/8$	$1/4$	$7/32$	$5/32$	$1/8$	$3/32$	$3/16$	$1/8$	$1/8$
$5/8 - 7/8$	$3/16$	$3/16$	$5/16$	$9/32$	$7/32$	$3/16$	$1/8$	$1/4$	$3/16$	$5/32$
$15/16-1\,1/4$	$1/4$	$1/4$	$7/16$	$11/32$	$11/32$	$1/4$	$3/16$	$5/16$	$1/4$	$3/16$
$1\,5/16-1\,3/4$	$3/8$	$3/8$	$11/16$	$15/32$	$15/32$	$3/8$	$1/4$	$7/16$	$3/8$	$5/16$
$1\,13/16-2\,1/4$	$1/2$	$1/2$	$7/8$	$19/32$	$5/8$	$1/2$	$3/8$	$5/8$	$1/2$	$7/16$
$2\,5/16-2\,3/4$	$5/8$	$5/8$	$1\,1/16$	$23/32$	$3/4$	$5/8$	$7/16$	$3/4$	$5/8$	$1/2$
$2\,7/8-3\,1/4$	$3/4$	$3/4$	$1\,1/4$	$7/8$	$7/8$	$3/4$	$1/2$	$7/8$	$3/4$	$5/8$
$3\,3/8-3\,3/4$	$7/8$	$7/8$	$1\,1/2$	1	1	$7/8$	$5/8$	$1\,1/16$	$7/8$	$3/4$
$3\,7/8-4\,1/2$	1	1	$1\,3/4$	$1\,3/16$	$1\,3/16$	1	$3/4$	$1\,1/4$	1	$13/16$
$4\,3/4-5\,1/4$	$1\,1/4$	$1\,1/4$	2	$1\,7/16$	$1\,7/16$	$1\,1/4$	$7/8$	$1\,1/2$	$1\,1/4$	1
$5\,3/4-6$	$1\,1/2$	$1\,1/2$	$2\,1/2$	$1\,3/4$	$1\,3/4$	$1\,1/2$	1	$1\,3/4$	$1\,1/2$	$1\,1/4$

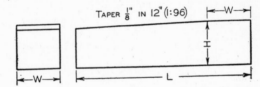

TAPER $\frac{1}{8}''$ IN 12" (1:96) — W — H — L

Square and Flat Stock Keys (American Standard)

Shaft Diameters d (Inches)	Square Stock Keys w (Inches)	Flat Stock Keys $w \times h$ (Inches)
$1/2, 9/16$	$1/8$	$1/8 \times 3/32$
$5/8, 11/16, 3/4, 13/16, 7/8$	$3/16$	$3/16 \times 1/8$
$15/16, 1, 1\,1/16, 1\,1/8, 1\,3/16, 1\,1/4$	$1/4$	$1/4 \times 3/16$
$1\,5/16, 1\,3/8, 1\,7/16, 1\,1/2, 1\,9/16, 1\,5/8, 1\,11/16, 1\,3/4$	$3/8$	$3/8 \times 1/4$
$1\,13/16, 1\,7/8, 1\,15/16, 2, 2\,1/16, 2\,1/8, 3\,3/16, 2\,1/4$	$1/2$	$1/2 \times 3/8$
$2\,5/16, 2\,3/8, 2\,7/16, 2\,1/2, 2\,5/8, 2\,3/4$	$5/8$	$5/8 \times 7/16$
$2\,7/8, 2\,15/16, 3, 3\,1/8, 3\,1/4$	$3/4$	$3/4 \times 1/2$
$3\,3/8, 3\,7/16, 3\,1/2, 3\,5/8, 3\,3/4$	$7/8$	$7/8 \times 5/8$
$3\,7/8, 3\,15/16, 4, 4\,1/4, 4\,7/16, 4\,1/2$	1	$1 \times 3/4$
$4\,3/4, 4\,15/16, 5, 5\,1/4, 5\,7/16, 5\,1/2$	$1\,1/4$	$1\,1/4 \times 7/8$
$5\,3/4, 5\,15/16, 6$	$1\,1/2$	$1\,1/2 \times 1$

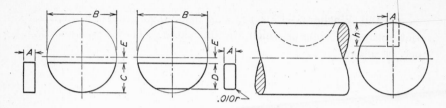

WOODRUFF KEYS (American Standard)

Key[1] Number	Nominal			Max.			Key[1] Number	Nominal			Max.		
	A	B	E	C	D	h		A	B	E	C	D	h
204	$1/16$	$1/2$	$3/64$	.203	.194	.1718	807	$1/4$	$7/8$	$1/16$	.375	.365	.2500
304	$3/32$	$1/2$	$3/64$	.203	.194	.1561	808	$1/4$	1	$1/16$	.438	.428	.3130
305	$3/32$	$5/8$	$1/16$	.250	.240	.2031	809	$1/4$	$1 1/8$	$5/64$	.484	.475	.3590
404	$1/8$	$1/2$	$3/64$	.203	.194	.1405	810	$1/4$	$1 1/4$	$5/64$	.547	.537	.4220
405	$1/8$	$5/8$	$1/16$	.250	.240	.1875	811	$1/4$	$1 3/8$	$3/32$	.594	.584	.4690
406	$1/8$	$3/4$	$1/16$	.313	.303	.2505	812	$1/4$	$1 1/2$	$7/64$	.641	.631	.5160
505	$5/32$	$5/8$	$1/16$	.250	.240	.1719	1008	$5/16$	1	$1/16$	.438	.428	.2818
506	$5/32$	$3/4$	$1/16$	.313	.303	.2349	1009	$5/16$	$1 1/8$	$5/64$	.484	.475	.3278
507	$5/32$	$7/8$	$1/16$	.375	.365	.2969	1010	$5/16$	$1 1/4$	$5/64$	.547	.537	.3908
606	$3/16$	$3/4$	$1/16$	.313	.303	.2193	1011	$5/16$	$1 3/8$	$3/32$	.594	.584	.4378
607	$3/16$	$7/8$	$1/16$	.375	.365	.2813	1012	$5/16$	$1 1/2$	$7/64$	.641	.631	.4848
608	$3/16$	1	$1/16$	.438	.428	.3443	1210	$3/8$	$1 1/4$	$5/64$	.547	.537	.3595
609	$3/16$	$1 1/8$	$5/64$	.484	.475	.3903	1211	$3/8$	$1 3/8$	$3/32$	.594	.584	.4065
							1212	$3/8$	$1 1/2$	$7/64$	.641	.631	.4535

[1] NOTE: Key numbers indicate the nominal key dimensions. The last two digits give the nominal diameter (B) in eighths of an inch and the digits preceding the last two give the nominal width (A) in thirty-seconds of an inch. Thus, 204 indicates a key $2/32 \times 4/8$ or $1/16 \times 1/2$ inch; 1210 indicates a key $12/32 \times 10/8$ or $3/8 \times 1 1/4$ inches.

DECIMAL EQUIVALENTS OF FRACTIONS OF AN INCH

Fraction	Decimal	Fraction	Decimal	Fraction	Decimal	Fraction	Decimal
$1/64$	= .015625	$17/64$	= .265625	$33/64$	= .515625	$49/64$	= .765625
$1/32$	= .03125	$9/32$	= .28125	$17/32$	= .53125	$25/32$	= .78125
$3/64$	= .046875	$19/64$	= .296875	$35/64$	= .546875	$51/64$	= .796875
$1/16$	= .0625	$5/16$	= .3125	$9/16$	= .5625	$13/16$	= .8125
$5/64$	= .078125	$21/64$	= .328125	$37/64$	= .578125	$53/64$	= .828125
$3/32$	= .09375	$11/32$	= .34375	$19/32$	= .59375	$27/32$	= .84375
$7/64$	= .109375	$23/64$	= .359375	$39/64$	= .609375	$55/64$	= .859375
$1/8$	= .125	$3/8$	= .375	$5/8$	= .625	$7/8$	= .875
$9/64$	= .140625	$25/64$	= .390625	$41/64$	= .640625	$57/64$	= .890625
$5/32$	= .15625	$13/32$	= .40625	$21/32$	= .65625	$29/32$	= .90625
$11/64$	= .171875	$27/64$	= .421875	$43/64$	= .671875	$59/64$	= .921875
$3/16$	= .1875	$7/16$	= .4375	$11/16$	= .6875	$15/16$	= .9375
$13/64$	= .203125	$29/64$	= .453125	$45/64$	= .703125	$61/64$	= .953125
$7/32$	= .21875	$15/32$	= .46875	$23/32$	= .71875	$31/32$	= .96875
$15/64$	= .234375	$31/64$	= .484375	$47/64$	= .734375	$63/64$	= .984375
$1/4$	= .25	$1/2$	= .5	$3/4$	= 75		

Pins and Washers.—Pins used as fastenings are made in a large variety of forms, some of which are illustrated. They may be straight, taper, or split.

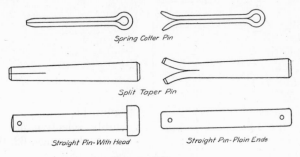

Spring Cotter Pin

Split Taper Pin

Straight Pin-With Head   *Straight Pin-Plain Ends*

Forms of Pins.

Dimensions for standard steel washers are given in the table. Cast iron washers may have proportions as follows:

$$A = d + \tfrac{1}{8}'', \qquad B = 3\tfrac{1}{2}\,d + \tfrac{1}{8}'', \qquad C = \tfrac{3}{4}\,d + \tfrac{1}{4}''.$$

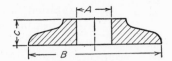

Cast Iron Washer.

DIMENSIONS OF PLAIN WASHERS
(Part of S. A. E. Standard)

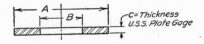

Bolt Diameter	B	A	C	Bolt Diameter	B	A	C
$1/4$	$9/32$	$5/8$	$1/16$	$3/4$	$13/16$	$1\tfrac{1}{2}$	$1/8$
$5/16$	$11/32$	$11/16$	$1/16$	$7/8$	$15/16$	$1\tfrac{3}{4}$	$1/8$
$3/8$	$13/32$	$13/16$	$1/16$	1	$1\tfrac{1}{16}$	2	$1/8$
$7/16$	$15/32$	$15/16$	$1/16$	$1\tfrac{1}{8}$	$1\tfrac{3}{16}$	$2\tfrac{1}{4}$	$1/8$
$1/2$	$17/32$	$1\tfrac{1}{16}$	$3/32$	$1\tfrac{1}{4}$	$1\tfrac{5}{16}$	$2\tfrac{1}{2}$	$5/32$
$9/16$	$19/32$	$1\tfrac{3}{16}$	$3/32$	$1\tfrac{3}{8}$	$1\tfrac{7}{16}$	$2\tfrac{3}{4}$	$5/32$
$5/8$	$21/32$	$1\tfrac{5}{16}$	$3/32$	$1\tfrac{1}{2}$	$1\tfrac{9}{16}$	3	$5/32$
$11/16$	$23/32$	$1\tfrac{3}{8}$	$3/32$				

INDEX

Accuracy, 10
of sketches, 87
Acme thread, 16
Addendum, 135
Aircraft rivets, 47A
Allowance, 58
Alloy identification for rivets, 47B
Alternate sectioning, 76
Aluminum rivets, 47A
American standard
arrangement of views, 13
volt heads and nuts, 23–27
C. I. flanges, 150
cap screws, 29
coarse thread, 19
fine thread, 22
flanged fittings, 148–150
gears, proportions for, 135
jam nuts, 33
line symbols, 4
machine screws, 31
pipe, 145
pipe thread, 145
rivet symbols, 47A
rivets, 44
screw threads, 15, 19
screwed fittings, 149
set screw heads, 32
sizes for drawings, 3
sizes of shafting, 115
slotted head cap screws, 29
symbols for materials, 73
wood screws, 35
woodruff keys, 269
Angles, 55
Arc welding symbols, 39
Arcs, 102
curves and, 54

hidden, 9
inking, 9
joining lines and, 9
Areas, projected, 12
Arms, pulley, 112A
Arrow heads, 48
Art gum, 11
Assembly, selective, 59
Assembly drawings, 62, 67
making, 68
Auto bolts, 34
Auxiliary views, 14, 81
classes of, 14A
Axes, isometric, 89
oblique, 90
Axioms for fixture designer, 127

Babbitted Bearings, 106
Ball bearings, 110
Ball cranks, 101
Basic dimensions, 58
Bearing metals, 106
Bearings, 105–111
Bell cranks, 99
Belt, drive, 112B
length, 113
Belts, horsepower transmitted, 113
pulleys, etc., 112–114
Bending and twisting, shaft for, 118
Bevel gears, 137
Bill of material, 69
"Blacked-in" section, 77
"Blocking-in" lines, 65
Blue printing, 67
Bold face letters, 5
Bolt, circle, 36
heads and nuts, 23–27
list, 69
stress, 37

271